EARLY AMERICAN
BOOK ILLUSTRATORS AND WOOD ENGRAVERS
1670-1870
VOLUME II · SUPPLEMENT

Early American
Book Illustrators and Wood Engravers
1670-1870

VOLUME II · SUPPLEMENT

A Supplement to the Main Catalogue,

issued in 1958, of a Collection of American Books

Illustrated for the most part with Woodcuts and Wood Engravings

in the Princeton University Library

BY SINCLAIR HAMILTON

PRINCETON, NEW JERSEY

PRINCETON UNIVERSITY PRESS

1968

Copyright © 1968, by Princeton University Press
Library of Congress Catalogue Card Number: 68-20870

Designed by P. J. Conkwright.
The vignettes on pages vii, ix, 1, and 27
are reproductions of wood engravings by William Macleod
from *Harper's New York and Erie Railroad Guide*,
N.Y. [cop. 1851], Item 1846.
Reproduced on page x is an advertisement
issued by J. W. Orr of New York in 1854, Item 1964.
The bookplate of the Hamilton Collection,
reproduced on the title-page, was designed by Bruce Rogers.

Printed in the United States of America
by Princeton University Press, Princeton, New Jersey
Plates by Meriden Gravure Company

PREFACE

Since the publication in 1958 of *Early American Book Illustrators and Wood Engravers, 1670-1870*, over 700 items, including the work of more than 80 additional illustrators, have been added to the collection catalogued therein. In view of these additions, it has seemed desirable to issue this Supplement to the Main Catalogue. All items numbered 1303 upwards will thus be found in the Supplement.

The Supplement is arranged precisely as the Main Catalogue was arranged and the statements in the Preface to the Main Catalogue with regard to the collection and the method of cataloguing apply to the Supplement as well.

In listing a 19th-century illustrator, about whom biographical data has already appeared in the Main Catalogue, the reader of the Supplement is referred to the appropriate page in the Main Catalogue. Biographical material is given in the Supplement only when the illustrator is not listed in the Main Catalogue or when it seemed desirable to give additional information about him.

As in the Main Catalogue, the word "woodcut" has been used in the Supplement to include a cut of which it is impossible to say definitely whether it is on wood or typemetal (see note on p. xxiii of the Main Catalogue). The word "cut" as used in the Supplement denotes a relief cut, whether on wood or metal. The words "wood engraving" denote a cut produced by the method of wood engraving as outlined in note 19 on p. xxxii of the Main Catalogue.

In the Supplement a little more attention has been paid to periodicals, especially their early numbers, although no attempt has been made to collect long shelf-filling runs. Complete runs of such leading magazines as *Harper's Monthly, Harper's Weekly, Leslie's Illustrated News*, etc. will be found elsewhere in the Princeton University Library, if any one desires to consult them.

The names of most of those mentioned in the Preface to the Main Catalogue as having been of great help in assembling the collection and in preparing the Catalogue deserve to be repeated here with respect to the Supplement. William S. Dix, Librarian of Princeton University, and his staff have once more been of the greatest assistance, but especial thanks should perhaps go to Alexander D. Wainwright (who very kindly read the galley proofs and made some excellent suggestions), Gillett G. Griffin, Earle E. Coleman, Barbara T. Ross and Orville J. Rothrock. The latter, now Curator of the Graphic Arts Division, has given liberally of his time and knowledge to the selection and arrangement of the illustrations. Dr. d'Alté A. Welch of Cleveland has been most generous in sharing some of his vast store of learning relating to children's books. Mr. Thomas L. Sloan of the Department of Art and Archaeology at Princeton University was good enough to read the galley proofs of Part II of the Supplement and a number of his helpful suggestions have been incorporated. John E. Alden, Keeper of Rare Books at the Boston Public Library, Sinclair Hitchings, Keeper of Prints at the same Library, and Edwin Wolf, 2nd, Librarian of The Library Company of Philadelphia, have all been extremely helpful. Marcus A. McCorison, Director of the American Antiquarian Society, was always prompt in answering my many inquiries and always had useful information to pass on. Finally, thanks are once again due to my secretary, Eleanor M. Beyhl, for all the work done in typing the manuscript and preparing the indices.

S. H.

CONTENTS

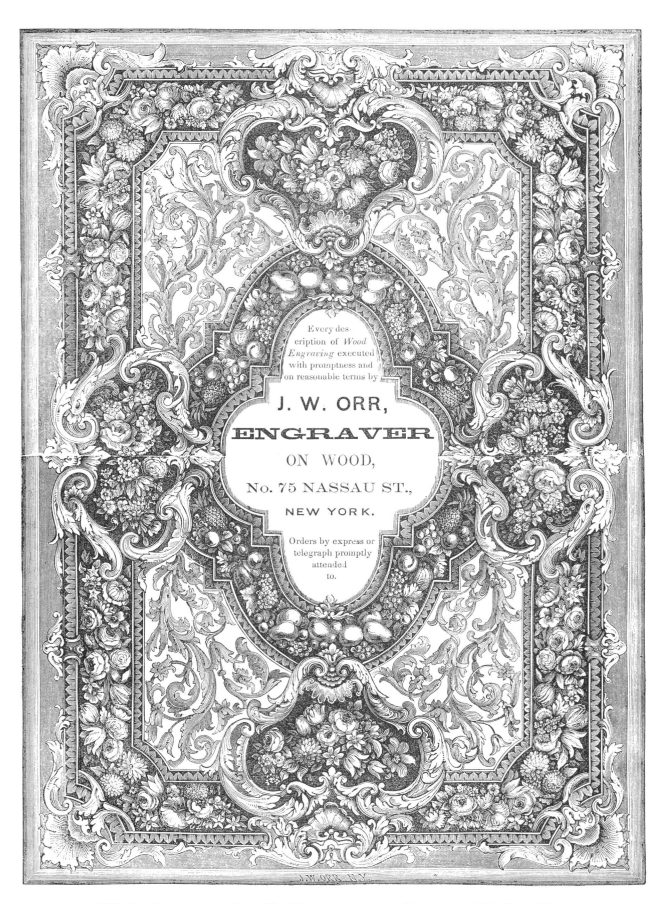

J.W. Orr. Advertisement from *The Illustrated American Biography*, 1854. (Item 1964)

LIST OF ILLUSTRATIONS

(Figures 1-8 between pages 26 and 27)

(Figures 9-18 between pages 58 and 59)

KEY TO ABBREVIATIONS

The abbreviations of works frequently referred to in the Main Catalogue and the Supplement will be found at p. xxii of that Catalogue. Some additional abbreviations found in the Supplement are:

B.A.L. *Bibliography of American Literature*, compiled by Jacob Blanck, New Haven, 1955-1963.

Bolton (3): Bolton, Theodore, *The Book Illustrations of Felix Octavius Carr Darley*, Worcester, 1952.

Drake: Drake, Milton, *Almanacs of the United States*, New York, 1962.

Howes: Howes, Wright, *U.S.iana (1650-1950)*, New York, 1962.

Mott: Mott, Frank Luther, *A History of American Magazines*, 3 vols., Cambridge, 1957.

Welch: Welch, d'Alté A., *A Bibliography of American Children's Books Printed Prior to 1821*, in Proceedings of the American Antiquarian Society for April 17, 1963, October 16, 1963, October 21, 1964, October 20, 1965, and April 19, 1967.

Wright II: Lyle H. Wright, *American Fiction 1851-1875*, San Marino, Calif., 1957.

Wright III: Lyle H. Wright, *American Fiction 1876-1900*, San Marino, Calif., 1966.

SUPPLEMENT · PART I

AMERICAN BOOK ILLUSTRATION PRIOR TO

THE NINETEENTH CENTURY

· 1706 ·

1303. THE JUST MAN'S PREROGATIVE. A SERMON PREACHED PRIVATELY, SEPT. 27, 1706. ON A SOLEMN OCCASION; FOR THE CONSOLATION OF A SORROWFUL FAMILY, MOURNING OVER THE IMMATURE DEATH, OF A PIOUS SON, VIZ. MR. SIMEON STODDARD, WHO WAS FOUND BARBAROUSLY MURDERED, IN CHELSEA-FIELDS NEAR LONDON, MAY 14, 1706. By S. Willard. Boston: N.E. Printed by B. Green. Sold by Nicholas Boone at his Shop, 1706. Evans 1286.

There is a wide black border surrounding the title-page, and cut out of the top of this border, and hence appearing in white, are crossbones, two skulls with what is probably meant for an hourglass between them, and a crossed spade and pickaxe. It is all so crudely done that it looks like local work and is probably an early attempt in this country at a mortuary border.

Samuel Willard was an eminent divine and a Vice President of Harvard. He died on September 12, 1707, not long after this sermon was delivered. John Danforth who wrote the "Pindaric Elegy" upon him (see Ford, No. 300) sings thus sweetly of Mr. Willard:

"Harvard! I'le call thy Head
   (for tis no Treason)
   Master of Reason;
Master of all the Wisdom of the Sages
   That's handed down to Later Ages."

Disbound. The name of Sam¹ Checkley and the date 1706 has been written on the title-page.

· 1712 ·

1304. AN ALMANACK OF THE COELESTIAL MOTIONS, ASPECTS & ECLIPSES, FOR THE YEAR OF THE CHRISTIAN AERA, 1712. BEING LEAP-YEAR, AND FROM THE CREATION, 5661 . . . By Daniel Travis. America Printed: Sold by N. Boone, at the Sign of the Bible, Boston, 1712. 16 pp. Drake 2944.

On the verso of the first leaf is a cut of the anatomical man which resembles the figure of the anatomical man used by John Foster in his almanac for 1678 and that used by John Tully in his almanac for 1693 [see Item 6]. Sewed.

· 1719 ·

1305. AN ALMANACK FOR THE YEAR OF OUR LORD, 1719 . . . By N. Whittemore. Boston: Printed by T. Fleet, for the Booksellers, and Sold at their Shops, 1719.

There are 8 leaves and on the recto of the final leaf is a cut of the "Man of Signs" or anatomical man, somewhat reminiscent of the cuts used by John Foster in 1678 and by Tully in 1693. Whittemore used a "Man of Signs" cut in his first almanac, that for 1705, and, with the exception of certain years, such as the almanac for 1715, continued to use such a cut. However, a comparison of the cut in the 1718 almanac with that in this 1719 almanac shows that the block has been recut. The 1719 almanac is the first of this series to bear the imprint of Thomas Fleet. Could the recutting have been done by Fleet's ingenious Negro [see Item 51]? Sewed.

· 1722 ·

1306. AN ORDINANCE FOR REGULATING AND ESTABLISHING FEES FOR THE COURT OF ADMIRALTY IN THE PROVINCE OF NEW-YORK, By His Excellency William Burnet, Esq., Captain General and Governour in Chief in and over Provinces of New-York, New-Jersey, and of all the Territories and Tracts of Land Depending thereon in America, and Vice-Admiral of the same, etc. In Council [New York: Printed by William Bradford, 1722]. 4 pp. The final page bears the date of July 16, 1722. Evans 2376.

On the front page is an ornamental headpiece, measuring 5¾ inches by 1¾ inches. It depicts 2 female figures, who appear to be half mermaids and half angels. At least they have the tails of fish, and wings sprout from their shoulders. On this page there is also a decorated capital letter, and on the final page there is an ornate tailpiece. All 3 cuts were probably done on typemetal.

It is, of course, very possible that these ornamental cuts were imported from England. It may be noted, however, that in Boston at about the time of this publication James Franklin was employing cuts, believed to have been his own work, on either wood or typemetal [see Items 9-13], which would certainly bear comparison with these, while in New York Zenger was using ornamental head- and tailpieces which may well have been homemade [see Item 14]. Furthermore, the cuts in this Item 1306 are somewhat crude in execution as compared with such English work of this period as the writer has seen. It would seem quite possible, therefore, that they were engraved on this side of the water. Preserved in cloth folder.

· 1727 ·

1306a. THE GREAT ASSIZE: OR DAY OF JUBILEE, IN WHICH WE MUST MAKE A GENERAL ACCOUNT OF ALL OUR ACTIONS BEFORE ALMIGHTY GOD. Delivered in Four Sermons upon the XXth Chap. of the *Revelations*, plainly shewing the happy State of the Godly & the woful Condition of the Wicked. Whereunto is annexed Two Sermons . . . By the Author Samuel Smith Minister of the Word. The Sixth and Fortieth Impression. Reprinted at Boston in N.E. Sold at the Sign of the Bible in Cornhill, 1727. Evans 2963.

The frontispiece or half title is a woodcut of

the Last Judgment, showing at the top the angel Gabriel blowing his horn and at the bottom the dead rising from their graves. It is tempting to suggest that it might have been cut by the man who engraved for Nicholas Boone the portrait of John Bunyan which appeared in 1728 in Boone's edition of *Come and Welcome to Jesus Christ* and in the following year in Boone's edition of *Grace Abounding to the Chief of Sinners* (Item 1307). Old calf, lacking last leaf and back cover.

· 1729 ·

1307. GRACE ABOUNDING TO THE CHIEF OF SINNERS: OR, A BRIEF AND FAITHFUL RELATION OF THE EXCEEDING MERCY OF GOD IN CHRIST TO HIS POOR SERVANT, JOHN BUNYAN . . . The Tenth Edition, Corrected, with the Remainder of his Life and Character; by a Friend since his Death. Boston: Reprinted for Nicholas Boone, at the Sign of the Bible in Cornhill, 1729. Evans 3143.

The frontispiece is a portrait of John Bunyan, a relief cut which probably is American work, copied, no doubt, from an English source. It first appeared in Bunyan's *Come and Welcome to Jesus Christ*, published by Nicholas Boone in Boston in 1728, copies of which, including the portrait, will be found at the Historical Society of Pennsylvania and the American Antiquarian Society.

This is not the first appearance of *Grace Abounding* in this country. A copy of an edition of 1717 will be found at the New York Public Library, but there is no portrait in this edition.* Copies of this 1729 edition will be found at the Boston Public Library and the American Antiquarian Society, both copies lacking the portrait, and at the Historical Society of Pennsylvania with the portrait repaired. Cont. calf.

· 1737 ·

1308. (1) THE BOSTON GAZETTE. From Monday May 16, to Monday May 23, 1737. Boston: John Boydell, 1737. The first leaf only, with good impressions of the masthead cuts. Fig. 2.

There are 2 of these masthead cuts, on the left a cut of a pine tree, and on the right one of a lighthouse and a ship. Both are signed with the initials "I.B." The use in *The Boston Gazette* of these cuts, which are somewhat larger than those formerly in use, was begun in 1735. At

* David E. Smith in his *"Illustrations of American Editions of The Pilgrim's Progress to 1870,"* in No. 1 of Vol. XXVI of *The Princeton University Library Chronicle*, at p. 18 (note), says that his examination

of the 1717 edition of *Grace Abounding* has led him to believe that a similar portrait had appeared there and suggests that this portrait may have been the work of James Franklin.

that time the newspaper was being printed by Bartholomew Green, Jr. for John Boydell, although the latter had ceased to be Post Master in 1734. While the words "Published by John Boydell" did not begin to appear at the masthead until May 24, 1736, it seems safe to assume that Boydell had something to do with the substitution of the new cuts in 1735, and, in view of the initials on the cuts, it is tempting to assume also that he engraved his own masthead. But it must be noted that Boydell died in 1739 and that John Draper used a tailpiece with the initials "I.B." in *The Lord Shall Rejoice in his Works*, a sermon preached in 1741 [Item 17]. It can, of course, be argued that Draper was a brother-in-law of Bartholomew Green and could have come into possession of the tailpiece from Boydell through Green. However, unless further evidence is forthcoming, it must be regarded as doubtful whether Boydell was the I.B. of the cuts and hence one of our earliest engravers.

(2) The Boston Gazette, or, Weekly Journal, Tuesday, August 21, 1744. Boston: Printed by S. Kneeland and T. Green at their Printing-House in Queen-street where Advertisements are taken in. Price 16s a Year, and 20s Seal'd.

At the masthead are 2 small cuts, that at the left showing a news carrier standing in a city square and holding a copy of the "Gazette or Journal" in his hand and that on the right showing a ship and lighthouse, but substantially smaller than the "ship and lighthouse" cut used by Boydell in (1) above.

The two larger cuts appearing in (1) above were used for a number of years. However, when Hannah Boydell, John's widow, died on October 15, 1741, Samuel Kneeland and Timothy Green became the proprietors of the newspaper and began to make changes. Boydell's large cuts appeared for the last time in the number for October 19, 1741. By that time they had become worn, and the "ship and lighthouse" cut was badly cracked. There was a number for October 20 without cuts and then in the number for October 27, the new small cuts, described above, made their first appearance. At the same time the name of the newspaper was changed to *The Boston Gazette, or, Weekly Journal*. These small cuts continued in use for many years.

1309. Obedience and Submission to the Pastoral Watch and Rule over the Church of Christ, Considered in a Sermon Preach'd at the Ordination Of the Reverend Mr. James Diman To the Pastoral Office over a Church of Christ in Salem; On the Eleventh Day of May,

1737. By Edward Holyoke, M.A., Pastor of a Church of Christ in Marblehead . . . Together with the Charge, by the Reverend Mr. Barnard; and the Right Hand Of Fellowship by the Reverend Mr. Clarke. Boston: Printed by Thomas Fleet, at the Heart and Crown in Cornhill, 1737. Evans 4145.

At the top of page (1) appears the cut of a battle scene which is also to be found in Item 16, *A Seasonable Caveat, etc.*, Boston, 1735. Since the present Item is a Fleet imprint, it definitely links the battle scene cut to the Heart and Crown printing office and makes it seem probable that the edition of *The Prodigal Daughter* described in Item 51(2), where the battle scene cut also appears, was issued by Fleet in the late 1730s and was an extremely early edition of that chapbook.

The tailpiece on the final page is also to be found in Item 16, and it seems likely that Fleet was the printer of that Item. Orig. wrappers.

· 1744 ·

1310. Broadside. By the Honorable George Thomas, Esq; Lieutenant Governor and Commander in Chief of the Province of Pennsylvania, and Counties of New-Castle, Kent, and Sussex on Delaware. A Proclamation. [Philadelphia: Printed by B. Franklin, 1744.] Evans 5473. Fig. 1.

This proclamation announces that on March 29, 1744, His Majesty had declared war on the French king and calls upon "all His Majesty's Subjects in this Province, capable of bearing Arms, forthwith to provide themselves with a good Firelock, Bayonet, and Cartouch Box and with a sufficient Quantity of Powder and Ball; that they may be prepar'd, not only to defend this His Majesty's Province, and their own Persons, Families and Estates, but to annoy the Enemy in case it shall be thought proper to attack them." It further invites his Majesty's subjects to fit out privateers to distress and annoy the French. It is dated June 11, 1744.

At the top appears a cut of the Penn coat of arms. This device was first used by Franklin as the masthead for his *Pennsylvania Gazette* [see Item 18(1)]. The impression of this cut on the broadside is somewhat clearer and more vivid than that in Item 18(1). Possibly the block had been recut. As Franklin says in his *Autobiography* that he "engraved several things on occasion," it is quite possible that he was the engraver of the cut, although this, of course, is purely surmise. In any event it makes a handsome heading for the Lieutenant Governor's stirring Proclamation, which is a rare piece of Franklin printing.

· 1749 ·

1311. (1) THE HISTORY OF THE HOLY JESUS. Containing a brief and plain Account of his Birth, Life, Death, Resurrection and Ascension into Heaven; and his coming again at the great and last Day of Judgment. Being a pleasant and profitable Companion for Children; composed on Purpose for their Use. By a Lover of their precious Souls. The Sixth Edition. Boston, Printed by J. Bushell and J. Green, 1749. Evans 6331. Rosenbach 34. Welch 532.5.

This is a complete copy of Item 28 with all 16 woodcuts intact except for various tears which have been mended. With orig. front marbled wrapper, the back wrapper replaced with old paper. In a half morocco case.

(2) Also facsimile of the only known complete copy of the 3rd edition of *The History of the Holy Jesus* printed for B. Gray in Boston in 1746. The original is in the Essex Institute at Salem, Mass. The facsimile was made in an edition of 1200 copies by the Meriden Gravure Company.

No copy of this 3rd edition was known to Albert C. Bates when he wrote his *The History of the Holy Jesus*, Hartford, 1911. It contains the same 16 cuts which appeared in the 4th, 5th, and 6th editions.

· 1756 ·

1312. THE LAW, OUR SCHOOL-MASTER. A SERMON, PREACHED AT LITCHFIELD, JUNE 8, 1756 . . . By Joseph Bellamy, A. M. Minister of the Gospel at Bethlem. Published with Great Enlargements. New-Haven: Printed by James Parker, and Company, at the Post-Office [1756]. Evans 7618.

This is an early publication of the first New Haven press which was founded by Parker late in 1754. At the top of p. 1 is a headpiece bearing the initials "F.H." This cut is probably of English origin. Parker's equipment was ordered for him by Benjamin Franklin from the Caslon foundry in England and included in the order were some head- and tailpieces. One of these, also signed "F.H.," will be found in Item 41. The headpiece in this Item 1312 is probably another. There is also a somewhat ornate tailpiece on p. 77 which perhaps was part of the same equipment.

This sermon is bound with another of Bellamy's sermons—*A Blow at the Root of the refined Antinomianism of the present Age.* Bos-

ton: S. Kneeland, 1763. This second pamphlet contains no cuts.

On the front flyleaf is written "This Book contains two pamphlets written by Dr. Bellamy & sent by himself thro the hands of Dr. Erskine of Edinburgh to J. Ryland, junr. who rec^d. them in July, 1787." Dr. Bellamy (1719-1790) was a follower of Jonathan Edwards and preached at Bethlehem, Conn., for 52 years. He was a powerful revivalist. Old boards with leather back.

· 1757 ·

1313. THE AMERICAN MAGAZINE AND MONTHLY CHRONICLE FOR THE BRITISH COLONIES. VOL. I. Containing from October 1757 to October [1758] inclusive. By a Society of Gentlemen. Philadelphia: Printed and Sold by William Bradford, at the Corner House in Front and Market-Streets.

Following the title-page are 6 pages of an "Index to the most remarkable Things in the American Magazine Vol. I. from October 1757 to October 1758 inclusive."

This Vol. I contains all the numbers of the magazine which were issued, except that for August 1758, which is missing. This August number will be found in Item 35, so that a complete file of the magazine is in the collection.

The title of the first number for October 1757 is "The American Magazine, or Monthly Chronicle for the British Colonies." The title of all the remaining numbers is "The American Magazine and Monthly Chronicle for the British Colonies." The number for October 1758 is called a Supplement to Vol. I. The postscript to this Supplement, in which the Proprietors announce the discontinuance of the magazine "at least for some time," is dated November 14, 1758.

Each number, except the final number or Supplement, contains the cut described in Item 35. Cont. calf, rebacked.

· 1758 ·

1314. AN ASTRONOMICAL DIARY; OR, AN ALMANACK FOR THE YEAR OF OUR LORD CHRIST 1759 . . . By Nathaniel Ames. Boston: Printed and Sold by Draper, Green & Russell, & Fleet [1758]. Evans 8072, who calls for 16 pages. There are actually 24.

Contains a cut of "The Solar System" on the front cover. Sewed.

· 1760 ·

1315. AN ALMANACK FOR THE YEAR OF OUR LORD CHRIST, 1761 . . . By Roger Sherman. Boston; New England: Printed by D. and J. Kneeland, for D. Henchman, J. Edwards, M. Dennis, J. Winter, T. Leverett, and S. Webb, 1761 [1760]. Evans 8734 differs slightly in the title and does not have the date 1761 at the end of the imprint.

On the title-page is a spirited cut of an Indian with bow and arrow. This appears to be printed from the block used later (1768) by John Waterman in his *Tom Thumb's Play-Book* [Item 50]. However, when Waterman made use of it the block had been cut down so that only about a quarter of the frame remained and the trees on the right and part of the Indian's bow had been cut away. Sewed.

· 1767 ·

1316. THE NEW BOOK OF KNOWLEDGE. SHOWING THE EFFECTS OF THE PLANETS AND OTHER ASTRONOMICAL CONSTELLATIONS; WITH THE STRANGE EVENTS THAT BEFALL MEN, WOMEN AND CHILDREN, BORN UNDER THEM . . . Boston: Printed for A. Barclay, near the Three Kings, in Cornhill, 1767.

Contains a full-page frontispiece of an astronomer. About ⅓ of the top of this cut has been torn off, without affecting, however, the main figure. In addition there are 5 (should be 6) small cuts in the text, 2 of which are repeated. Another edition of the book was published by Zechariah Fowle in Boston in the same year. Except for the imprint, these two 1767 editions are identical both as to the cuts and as to the setting of the type. The American Antiquarian Society has copies of both editions. In their copy of the Fowle edition Isaiah Thomas has written "Printed and Cuts Engraved wholly by I. Thomas, then 13 years of age, for Z. Fowle when I.T. was his apprentice" (see pp. 22 and 23 of Main Catalogue). Thomas would have become 13 in 1762 and it has been assumed that an edition of the book was issued by Fowle, with Thomas's cuts, in that year (see Evans 9200), but no copy of such an edition has been located. Whether or not there was such an earlier edition, it seems clear that the cuts in this Item 1316 constitute some of Thomas' earliest work as an engraver.

The small cuts in the text are as crude as one would expect from a lad of 13 years. The frontispiece, however, seems considerably more sophisticated. It will also be found in *The Massachusetts Calender* for 1772, printed in Boston by Isaiah Thomas [Item 59], and Ezekiel Russell used it, copied in reverse, in some of his publications [see Items 80, 89, and 103]. One's first impulse is to question whether Thomas meant to include this frontispiece when

he wrote his inscription in the copy at the American Antiquarian Society, and yet the inscription is written on the back of the frontispiece itself so that, unless he merely used the first blank page that was handy, it would seem that he did lay claim to the frontispiece as well as to the smaller cuts.

In the present copy 16 pages are missing, viz.: v-viii, 17-20, 137-40 and 161-64. None of these missing pages contains any cuts, except p. 164 which has a cut of a sextant. Cont. calf.

1316a. THE NEW-ENGLAND PRIMER IMPROVED FOR THE MORE EASY ATTAINING THE TRUE READING OF ENGLISH. TO WHICH IS ADDED, THE ASSEMBLY OF DIVINES, AND MR. COTTON'S CATECHISM. Boston: Printed for, and Sold by Timothy White, a little above the Market, 1767. 40 leaves, A-E⁸.

The frontispiece is quite an interesting cut of George III. There are 24 small cuts for the rhymed alphabet beginning on the recto of [A⁶]. On the verso of [B⁷] is the usual cut of the martyrdom of John Rogers which, according to the text, took place in Queen Mary's reign on February 14, 1754 [*sic*].

Following the primer are prayers and verses for children; "Some proper Names of Men and Women, to teach Children to spell their own"; rhymed advice of Rogers to his children written "Some few Days before his Death"; The Shorter Catechism; "Spiritual Milk, for American Babes. Drawn out of the Breasts of both *Testaments*, for their Souls Nourishment" by John Cotton; A Dialogue between Christ, Youth and the Devil; and the advice to his children of the "late Reverend and Venerable Mr. Nathanael Clap of Neport [*sic*] on Rhode Island."

This appears to be the only recorded copy of this edition. It is the George Parker Winship copy, No. 27 in George F. Heartman's *The New England Primer*, New York, 1934.

Orig. wooden boards (about one-quarter of front cover lacking) with orig. calf back, in a full morocco box.

· 1768 ·

1317. THE FAMOUS TOMMY THUMB'S LITTLE STORY-BOOK: CONTAINING, HIS LIFE AND SURPRISING ADVENTURES; TO WHICH ARE ADDED, TOMMY THUMB'S FABLES, WITH MORALS: AND, AT THE END, PRETTY STORIES, THAT MAY BE SUNG OR TOLD. (Adorned with many curious Pictures.) Boston: Printed and Sold by W. M'Alpine on Marlborough-street, 1768. Fig. 4.

This appears to be the only known copy of this edition. The only edition of the book listed by Evans is one published in Boston in 1771 (No. 12040). This 1771 edition, a copy of which is in the Boston Public Library, and which is closely similar to the 1768 edition, has 32 pages, and it is probable that this was also true of the 1768 edition. Unfortunately in the present copy the leaf containing pp. 31 and 32 is missing. This copy also lacks pp. 23-26 which probably contained the fables "The Ape and the Fox" and "The Tortoise and the Eagle," with their accompanying cuts. If the missing leaves were present, the collation would be A-B⁸. This copy has the full-page frontispiece and 6 (instead of 8) smaller cuts in the text. The cuts in this edition and in the 1771 edition appear to be the same, and the small cuts in the text are apparently very crude copies of those in an edition printed in London by S. Crowder about 1760, a copy of which is in the collection of d'Alté A. Welch of Cleveland. This London edition contains one fable which is not to be found in either Boston edition, that of "The Nurse and Cross Child." A crude copy of the English cut for this fable has been used on the title-pages of the Boston editions.

Crowder's London edition of *The Famous Tommy Thumb's Little Story-Book* is one of the important source books of Mother Goose Rhymes (see Welch, p. 142). Both Boston editions follow this London edition pretty closely. There are certain discrepancies such as the omission of the fable above noted, the use of the frontispiece, depicting most realistically Tommy's deliverance from the Cow's Belly, which does not appear in the English edition, and an occasional change in a word (such as "Cock Robbin" for "Cock Robin"), but, on the whole, the two Boston editions are clearly based, directly or indirectly, on Crowder's London edition.

The Boston 1768 edition is the fourth book, and the first American book,* to contain a group of more than 3 Mother Goose Rhymes. Those which will be found in the present copy are "There was a man of Thessary," "Sliding on the Ice," "Cock Robbin [*sic*]," and "When I was a little Boy." Unfortunately, owing to the last leaf not being present, it lacks "O my Kitten," "This Pig went to Market," "The Sow came in," "Boys and Girls," and (most lamentable of all) "Little Boy Blue." All of these missing rhymes will be found in Crowder's London edition of *ca.* 1760 and in the Boston

* It should, perhaps, be noted that in *The Renowned History of Giles Gingerbread* [Item 49], printed by Mein & Fleeming in Boston in 1768, there appeared a list of "Books for Children to be had of John Mein at the London Bookstore" and in this list was "The Famous Tommy Thumb's Little Story-Book." As Dr. Welch points out (see Welch, p. 142),

1771 edition. For much of the foregoing information, I am indebted to Dr. d'Alté A. Welch.

Front wrapper present but back wrapper missing. Covered with old brown paper.

· 1769 ·

1318. BICKERSTAFF'S BOSTON ALMANACK. FOR THE YEAR OF OUR LORD 1770 . . . [By Benjamin West.] Printed by Mein and Fleeming, and to be Sold by John Mein, at the London Book-Store, North-side of King-Street [1769]. Evans 11526, who locates no copies.

On the title-page is a woodcut portrait of "The Hon. James Otis, jun. Esq." Sewed. Lacks two leaves.

1319. FATHER ABRAHAM'S ALMANACK, FOR THE YEAR OF OUR LORD, 1770 . . . By Abraham Weatherwise, Gent. Philadelphia: Printed by John Dunlap, at the Newest-Printing-Office, the South Side of the Jersey Market, and three Doors below Second-street [1769]. Evans 11521.

On the front wrapper is the astronomer cut which is to be found in Item 36. The initials "H.D." in the lower right-hand corner have become so worn as to be almost indecipherable. ¾ calf.

· 1770 ·

1320. THE AMERICAN INSTRUCTOR: OR, YOUNG MAN'S BEST COMPANION . . . By George Fisher, Accomptant. The Fourteenth Edition, Revised and Corrected. New-York: Printed and sold by H. Gaine, at the Bible and Crown, in Hanover-Square, 1770. Contains a frontispiece, signed with the initials of Henry Dawkins, showing a teacher with his pupils. This cut was used by W. Dunlap of Philadelphia in his *Father Abraham's Almanack* for 1766 [Item 38].

Evans does not give this edition of *The American Instructor*, but he does give an edition (the 15th edition) printed by Dunlap in Philadelphia also in 1770 (Evans 11859) which contains the same cut as a frontispiece. There was evidently some interchange between Dunlap and Gaine. They both published a *Father Abraham's Almanack* for 1759 containing Henry Dawkins' astronomer cut and other cuts [see Items 32 and 36]. Just how the frontispiece for

this may have been an English book or an American reprint no longer extant. It raises the possibility, however, that another American edition of *The Famous Tommy Thumb's Little Story-Book* was published by Mein & Fleeming in about 1768, of which no copy has come down to us.

The American Instructor, which had been used by Dunlap in 1765 or 1766, got into Gaine's hands for the 14th edition of *The American Instructor* and into Dunlap's hands for the 15th edition raises an interesting question.

Cont. calf.

1321. BROADSIDE. The following Lines were occasioned by the Death of Richard Brown, Samuel Brown, John King & Peter Brown who belonged to Oyster-Ponds on Long Island, And were all Drowned by the over-setting of their Boat, as they were attempting A Passage from East-Hampton, to the Oyster-Ponds, March 9th, 1770. [Then follow 3 columns of lugubrious and mediocre verse.] East-Hampton . . . March 20th, 1770. Printed and Sold in New-London.

At the top of this broadside is the conventional mortuary cut which was used so often in the early part of the 18th century. It is reproduced by Winslow, pp. 7, 23, 31, and 37, and by Ford, p. 44. The words proceeding from Death's mouth "Memento Mori, Remember Death" have been changed to read "Young & Old Remember Death," and no doubt the block itself had been frequently copied or recut during the intervening years.

This mortuary cut is to be found on a memorial broadside commemorating the death of Mrs. Lydia Minot, who was buried January 27, 1667, and for a time it was thought that this was the date of the woodcut and hence that it antedated the portrait of Richard Mather [Item 1]. However, as Miss Winslow points out (p. 6), this *Memento Mori* cut did not begin to appear with any frequency until 1708, and she suggests that, in the case of Lydia Minot, the broadside is a reissue of the original verses issued at the time of Mrs. Minot's death with the *Memento Mori* heading added. In any event the cut, in its accentuation of the power of death, must have been an awe-inspiring one to the original settlers of New England.

1322. A NEW GUIDE TO THE ENGLISH TONGUE; IN FIVE PARTS . . . The Whole, being recommended by several Clergymen and eminent Schoolmasters, as the most useful Performance for the Instruction of Youth, is designed for the Use of Schools in Great Britain, Ireland, and America. By Thomas Dilworth, Author of the Schoolmaster's Assistant; Young Book-keeper's Assistant, etc. etc. Philadelphia: Printed and Sold by Thomas & William Bradford, Wholesale and Retail Booksellers and Stationers, No. 8, South Front Street [*ca.* 1770]. Evans 11634. Rosenbach 65.

* The only recorded copy of this is in the Columbia University Library. It appears to be the first Amer-

The 4 unnumbered pages before the title contain a woodcut portrait of Dilworth and 26 cuts illustrating the alphabet. Beginning with p. 141 there are 12 fables each with a cut at its head. A comparison of these cuts with those used by Benjamin Franklin in his edition of 1747* shows that, while they illustrate the same subjects, they are substantially different. Franklin's cuts are more freely drawn, while those in this later edition are rather tight in drawing. They are, however, better printed and hence clearer. The cuts also differ from those appearing in Dunlap's Philadelphia edition of 1772 which are signed with Henry Dawkins' initials [see Item 63]. Orig. boards with leather back.

1323. (1) VOLLSTÄNDIGES MARBURGER GESANG-BUCH, ZUR UEBUNG DER GOTTSELIGKEIT, IN 649 CHRISTLICHEN UND TROSTREICHEN PSALMEN UND GESÄNGEN HRN. D. MARTIN LUTHERS, UND ANDRER GOTTSELIGER LEHRER . . . Germantown, Gedruckt und zu finden bey Christoph Saur, 1770. Evans 11714.

With frontispiece cut showing Martin Luther standing in his library. Behind him is a large, plump goose. Justus Fox was very busy around this time engraving cuts for Sower [see Items 39, 39a, and 61], and perhaps this cut is his work.

Charles R. Hildeburn in his *The Issues of the Press in Pennsylvania*, Philadelphia, 1886, No. 2561, locates a copy of this book at the Historical Society of Pennsylvania. Cont. calf with clasps.

(2) A copy of a later edition published by Sower in Germantown in 1777, with the same frontispiece as in (1) above, with 31 additional songs. Evans 15387. Cont. calf, clasps missing.

· 1771 ·

1324. THE HISTORY OF THE HOLY JESUS. CONTAINING A BRIEF AND PLAIN ACCOUNT OF HIS BIRTH, LIFE, DEATH, RESURRECTION AND ASCENSION INTO HEAVEN; AND HIS COMING AGAIN AT THE GREAT AND LAST DAY OF JUDGMENT. Being a pleasant and profitable Companion for Children; composed on Purpose for their Use. By a Lover of their precious Souls. The Eleventh Edition. New-Haven: Printed by T. and S. Green, 1771. Welch 532.19.

Contains the 16 cuts which appeared in the early editions of the 1740s, apparently printed from the original blocks, except that one or two may have been reworked (see, for example, the cut of "The Careful Mother" on A⁴ recto)

ican edition of an extremely popular speller.

and except also that the ornate border surrounding the cut of the ship on A⁸ verso has been replaced by straight rules. The small cut of a tree on B⁵ verso also differs from the cut used in the earlier editions.

In addition to the usual 16 cuts this edition contains on the final page a 17th cut which is quite interesting and seems to have little, if any, relation to *The History of the Holy Jesus*, although Welch (532.8) suggests that the cut may be a supplementary illustration of the Murder of the Innocents. To the writer, however, it would seem to be an attempt to depict an incident in a French and Indian raid. On the left are shown some soldiers who have secured an old man and a woman as their prisoners. A corpse lies in the middle foreground while on the right, behind some trees, a figure, which might be that of an Indian, is seen scalping a child. The writer has been unable to ascertain where the cut was first used. It will also be found in the 8th edition of *The History of the Holy Jesus*, printed by T. Green in New London in 1762, a copy of which is owned by the Connecticut Historical Society, and in the 10th edition of 1769, also printed by T. Green in New London, a copy of which is in the Yale Library.

It might be noted that in the 8th edition of 1762 there is an additional or 18th cut which is not found in any of the other early editions. It is the portrait of a military looking man. In the background is what appears to be a group of cavalrymen and, in the farther distance, the spires of a city.

This copy of the 11th edition of 1771 appears to be the only known copy. 19th-century leather.

· 1772 ·

1325. ANDERSON IMPROVED: BEING AN ALMANACK, AND EPHEMERIS, FOR THE YEAR OF OUR LORD 1773 . . . By John Anderson, Philom. Newport, Rhode-Island: Printed by Solomon Southwick, and to be Sold, Wholesale and Retail, at his Office in Queen-Street, as cheap as any in New-England [1772]. Evans 12310.

On the front wrapper is a woodcut of an astronomer looking through a telescope. This is an earlier and considerably better impression of the cut than that found in Item 65. Lacks final signature of 4 leaves which contain no cuts. Sewed.

1326. AN ASTRONOMICAL DIARY; OR, ALMANACK FOR THE YEAR OF CHRISTIAN AERA, 1773 . . . By Nathanael Low, a Student in Physic. Boston: Printed and Sold by J. Knee-

land, in Milk-Street, 1773 [1772]. Evans 12438. With a woodcut portrait of John Dryden on the title-page. Sewed. Lacks one leaf.

1327. NEÜ-VERMEHRT-UND-VOLLSTÄNDIGES GESANG-BUCH . . . Germantown: Gedruckt und zu finden bey Christoph Saur, 1772. Evans 12534.

This is the 3rd edition of this German psalter and hymn book and contains the same cut which was used in the earlier editions [see Items 33(1) and 33(2)], showing David playing the harp and signed with the initial "S," which suggests Sower himself as the possible engraver. Cont. calf with the bookplate of Samuel W. Pennypacker.

1328. THE NORTH-AMERICAN'S CALENDAR AND GENTLEMEN AND LADIES DIARY, BEING AN ALMANACK FOR THE YEAR OF THE CHRISTIAN AERA 1773 . . . By Samuel Stearns. Boston: Printed and Sold by Edes & Gill and T. & J. Fleet [1772]. Evans 12566.

On the title-page is a cut of "A Projection of the Twelve Signs of the Zodiack." On the second page is a cut of "The Anatomy of Man's Body" (the anatomical man), and on the third page is a cut of the "Eclipses." These 3 typemetal cuts were engraved by Paul Revere in the Fall of 1772, and for them he charged Edes & Gill the sum of 1£, 16s. (See Brigham, p. 136, who reproduces all 3 cuts on Plate 72.) Sewed.

1328a. THE PENNSYLVANIA CHRONICLE, AND UNIVERSAL ADVERTISER. From Saturday, September 19, to Saturday, September 26, 1772. [Philadelphia: Printed by William Goddard, at the New Printing-Office in Front-Street, near Market-Street, on the Bank Side, and almost opposite to the London Coffee-House. . . .] See Evans 12508.

On the third page appears a cartoon, cut on wood or typemetal, showing "Americanus" [Joseph Galloway] on his way to the Bucks County election, accompanied by the Buckram Marquis of New Barrataria [Thomas Wharton]. He carries the 5 Mile Stone on his back, and is trampling on the Goddess Liberty, the Bill of Rights, and the Pennsylvania Charter, while the devil whispers in his ear "Don't flinch, my Dear Galloway. I'll support you."

Galloway at this time was a leader of the bar and a man of some prominence. For a number of years he had been speaker of the Pennsylvania Assembly and in 1774 he became a delegate to the First Continental Congress. In 1776, however, at a time when the rebellious colonies seemed headed for defeat, he defected to the British and later became civil administrator of Philadelphia on its occupation by Howe.

The cartoon in the *Chronicle* is accompanied by a vicious attack upon Galloway signed by the paper's publisher, William Goddard. Galloway and Goddard, at one time partners, had quarreled and become bitter enemies. Goddard was attempting to prevent Galloway's reelection to the Assembly. The mysterious reference in the cartoon to the 5 Mile Stone relates to another controversy between Galloway and Goddard. Early in 1772 Galloway received a letter demanding a loan of 50£, the money to be left under the 5 Mile Stone on the Darby Road. Galloway accused Goddard of being the writer, which the latter indignantly denied. Thereafter the *Chronicle* referred to the 5 Mile Stone as Galloway's "monument."*

According to Murrell (Vol. I, pp. 12-13) the real political cartoon first made its appearance in this country in Philadelphia in 1764. This cartoon of 1772 in the *Pennsylvania Chronicle* is, therefore, a comparatively early one and, as it relates to purely local controversies, it was, no doubt, the product of some Philadelphia craftsman. Murrell (p. 20) attributes some of the cartoons of the 1760s, which he describes, to Henry Dawkins, and it is interesting to note that John Dunlap, the Philadelphia publisher, advertises his *Father Abraham's Almanack* in this issue of the *Chronicle* and that Dawkins had not only made engravings for this almanac in the past [see Items 36 and 38] but had also engraved the cuts for John Dunlap's 1772 edition of *A New Guide to the English Tongue* [Item 63]. It is, within the realm of possibility that Dawkins had some hand in this 1772 cartoon of Joseph Galloway.

· 1773 ·

1329. AN ASTRONOMICAL DIARY; OR, ALMANACK FOR THE YEAR OF CHRISTIAN AERA, 1774 . . . By Nathanael Low. Boston: Printed and Sold by J. Kneeland, in Milk Street: Sold also by the Printers & Booksellers. 1774. [1773.] Evans 12837. On the title-page is a woodcut portrait of Cromwell. Sewed.

1329a. DIVINE SONGS ATTEMPTED IN EASY LANGUAGE FOR THE USE OF CHILDREN. By I. Watts, D.D. The Sixteenth Edition. Philadelphia: Printed by Joseph Crukshank, for R. Aitken, Bookseller, opposite the London Coffee-House, in Front-street. [n.d., but probably about 1773. This is the date which the American Antiquarian Society has assigned to its copy, a date based on an entry in the Aitken *Waste Book* at the American Philosophical Society. See also Evans 13065.]

The frontispiece is an oval portrait of Dr. Watts, surrounded by a graceful border of type ornaments. It shows only the Doctor's head and shoulders and is totally different from the frontispiece in the Boston edition of 1771 [Item 58] which purported to show Dr. Watts in his pulpit, although it was actually a cut used probably in early 1771 to depict George Whitefield preaching. It is also totally different from the frontispiece of the 3 editions of the *Divine Songs* issued in 1775 [see Item 1335], which also purported to show Dr. Watts in his pulpit, but which stemmed from the 1771 cut of Whitefield. Perhaps this Philadelphia cut was copied from an earlier English cut which was really trying to give some authentic idea of what the worthy Isaac looked like.

At the end of the volume is an interesting list of children's books for sale by Aitken. The only other copy of this edition known to the writer is that at the American Antiquarian Society. Orig. marbled wrappers, in cloth case.

1330. FREEBETTER'S CONNECTICUT ALMANACK, FOR THE YEAR OF OUR LORD CHRIST 1774 . . . [By Nathan Daboll.] The Second Edition. New-London: Printed and Sold by T. Green [1773]. 24 pp.

On the title-page is "a curious cut of his M . . . y's Wig." The portrait with its wig is hardly flattering to King George, and the cut is one of those increasingly frequent signs of colonial discontent. Disbound.

1331. THE PENNSYLVANIA PACKET. AND THE GENERAL ADVERTISER. Philadelphia: Printed by John Dunlap, at the Newest Printing-Office, in Market-Street, "where Subscriptions at Ten Shillings *per Annum*, Advertisements, Etc. are thankfully received for this Paper." See Evans 12186.

Two bound volumes containing the issues of this paper from January 4, 1773, to May 22, 1775, both inclusive, lacking 11 numbers. In all there are 114 numbers together with many supplements and 2 extra numbers. These num-

---

* For an interesting account of the Galloway-Goddard feud, see article by Arthur W. Schlesinger in *The Pennsylvania Magazine of History and Biography*, No. LX, p. 309 (October 1936), and for the explanation of the reference to the "5 Mile Stone" see article by Fred Perry Powers on "Mile Stones and Highways" in *Philadelphia History*, Vol. II, No. 6.

published by the City History Society of Philadelphia in 1922, where the cartoon is reproduced. Both these articles were called to the writer's attention by Mrs. William E. Decker, of the Bucks County Historical Society, who was most helpful in connection with this Galloway cartoon.

bers contain many articles and much news of historical interest, such as, for example, matters relating to the duty on tea, an account of the battles of Lexington and Concord, etc., etc.

At the masthead of the number for January 4, 1773, and of many numbers following is a cut of a sailing ship with its bow toward the spectator, the foreshortening not badly handled. This cut had been in use since the start of the paper on October 28, 1771. For some unexplained reason, this cut, although not very much worn, was abandoned with the issue of October 25, 1773, and a new cut, somewhat more eye-catching of a three-masted sailing ship, seen broadside, was substituted. Henry Dawkins was in Philadelphia in the early 1770s and had done engraving both for John Dunlap and for his predecessor William Dunlap [see Items 63, 36, and 38]. Possibly he had something to do with these mastheads. With the issue of October 25, 1773, where this change was made, the entire masthead was rearranged and the name of the paper changed to read "Dunlap's Pennsylvania Packet, or, the General Advertiser."

The paper is full of small advertising cuts, many of them used time and time again. Probably they were kept in stock by Dunlap for use, at a price, by those wishing to advertise. The most common are cuts of sailing vessels with notices of departures for Liverpool, Bristol, Dublin, Charlestown, S.C., and other ports; cuts of runaway servants, sometimes male and sometimes female and sometimes in pairs when more than one had taken French leave; cuts of handsome horses, some of them quite elaborately drawn, to be used for breeding purposes; cuts of the Philadelphia and New York stage coaches which set off "at or before sun rising on every Tuesday and Friday to Prince-town, where the New-York coach meets and exchanges passengers"; cuts of stolen cows and cuts of houses for sale or rent. Many of these cuts are reasonably well drawn, and they afford interesting examples of the commercial cuts in use during this period.

The 2 volumes are not in uniform bindings. The first carries the bookplate of Samuel W. Pennypacker.

1332. The Schoolmaster's Assistant: Being a Compendium of Arithmetic, both Practical and Theoretical . . . The Seventeenth Edition. By Thomas Dilworth. Philadelphia: Printed and Sold by Joseph Crukshank, in Third-street, opposite the Work-house, 1773. Evans 12752. The frontispiece is a portrait of Dilworth, probably cut on typemetal. Crukshank used it again in his edition of 1790 [Item 134]. It appears to be the same cut used by Dunlap

in his 1772 edition of Dilworth's *A New Guide to the English Tongue* [Item 63].

This is the first American edition of *The Schoolmaster's Assistant*. Orig. calf.

· 1774 ·

1333. Daboll's New-England Almanack, for the Year 1775 . . . [By Nathan Daboll.] New London: Printed and Sold by T. Green [1774]. 32 pp.

On the title-page is a portrait, largely in white line, of Dr. Jonathan Shipley, Lord Bishop of St. Asaph. The almanac contains Shipley's celebrated speech, "intended to have been spoken on the Bill for altering the Charter of the Province of the Massachusetts Bay; but want of Time, or some other Circumstance, prevented his delivering it in the House of Lords." The speech was popular in the colonies and there were a number of printings of it here in 1774. It contains the sentence, "My Lords, I look upon North-America as the only great nursery of freemen now left upon the face of the earth."

On the last page of the almanac there is a cut of a lunar eclipse. Disbound.

· 1775 ·

1334. Bickerstaff's New-England Almanack, For the Year of our Redemption, 1776 . . . Newburyport: Printed and Sold by Mycall and Tinges [1775]. On the title-page is an extremely crude woodcut depicting "Mercury introducing Concord, Agriculture, and the Arts, to America." Concord's nose appears to be broken and Mercury is quite bald. Sewed.

1335. Divine Songs, Attempted In easy Language, For the Use of Children. By I. Watts, D.D. The Fourteenth Edition. Printed for, and Sold by Mascoll Williams, at the sign of the Bible, in King-Street. Salem. 1775. 24 leaves, A-D⁶. Fig. 3.

This appears to be the only recorded copy of this edition. On the verso of the title-page is a cut of Dr. Watts in his pulpit. While differing in a number of respects and drawn in reverse, it evidently stems from the cut of George Whitefield preaching which appeared in several publications shortly after Whitefield's death in 1770 [see Item 63a and Winslow, No. 81]. In the lower left-hand corner of the cut is a comparatively large "N" followed by an equally large initial which is probably "C."

3 editions of *The Divine Songs* were published in 1775:

(1) A Boston edition "Printed and Sold, by N. Coverly near Christ-Church, North-End"

(see Roger P. Bristol, *Supplement [Checking Edition] to Evans' American Bibliography*, Charlottesville, 1962, p. 250).

(2) The present Salem edition which was "Printed for, and Sold by Mascoll Williams."

(3) A Boston edition "Printed for and sold by A. Barclay" (see Bristol's *Supplement*, above cited, at p. 250).

All 3 editions appear to have been printed from the same type, have the same number of leaves, are called "The Fourteenth Edition,"* and have the same frontispiece of "Dr. Watts." In the Barclay edition the lower portion of this cut, the portion with the "N.C." initials, is missing, but it does not seem to have been deliberately cut off, as the break is not a clean one and lines forming part of the lower portion of the cut are still to be seen, giving a rather unsightly appearance. It seems likely that the block or plate met with an accident and the lower portion was in some way broken off.

In editions (1) and (3) the final page has a cut of Cromwell in an oval frame, a cut which will also be found in *An Astronomical Diary . . . for . . . 1774* (Item 1329). This cut does not appear in edition (2). In its place is a full-page advertisement of books and other things sold by Williams at Salem, including a paragraph to the effect that he did binding work of all sorts "in the best and neatest Manner." Williams apparently was commercially minded and preferred an advertisement to an embellishment.

In view of the wording of the 3 imprints and the break in the cut in edition (3), it seems probable that the 3 editions appeared in the order given above and that Coverly printed all of them. As initials which are probably "N.C." appear on the cut of "Dr. Watts," it would also seem reasonable to suggest that Coverly himself engraved it.

In the present copy of the Salem edition the final page, when the book was acquired, was pasted down to the back wrapper, completely obscuring Mr. Williams' advertisement. This, as Dr. d'Alté A. Welch has suggested, may mean that the wrappers are not the original ones, although they appear to be contemporary. It is a charming little book with a string of small woodcut bees introducing the famous lines "How doth the little busy Bee Improve each shining Hour." In cont. wall-paper wrappers, in a cloth case.

Accompanying the book are xerox prints of the title-page, the Watts portrait, the first page of text, and the last page with its portrait of Cromwell(?) from the Coverly edition, kindly furnished by the American Antiquarian Society,

and a docustat of the Watts portrait and the first page of text from the Barclay edition, kindly furnished by the Boston Public Library.

· 1776 ·

1336. A NEW MILITARY, HISTORICAL, AND EXPLANATORY DICTIONARY: INCLUDING THE WARRIORS GAZETEER OF PLACES REMARKABLE FOR SIEGES OR BATTLES. By Thomas Simes, Esq.; Philadelphia: Sold by Humphreys, Bell, and Aitken, 1776.

There is a copper engraved frontispiece and the text is livened by numerous small woodcuts of fortifications and military equipment. It is possible that Robert Aitken, who was an engraver [see Item 76], was responsible for the illustrations.

Evans (15083) lists this as the second volume of Simes' *The Military Guide for Young Officers*, but there is nothing in the present volume to mark it as part of a larger work. Possibly the *Dictionary* was published in a separate edition as well as part of *The Military Guide*. Modern cloth. Presented by James H. Farrell.

1337. (1) THE NEW YORK PACKET AND THE AMERICAN ADVERTISER. Thursday, July 11, 1776. Printed by Samuel Loudon, in Water-Street, between the Coffee-House and the Old Slip.

The masthead consists of a cut of a full-rigged ship, and at the bottom are initials which look like "I.D." but which an examination of the issue of June 13, 1776 [no. (2) below] shows clearly to be "H.D." Henry Dawkins left Philadelphia in 1774 and came to New York City where he was arrested in May 1776, for counterfeiting. As *The New York Packet* began publication in January 1776, it seems probable that Dawkins cut this masthead sometime in the latter part of 1775.

On the second page of this issue of *The New York Packet* is printed the Declaration of Independence, a very early New York printing. This issue also contains an interesting paragraph reading "Same day [July 9, 1776], in the evening, the statue of King George the Third, on horseback, in the Bowling-green, was taken down, broken to pieces, and its honour levelled with the dust."

The New York Packet was established by Loudon January 4, 1776, but was suspended with the issue of August 29, 1776, immediately prior to the entry of the British into New York. Loudon reestablished the paper at Fishkill in

---

* There appear to have been other "Fourteenth Editions" [see Item 58].

January 1777. Only 3 other copies of this July 11, 1776, issue have been located, those at the Library of Congress, the New York Public Library, and the Massachusetts Historical Society (see Clarence S. Brigham, *History and Bibliography of American Newspapers*, Worcester, 1947, Vol. I, p. 675).

(2) Also the issue of *The New York Packet* for June 13, 1776. This contains a better impression of the masthead which plainly shows the initials "H.D."

1338. THE NORTH AMERICAN'S ALMANACK, FOR THE YEAR OF OUR LORD CHRIST, 1777 . . . By Isaac Warren. Student in Astronomy. Worcester: Printed and Sold by W. Stearns and D. Bigelow, also to be sold by the Author in Lancaster, at 3/6 per Dozen, and 8 coppers single [1776]. Evans 15212.

On [A²] verso is a woodcut map of the environs of New York City, showing the "Island of New-York" with the city at its Southern tip, the Fort at Powle's Hook, the North River, King's Bridge, Hell-Gate, Governor's Island, part of Long Island, the Narrows full of shipping, part of Staten Island, and the New Jersey shore with the city of Newark. Sewed.

1339. THE PRODIGAL DAUGHTER: OR, A STRANGE AND WONDERFUL RELATION, SHEWING HOW A GENTLEMAN OF A VAST ESTATE IN BRISTOL, HAD A PROUD AND DISOBEDIENT DAUGHTER, WHO, BECAUSE HER PARENTS WOULD NOT SUPPORT HER IN ALL HER EXTRAVAGANCE, BARGAINED WITH THE DEVIL TO POISON THEM. HOW AN ANGEL INFORMED HER PARENTS OF HER DESIGN. HOW SHE LAY IN A TRANCE FOUR DAYS; AND WHEN SHE WAS PUT IN THE GRAVE SHE CAME TO LIFE AGAIN, AND RELATED THE WONDERFUL THINGS SHE SAW IN THE OTHER WORLD. Likewise the Substance of a Sermon preached on the Occasion, by the Rev. Mr. Williams, from Luke xv. 24. Danvers: Printed and Sold by E. Russell, next Bell-Tavern [*ca.* 1776-1777].

Contains 4 woodcuts which illustrate the same scenes which are illustrated in the Fleet editions [see Item 51] and in the Fowle and the Thomas editions [see Item 45], but the designs have substantial differences. The cut on the title-page, which is repeated on p. 12, will be found in Philip James, *Children's Books of Yesterday*, London, 1933, reproduced from a copy of *The Prodigal Daughter*, printed by Russell in Boston in 1797. Old paper wrappers, sewed.

· 1777 ·

1340. THE NEW-ENGLAND PRIMER IMPROVED. FOR THE MORE EASY ATTAINING THE TRUE READING OF ENGLISH. TO WHICH IS ADDED THE ASSEMBLY OF DIVINES, AND MR. COTTON'S CATECHISM. Boston: Printed by Edward Draper, at his Printing-Office, in Newbury-Street, and Sold by John Boyle, in Marlborough-Street. 1777. Evans 15450. Heartman 60.

On the front wrapper is a woodcut portrait of John Hancock apparently printed from the same block as the portrait in *Bickerstaff's Boston Almanack* for 1777 [Item 79]. Beginning on A⁶ recto are the small cuts illustrating the letters of the alphabet. On B⁷ verso is the cut of the burning of John Rogers.

In 1843 Ira Webster of Hartford, Conn., published a reprint of this edition, so that it became one of the best known of 18th-century editions. On the back of the front cover of this copy are written the words "Ira Webster's," so that this may have been the copy actually used by Webster in making the reprint. Old calf over wooden boards.

Accompanying the book is a copy of Ira Webster's reprint.

· 1778 ·

1341. THE EVENING POST; AND THE GENERAL ADVERTISER. Saturday, October 31, 1778. Boston: Printed by White and Adams, at their Printing-Office in School-Street, next Door to the Cromwell's Head Tavern . . . Vol. I, No. 3. Evans 15792.

At the masthead is a large cut showing a female figure, possibly intended for Columbia, holding in one hand a spear surmounted by the liberty cap and in the other an olive branch, with a sailing ship in the lower left-hand corner. Under it are the words "Hail Liberty Divine, and Peace, First-born of Heaven!"

This was a shortlived newspaper which began publication with the number for October 17, 1778, and expired with the number for May 11, 1780.

1342. THE LAST WORDS AND DYING SPEECH OF JAMES BUCHANAN, EZRA ROSS AND WILLIAM BROOKS, WHO ARE EXECUTED THIS DAY AT WORCESTER, FOR THE MURDER OF MR. JOSHUA SPOONER. Boston: Printed and Sold by Draper and Folsom, at the Corner of Winter-Street [*ca.* 1778].

This is a broadside giving the detailed confession of the murderers of the unfortunate Mr. Spooner, whose wife had taken a dislike to him and accordingly arranged his demise. At the upper left-hand corner is a cut of Satan with a hangman's noose in his hand, while at the upper right-hand corner is a cut of a skull and bones.

· 1780 ·

1343. (1) AMERICANISCHER HAUS- UND WIRTHSCHAFTS-CALENDER AUF DAS 1781ste JAHR CHRISTI . . . Zum Zweytenmal heraus gegeben. Philadelphia: Gedruckt und zu haben bey Steiner und Cist, in der Zweyten-strasse, vier Häuser oberhalb der Rees-strasse [1780]. 20 leaves, A-K². Evans 16696. Fig. 7.

Beginning on H¹ verso is a report of Benedict Arnold's treason and of Andre's execution contained in extracts from 2 letters written from Tapan (sic), one dated September 28, 1780, and the other October 2, 1780. There then follows a short description of the figures which, on receipt of the news of the treason, had been paraded through the streets of Philadelphia on September 30, 1780. Between signatures H and I a long folding woodcut has been sewed in, showing this Philadelphia parade. Arnold, with two faces, one looking forward and the other back, is seen sitting in a cart, and behind him stands the figure of the devil, holding a money bag in one hand and a pitchfork in the other. On a transparency in front of Arnold appear two bodies hanging from a gallows. Over them are the words "Spy" and "Traytor" and underneath the names "I. Smith" and "Andre."* Fifers and drummers (playing the Rogues-March) and a file of soldiers surround the cart and in front of it is to be seen the bonfire in which the effigies will be burnt. It is a most unusual and interesting cut. Drake (10105) locates 8 copies of the almanac, but in only one of them (that belonging to The Historical Society of Pennsylvania but now in the custody of the Library Company of Philadelphia) has the folding cut been preserved. Actually there are 9 copies, as the Historical Society of Pennsylvania has 2, but only one of these has the cut.

A cut of this same Philadelphia parade appeared in The Continental Almanack for 1781, published in Philadelphia by Francis Bailey. This cut, since it depicts the same scene, corresponds in a general way to the cut in the Americanischer Haus- und Wirthschafts-Calender, but is radically different in its details as well as in its spirit and draftsmanship. In the cut in the German almanac the figures are better drawn and are far more lively than are those in the other almanac. Indeed it is so well done that one wonders whether the services of Justus Fox [see Item 39], whose cuts had appeared in many of the German almanacs issued by the Sowers, might not have been availed of.

In about 1872 the cut of The Continental Almanack was re-engraved to illustrate Thompson Westcott's A History of Philadelphia, which was published in Philadelphia in the Sunday Dispatch from January 6, 1867, to March 24, 1878. The re-engraved cut appeared in the issue for June 30, 1872. Murrell (Vol. I, p. 32) refers to the cut in The Continental Almanack (inadvertently called by Murrell the Almanack for 1780) and reproduces the cut in Fig. 25, but, as Mr. Edwin Wolf, 2nd, of the Library Company of Philadelphia, has pointed out to the writer, a comparison indicates that Murrell's reproduction is based on the re-engraved cut made for the Sunday Dispatch rather than on the original cut. A copy of The Continental Almanack for 1781 will be found at the Metropolitan Museum of Art in New York City.

Throughout the Americanischer Haus- und Wirthschafts-Calender for 1781 are 12 cuts of the occupations of the months. These are copied in reverse from those appearing in Armbrüster's German Almanac for 1754 [Item 32], except that, due to a mistake, the cut for October appears under June and that for June under October. On the recto of I¹ is a cut of the Ant-Bear, rather well done. Sewed.

Accompanying the Almanac is a photostat of the cut in The Continental Almanack for 1781 from the copy at the Metropolitan Museum of Art in New York City and a photostat of the issue of the Sunday Dispatch for June 30, 1872.

(2) AMERICANISCHER HAUS- UND WIRTHSCHAFTS-CALENDER AUF DAS 1783ste JAHR CHRISTI . . . Gedruckt und zu haben bey Carl Cist, in der Markt-strasse, zwischen der Vierten- und Funften-strasse [1782]. Evans 17455.

On the title-page are cuts showing on the left side the implements of war and on the right side the implements of peace. These cuts will also be found on the title-page of (1) above, but that page is badly soiled so that it is hard to distinguish the design.

Beginning on B² recto are the same cuts of the occupations of the months which appear in (1) except that the mistake noted above has been corrected. Sewed.

1344. GEORGE'S ALMANACK FOR THE YEAR OF OUR LORD 1781 . . . [By Daniel George.] Newburyport: Printed and sold by John Mycall, and by the Book-sellers and Shop-keepers [1780].

---

* Actually the words written underneath the gallows were, according to the text as translated, "Andrie, General Adjutant of the British Army and Joe Smith, the first hanged as a spy and the other as a traitor to his country." This seems a little premature on September 30, 1780, as Andre was not executed until October 2, and Smith was later acquitted.

[13]

Evans 16785. With a cut of an elephant on the title-page. Sewed.

· 1781 ·

1345. THE NEW-ENGLAND PRIMER. IMPROVED, FOR THE MORE EASY ATTAINING THE TRUE READING OF ENGLISH. TO WHICH IS ADDED, THE ASSEMBLY OF DIVINES, AND MR. COTTON'S CATECHISM. Boston: Printed and Sold by John D. M'Dougall and Company, 1781. Evans 17244.

On p. [5] appears a portrait, probably engraved on typemetal, of General Washington. This portrait will also be found in *Weatherwise's Town and Country Almanack for . . . 1781*, also published by John D. M'Dougall and Company [see Item 90]. Probably the first appearance of the cut was in the almanac.

On October 26, 1781, Paul Revere wrote to his cousin Mathias Rivoire in France enclosing in his letter a small engraving of General Washington and saying "it is said to be a good likeness and it is my engraving." Largely on the strength of this letter, Charles Henry Hart in his *Catalogue of the Engraved Portraits of Washington*, New York, 1904, was prepared to accept this typemetal cut, crude as it may seem, as the work of Revere, "until the ascription is disproved by the production of a copper-plate print bearing his name as engraver." Brigham, at p. 108, says "Mr. Hart's opinion may be correct. The style of engraving in a way is like Revere's work, and the evidence of the letter to the cousin is interesting, if not conclusive. Perhaps some day the problem will be solved." As yet, however, no further light has been thrown on the problem.

As Brigham points out, the cut was apparently copied from the John Norman copperplate portrait of Washington in the *Philadelphia Almanack* for 1780, engraved and printed in broadside form by Norman and Bedwell in Philadelphia and reproduced by Brigham opposite p. 108, in Plate 50.

This edition of *The New-England Primer* contains the cuts of the alphabet on pp. 10-13 and the cut of the burning of John Rogers on p. 28. All these cuts are in good impressions in this copy. Orig. boards with leather back.

1346. RUSSELL'S AMERICAN ALMANACK, FOR THE YEAR OF OUR REDEMPTION, 1782 . . . [By Benjamin West.] Boston: Printed by E. Russell, at his Printing-Office in Essex-street, near Liberty-stump, South-end [1781].

On the title-page is a cut of a military man which Evans (17434), with some hesitation,

suggests is meant for Washington. If so, it is even more "unpleasant and lop-sided" than the portrait of Washington which appears in *Weatherwise's Town and Country Almanack for . . . 1781* [Item 90] and which has been attributed to Paul Revere.* This almanac also contains the 12 cuts of the occupations of the months. Sewed.

· 1783 ·

1347. BICKERSTAFF'S BOSTON ALMANACK FOR THE YEAR OF OUR REDEMPTION, 1784 . . . [By Benjamin West.] Boston: Printed and sold by E. Russell, near Liberty-Pole; and by Adams and Nourse, Marlboro'-street [1783]. See Evans 18304, with slight differences in the imprint.

On the title-page is the cut of an astronomer which will be found in Items 80, 89, and 103. The 12 cuts of the occupations of the months are the same as those which appear in Items 78, 82, and 103, but for some reason the impressions of these cuts in this 1784 almanac seem somewhat sharper. These cuts of the months are rather poor copies of those to be found in *Father Abraham's Almanack* for 1760, 1761, and 1766 [Item 38].

On A² verso of this 1784 almanac is a cut of a group of monkeys surrounding one in a rich embroidered coat and periwig. It illustrates the fable of "The Monkey who has seen the World." Sewed.

1348. THE HISTORY OF LITTLE GOODY TWO-SHOES; OTHERWISE CALLED MRS. MARGERY TWO SHOES. WITH THE MEANS BY WHICH SHE ACQUIRED HER LEARNING AND WISDOM, AND IN CONSEQUENCE THEREOF HER ESTATE . . . Boston: Printed and sold by Nathaniel Coverly, Near the Sign of the White-Horse, 1783. A-B¹⁶, 64 pp. See Welch, No. 427.2.

Contains 31 small cuts. Many of the cuts seem to have been copied in reverse from Hugh Gaine's 1775 edition [Item 75(b)], which is usually accepted as the first American edition, but a few are entirely different. This 1783 edition appears to be the 2d American edition of *Little Goody-Two Shoes*. It is true that Wilbur Macy Stone in his *History of Little Goody-Two Shoes*, Worcester, 1940, lists 3 other editions prior to 1783, viz., Hugh Gaine, New York, 1774 and 1776, and Robert Bell, Phila., 1776, the latter also listed by Evans, No. 14799, but no copy of any of these editions has been located, and there appears to be no reason to infer, from the advertisements on which they were based, that the editions advertised were American imprints.

---

* See p. xxx of Main Catalogue and Item 1345.

Welch locates only 3 other copies of this 1783 edition, all imperfect in one way or another. This copy is complete except that it is preserved in an old homemade paper wrapper which probably displaced the original wrappers.

1348a. THREE SERMONS TO LITTLE CHILDREN. ON THE NATURE AND BEAUTY OF THE DUTIFUL TEMPER. [Published by Desire.] By Samuel Spring, A.M. Pastor of the North Church, in Newbury-Port. Boston: Printed and Sold by Nathaniel Coverly, Opposite the White-Horse-Tavern, 1783. Evans 18195. A-F⁶.

Contains 2 small cuts (pp. 22 and 44). These are entirely different from, and not quite as ingratiating as, those which appear in the later New York edition of 1790 (Item 135). Cont. calf over wooden boards.

· 1785 ·

1349. BICKERSTAFF'S BOSTON ALMANACK, FOR THE YEAR OF OUR LORD 1786 . . . [By Benjamin West]. Boston: Printed and Sold (Wholesale and Retail) by John W. Folsom [1785]. Evans 19371.

On the title-page is a cut showing a dog biting a man and illustrating the well-known elegy which ends

"The man recover'd of the bite,
The dog it was that dy'd."

Sewed, in old paper wrappers.

1350. THE MOST DELIGHTFUL HISTORY OF THE KING AND THE COBLER: SHEWING: HOW THE KING FIRST CAME ACQUAINTED WITH THE COBLER, AND THE MANY PLEASANT HUMOURS WHICH HAPPENED THEREUPON, &C. Boston: Printed and sold at the Bible & Heart in Cornhill [ca. 1785-1790]. Welch 679.3.

With 2 woodcuts on the title-page, the first showing "The Cobler sitting and whistling in his Stall" and the other showing "The Cobler's Reception and Behaviour at Court." The latter is repeated on the final page. The cuts appear to be printed from the identical blocks used by the Fleets in their edition of this chapbook issued prior to 1776 when they were still using the "Heart and Crown" imprint (see Rosenbach 66). Rosenbach dates his copy ca. 1770, but the impressions look as if the blocks were worn and the cuts may be of considerably older vintage than this. Perhaps they are the work of Fleet's ingenious Negro [see Item 51]. In this "Bible & Heart" edition the type differs substantially from that used in Rosenbach 66.

The American Antiquarian Society has a copy of an edition of this chapbook printed without date by John Boyle of Boston. Clarence S.

Brigham put the date as ca. 1773. There are also copies of an undated Boyle edition at the William L. Clements Library and in the d'Alté A. Welch Collection which Welch dates as ca. 1774 (see Welch 679.1). Probably these are copies of the same edition as that at the American Antiquarian Society. Apart from these 3 copies, the Rosenbach copy of the early Fleet edition and the present copy, no American 18th-century copies of this chapbook have been located. Sewed.

1351. WEATHERWISE'S TOWN AND COUNTRY ALMANACK, FOR THE YEAR OF OUR LORD, 1786 . . . By Abraham Weatherwise, Philom. [David Rittenhouse]. Boston: Printed for and sold by J. Norman near the Boston Stone Where may be had the second Edition of the Massachusetts Harmony, with a large addition of new tunes lately published in London. Likewise Wats' (sic). Psalms and Hymns, by the Groce or Dozen [1785]. Evans 19224. Fig. 6.

On the recto of the leaf preceding the title-page is a cut of "General Washington's Jack Ass" and under it the following:

"This is the true picture of that Celebrated Animal, which his Most Catholick Majesty the King of Spain Bought with his own money and Shipped at his own Expence, for a present to our beloved General.

Hero merit takes, and Gallant Actions shine
Or Mighty Sir, this Ass had ne'er been thine,
Though droll the Gift, yet from a King tis' good;
Asses, Kings, Ministers are all one blood."

Sewed and covered with a bit of green wall-paper.

· 1786 ·

1351a. THE HOLY BIBLE ABRIDGED: OR, THE HISTORY OF THE OLD AND NEW TESTAMENT. Illustrated with Notes, and adorned with Cuts. For the Use of Children. The First Worcester Edition. Worcester (Massachusetts), Printed by Isaiah Thomas, and sold at his Book Store. 1786. A-L.⁸ Evans 19506.

Contains full-page frontispiece and 56 (should be 61) smaller cuts in the text depicting Biblical scenes. 10 pages (35, 36, 45, 46, 65, 66, 129, 130, 143, and 144), containing 5 cuts, are missing. The missing cuts are those of Cain killing Abel, the burning of Sodom and Gomorrah, the sacrifice of Isaac, the flight of quails, and the baptism of Christ.

The same cuts were used in the Second Worcester Edition [Item 170], except that the 1st edition has accurate cuts for the flight of quails and for Jezebel being devoured by dogs, whereas the 2d edition repeats, for the first of these, the cut of Elijah and the ravens and, for the second, Lazarus with the dogs licking his sores.

There were 2 issues of this First Worcester Edition, one (Welch 560.3) with the words in the imprint "Sold also by E. Battelle, Boston," and one (Welch 560.4) without these words. Of the issue carrying the Battelle name, Welch locates 2 copies, one perfect and the other with 2 pages mutilated. Of the other issue, to which the present copy belongs, Welch locates 2 copies, both quite defective.

Orig. boards, with a cut of the fox and the grapes on the front cover and another cut, also derived from Aesop, on the back cover. On the front flyleaf is a presentation inscription, dated April 3, 1795.

Accompanying the book is a set of photostats and a set of xerox prints of the missing pages, the former kindly furnished by the American Antiquarian Society and the latter, with like kindness, furnished by Miss Ruth E. Adomeit and Dr. d'Alté A. Welch of Cleveland, Ohio.

· 1787 ·

1352. BICKERSTAFF'S BOSTON ALMANACK, OR, THE FEDERAL CALENDAR, FOR . . . 1788 . . . [By Benjamin West]. Fourth Edition. Boston: Printed by E. Russell [1787]. Evans 20877.

On the title-page is a woodcut showing Washington and Franklin "triumphantly seated in the Federal Chariot drawn by 13 Freemen, figurative of the happy Union now forming by these States." Washington holds in his hand the Federal Constitution while "the sagacious and philosophick Franklin sits attentive with Spectacles on, having just scan'd over the Glorious Work, which will prove the political Salvation of his Country . . ."

Murrell reproduces this cut on p. 35 and says that it is "the only cartoon so far discovered showing Washington and Franklin together."

On the recto of [A³] begins the story of the strange and wonderful Discovery of the remarkable Virginia Hermit by Captain James Buckland and Mr. John Fielding [see Item 110], and a woodcut of the Hermit himself appears on the verso of [C³].

The only copy of this almanac located by Evans is at the Library of Congress, but another, as stated by Murrell, was at one time in the possession of Mrs. Harry MacNeill Bland. Sewed, last leaf missing.

1353. THE DEATH AND BURIAL OF COCK ROBIN; WITH THE TRAGICAL DEATH OF A. APPLE PYE: THE WHOLE TAKEN FROM THE ORIGINAL MANUSCRIPT IN THE POSSESSION OF MASTER MEANWELL. The First Worcester Edition. Printed at Worcester, Massachusetts, by Isaiah Thomas, and sold, Wholesale and Retail, at his Book-Store, 1787. Evans 20319. Welch 205.1.

Contains 19 small woodcuts with 4 additional cuts on the front and back wrappers. The majority of these cuts are in excellent impression. The well-known elegy which commences "Who killed Cock Robin?" begins on p. 14.

This copy originally lacked the first and last leaves and the wrappers, but the missing leaves and wrappers were very generously supplied by the American Antiquarian Society from a defective copy in their possession, thus making this a complete copy. The only other recorded complete copy is at the American Antiquarian Society. The back wrapper, on which the final leaf is pasted, has been repaired with the loss of a few words on p. 31. Orig. wrappers.

· 1788 ·

1354. BICKERSTAFF'S BOSTON ALMANACK, OR, THE FEDERAL CALENDAR, FOR THE YEAR OF OUR REDEMPTION, 1789 . . . [By Benjamin West]. Boston: Printed by E. Russell, next Liberty-Pole [1788]. Evans 21592, except that the words "Washington and Liberty Forever" do not appear on the title-page.

On the title-page is a woodcut depicting "The Rising Glory of the American Empire." Sewed.

1355. JACKY DANDY'S DELIGHT: OR THE HISTORY OF BIRDS AND BEASTS; IN VERSE AND PROSE. The First Worcester Edition. Printed at Worcester, Massachusetts, By Isaiah Thomas. Sold at his Bookstore, 1788. Evans 21174. 16 leaves.

Contains 20 woodcuts. This copy lacks 2 leaves (pp. 15-18, with 3 woodcuts) and the final blank leaf and the wrapper to which it was pasted. The front wrapper is present, the frontispiece being pasted to it. There is a copy of this book at the American Antiquarian Society and another, lacking the first and last leaves, at the Free Library of Philadelphia.

1356. A LITTLE LOTTERY BOOK FOR CHILDREN: CONTAINING A NEW METHOD OF PLAYING THEM INTO A KNOWLEDGE OF THE LETTERS, FIGURES, ETC. EMBELLISHED WITH ABOVE FIFTY CUTS, AND PUBLISHED WITH THE APPROBATION OF THE COURT OF COMMON SENSE. First Worcester Edition. Printed at

Worcester, Massachusetts, by Isaiah Thomas. Sold at his Bookstore in Worcester, and by him and Company in Boston [1788]. 64 pp., including advertisements at end, pp. 1 and 64 blank. Evans 21205. Welch 713.2.

See also Charles L. Nichols, *Bibliography of Worcester*, Worcester, 1918, No. 136, who describes an imperfect copy and says, "A copy with a perfect title-page has not been found." In the present copy, the title-page, which contains no cuts, is in facsimile. The only other copy of the book which the writer has been able to locate is at the American Antiquarian Society. It is a perfect copy.

Contains a cut on the first leaf and 52 other cuts, 2 for each letter of the alphabet. Orig. floreated wrappers, in cloth case.

· 1789 ·

1357. BICKERSTAFF'S BOSTON ALMANACK, OR, FEDERAL CALEDNAR [*sic*], FOR 1790 . . . [By Benjamin West.] [Boston]: Printed by E. Russell, next Liberty-Pole: Where may be had cheap to Travelling-traders, &c. the Bloody Register, N°. 4 [1789]. Evans 22268.

On the title-page is an ornamental cut enclosing portraits of George Washington and Horatio Gates. On the recto of [A²] begins a poem on Washington—"Composed in 1782, but never before published—by J. Plumer, a Citizen of the World." There were a 2d and a 3rd edition of this almanac. Sewed.

· 1791 ·

1358. BICKERSTAFF'S GENUINE MASSACHUSETTS, NEW-HAMPSHIRE, VERMONT, RHODE-ISLAND, AND CONNECTICUTT ALMANACK, FOR THE YEAR OF OUR LORD, 1792 . . . [By Benjamin West.] Boston: Printed and sold by Nathaniel Covely [*sic*], 1792 [1791]. Evans 23984 or 23985.

On the title-page are 2 small cuts, one showing a man sitting under a tree and talking with a woman, with a large house in the background, the other showing a landscape with a tree in the foreground. Sewed.

1359. THE HOLY BIBLE, CONTAINING THE OLD AND NEW TESTAMENTS: WITH THE APOCRYPHA. Translated out of the Original Tongues, and with the former Translations diligently compared and revised, by the special Command of King James I, of England. Worcester: Printed at the Press in Worcester, Massachusetts, by Isaiah Thomas. Sold by him in Worcester; and

by him and Company, at Faust's Statue, No. 45, Newbury Street, Boston, 1791.

On p. [5] at the beginning of the book of Genesis there is a woodcut of Adam and Eve in the Garden of Eden. On p. [637] at the beginning of the Apocrypha there is a woodcut of Judith with the head of Holofernes. On p. [789] at the beginning of the Gospel according to Saint Matthew there is a woodcut of the Crucifixion. The first of these cuts is signed "Hill," and the other two resemble the first so closely that it seems almost certain that Hill was responsible for all three.

Samuel Hill, a Boston engraver, active from about 1789 to 1804, is best known for his copperplate engravings, but he did occasionally do relief work, although such work of his is hard to find (see Sinclair H. Hitchings, "Samuel Hill's Relief Engraving," in *PAGA*, Vol. VIII, No. 1, Lunenburg, Vermont, March 1960).

There are also a number of tailpieces in this Bible (pp. 2, 635, 786, 991, 1008, 1011, and 1012), some of which might possibly be the work of Hill also (see the article in *PAGA* referred to above).

There are 50 copperplate engravings. Of these, 6 were engraved by Samuel Hill, viz., the frontispiece and those facing pp. 191, 195, 229, 232, and 878. Of the remaining plates, 32 were engraved by Joseph H. Seymour, who was in Thomas' employ between 1791 and 1795 (see Groce and Wallace, p. 570), 5 by John Norman, and 1 by Doolittle of New Haven. The others are unsigned.

Thomas published 2 editions of the Bible in 1791, one his Folio Bible and the other his Royal Quarto. This is a copy of the Folio Bible. The 3 relief cuts referred to above do not appear in the Quarto edition. Thomas was attempting to produce a Bible which would to some extent take the place of the many being imported from abroad. In his foreword, addressed to "Christians of every Denomination," he writes "Though many difficulties impeded this work in the press, yet both Editions were executed in a little more than twelve months, solely at the expense of the Editor.—How far he has succeeded in his endeavor, you will judge by a comparison of his copies with those printed in Europe of the quality which his are done to imitate.—If, on inspection, the execution of the work should be satisfactory, he flatters himself that he may rely on all the Friends of Revelation, and on all the Patrons of the Arts, to succeed his endeavors, and reward his exertions, by giving his Editions a preference to those imported from abroad."

Cont. calf rebacked. Presented by Gillett Griffin.

· 1792 ·

1360. THE AMERICAN PRIMER, IMPROVED, OR, AN EASY AND PLEASANT GUIDE TO THE ART OF READING. ADORNED WITH CUTS. TO WHICH IS ADDED, THE ASSEMBLY OF DIVINE'S CATECHISM. Boston: Printed by Nathaniel Coverly for James Gardner, of Providence [1792?]. See Evans 24574.

The cut on the verso of the title-page appeared in *The Holy Bible Abridged*, printed in Boston about 1782 by Robert Hodge for Nathaniel Coverly [Item 96]. In addition to this cut there are small cuts illustrating the letters of the alphabet on the recto and verso of A⁴, cuts illustrating "In Adam's fall We sinned all" etc. on A⁶, A⁷, and A⁸, cuts of animals on B⁴, B⁵, and B⁶, with the John Rogers cut on the verso of B⁶. Leaf A⁵ is missing.

The only other recorded copy of this primer is in the Monroe, Wakeman, and Holman Collection of the Pequot Library, Southport, Conn., which has been deposited in the Yale University Library. In the *Catalogue of the Monroe, Wakeman, and Holman collection of the Pequot Library*, New Haven, 1960, No. 25, appears the following entry in connection with this primer, which is there given the date [1792?]: "Apparently identical with Evans 24574, and Chas. F. Heartman, American primers, Highland Park, N.J., 1935, No. 8. Heartman locates no copy under this number, but lists a unique Pequot copy under number 3, which has the same title, imprint, and collation, but bears the, presumably conjectured, date 1776. It would seem that the two entries refer to the same edition. Imperfect: last leaf very slightly mutilated."

In view of this entry, the 1792 date of Evans and of the Pequot catalogue has here been accepted and the 1776 date of Heartman no. 3 has been rejected in spite of its reference to the Pequot copy. While it is true that Coverly was printing American Primers as early as 1776 (see Heartman, No. 4), the use of a cut from Hodge's *The Holy Bible Abridged*, which could hardly have been cut at so early a date, makes it seem reasonably clear that this edition of *The American Primer* was of a later vintage than 1776.

Orig. board covers, with leather back.

1361. BICKERSTAFF'S GENUINE BOSTON ALMANACK OR FEDERAL CALENDAR, FOR 1793. [By Benjamin West.] First after Leap-Year; seventeenth of Independence. [Boston]: Printed by E. Russell, cheap to Travelling-Traders and others [1792]. Evans 25015.

On the title-page is Russell's astronomer cut as found in his *The Strange and Remarkable Swansey Vision* of 1776 [Item 80] and his *American Almanack* for 1781 [Item 89]. On the recto of [A²] is the cut which Russell had formerly used as the cut of February in the occupations of the months, now apparently intended to illustrate a scene in the life of a chimney sweep. On the verso of this leaf is the cut used by Russell to represent George Washington in *Bickerstaff's Boston Almanack* for 1778 [see Item 82]. It was also used in Item 1369. On the recto of C¹ is a cut of a woman holding a musket in one hand and a powder horn in the other. It is used to illustrate an article on "Female Heroism. Lately displayed in a most surprising and courageous Adventure by a young Lady in France." While differing in many details, it seems to stem from the portrait of Hannah Snell, the female soldier, used by Isaiah Thomas in his *New England Almanack* for 1775 [see Item 72]. It was used in the broadside *A New Touch on the Times* (Winslow, No. 90, and Ford, No. 2161) published probably about 1779, and what appears to be a copy of it will be found in a broadside published by Russell about 1793 (Ford No. 2700). There are some other small cuts, including an interesting one on C² verso which shows a night scene with one woman apparently pummeling another in front of a dark and sinister house. Sewed.

1362. BILL OF LADING, printed by J. Crukshank in Philadelphia not later than 1792. It is dated October 20, 1792, the 1792 being printed except for the final figure 2 which is written. In the upper left-hand corner is a woodcut initial S, showing a square-rigged ship under full sail. It is not badly drawn.

1363. THE HOLY BIBLE ABRIDGED OR, THE HISTORY OF THE OLD AND NEW TESTAMENT. ILLUSTRATED WITH NOTES AND ADORNED WITH CUTS, FOR THE USE OF CHILDREN . . . New-York: Printed by William Durell, No. 19, Queen-Street, 1792. Welch 560.9.

In the Old Testament there are 2 full-page cuts, the frontispiece, which represents the slaying of Abel with Adam and Eve, horrified and grief-stricken, looking on at the right, and another on p. 105 depicting the feast of Belshazzar. There are 15 smaller cuts in the text. In the New Testament there are also 15 small cuts. The New Testament has a separate title-page and new pagination. The title-page reads "The Testament Abridged: or, The History of the New Testament. Adorned with Cuts. For the use of Children. . . . New-York: Printed by William Durell, 1792." The type ornament border differs in the two title-pages.

Copies of this book will be found at Columbia

University in the Plimpton collection, at the Connecticut Historical Society, and in the collection of Mrs. A. M. Greenwood. Orig. boards, covered with floreated paper.

1364. A True and Particular Narrative of the late Tremendous Tornado, or Hurricane, at Philadelphia and New-York, on Sabbath-Day, July 1, 1792: When several Pleasure-Boats were lost in the Harbor of the latter and Thirty Men, Women and Children, (taking their Pleasure on that sacred Day) were unhappily drowned in Neptune's raging and temptestuous Element!!!!!! . . . Tell this not in Massachusetts! Publish it not in the Streets of Connecticut! lest their sober-minded young Men and Maidens should bitterly reproach thee in the Day of thy Calamity, and triumph over thee when thy Desolation cometh; and ask of thee, Where are thy Magistrates? . . . Or do they bear the Sword of the Lord in vain? . . . Where are thy Watch-men? . . . Have they deserted their Watch-Tower? Or have they fallen asleep? . . . Boston: Printed and Sold by E. Russell, next the Stump of Lib. Tree. [Pr. Six Pence.] Where may be had, Mary and Martha, &c.

At the foot of this broadside is a line which is very difficult to decipher. In part it reads as follows: "Printed for and Sold by Tho. Bassett, of Dunbarton, N.H., who has . . . printed . . . a curious Account of a remarkable Vision; . . ." Evans 24864.

At the top of the broadside are cuts of 30 coffins, and there are also a number of small cuts, some of ships printed upside down to indicate how "topsaturvy" ships become in a real hurricane. Following a description of the effects of the hurricane, the final half of the broadside is taken up with the poem "The New-York Tragedy" which commemorates the awful carnage of that first day of July and makes clear how much wiser it is to go to church on the Sabbath, rather than to desecrate the day in pleasure boating. At the top of this poem appears a cut of a skeleton on horseback, a cut which will be found in another publication of Russell [see Item 1366].

There were at least 3 different issues of this broadside.

(a) The copy at the New York Historical Society which is reproduced by Winslow, No. 37. The copies at the Huntington Library and the Massachusetts Historical Society are similar to this. 20 coffins appear at the top of this issue.

(b) The present copy, which is similar to that at Brown University, except that the latter does not contain the line at the bottom regarding Tho. Bassett of Dunbarton, N.H. At the top are

30 coffins, which is the number of persons drowned as stated in the title of the broadside and the title of the poem.* Otherwise the same cuts appear here as in (a) above. The wording of the description of the hurricane and the arrangement of the lines also correspond with (a). A number of fairly substantial changes, however, appear in the poem. Thus, for example, the last 2 lines of verse 4 read:

"He lays the proud and haughty low
And drives their counsels too and fro"

While these lines in (a) read:

"He lays the proud and haughty down
And gives the meek a glorious crown"

Other changes will be found in verses 12, 14, 19, 20, 21, 26, 28, 34, 35, 36, 37, and 43. It seems probable that (b) is a later issue than (a).

(c) This is a totally different issue from either (a) or (b). The only copy which the writer has been able to locate is at the Rosenbach Foundation in Philadelphia. It has 20 coffins at top, and in its text, including that of the poem, it is substantially similar to (a), although there are some slight variations—see, for example, verses 19, 27, and 32. It lacks all of the cuts of (a) and (b) and has only 2 small cuts of vessels near the top. The arrangement of its lines differs materially from (a) and (b), and it has no imprint. It may have been the copy used by Wegelin in his *Early American Poetry*, No. 804, although there are some slight discrepancies.

The type used in (c) looks very much like Russell's type, but it is interesting to note that in (a) and (b), which bear Russell's imprint, Captain Scott, the hero of the hurricane, is described as of Groton "in this Commonwealth," whereas in (c) he is described as of Groton "in Massachusetts." This change, together with the complete difference in the setup, the difference in the design of the 20 coffins at the top, and the failure to use any of Russell's cuts, makes it seem likely that a different printer was responsible for it.

The present copy is backed with linen. It is accompanied by photostats of the copies at the Huntington Library, the Massachusetts Historical Society, Brown University, and the Rosenbach Foundation.

1364a. A Wonderful Discovery of an Old Hermit, Who lived upwards of two Hundred Years. Windham [Conn.], Printed [by J. Byrne], 1792. Evans 24154.

* A reading of the description of the hurricane would indicate, however, that the New York casualties totaled 20, with only one casualty in Philadelphia.

This appears to be the final 18th-century issue of this incredible tale which was the best seller of 1786 (see Item 110). The frontispiece, which the Library of Congress card describes as a typemetal cut, shows the hermit at the entrance to his cave. Thanks to a generous use of white line, it is an effective cut. A title vignette contains the printer's initials. Old paper wrappers.

· 1793 ·

1365. THE APOLLO: BEING A COLLECTION OF ENGLISH SONGS INCLUDING A SELECTION OF MASONIC SONGS, ANTHEMS, ODES, PRELUDES, PROLOGUES, EPILOGUES, TOASTS, &c. A New Edition, with Additions. Philadelphia: William Spotswood, 1793. With a woodcut of a charming pastoral scene on the title-page. Modern boards with morocco back.

1366. A DIALOGUE BETWEEN A BLIND-MAN AND DEATH. By Richard Standfast. London; Printed: Boston; Re-printed, (at the earnest Request of a Number of well-disposed Christians) by E. Russell, next Liberty-Stump, for T. Grant, of Chelmsford, 1793. Evans 26200.

On the title-page is a small cut of death riding on a horse. On the next page is the cut first used to represent Whitefield preaching, which will be found in Item 58 and in Item 63a. On p. 3 is a cut of 4 coffins and a very small cut showing death snuffing out a candle. Old paper wrappers, sewed.

1366a. THE PLEASING HISTORY OF PAMELA; OR, VIRTUE REWARDED. BEING AN ENTERTAINING HISTORY OF A BEAUTIFUL YOUNG DAMSEL, WHO ROSE FROM ALMOST THE LOWEST TO THE HIGHEST SITUATION OF LIFE, WITH MANY IMPORTANT AND ENTERTAINING SUBJECTS, INTENDED TO CULTIVATE THE PRINCIPLES OF VIRTUE AND RELIGION IN THE MINDS OF BOTH SEXES. [By Samuel Richardson.] Boston: Printed and sold by Samuel Hall, No. 53, Cornhill [1793]. Evans 26088. Welch 994.1. With full-page frontispiece and 2 other delightful cuts in the text. A typical Hall juvenile. Orig. boards with leather back.

1367. THE TRAGEDY OF LOUIS CAPET: BEING A TRUE AND AUTHENTIC NARRATIVE OF THE HORRID AND BARBAROUS EXECUTION OF THE LATE UNFORTUNATE MONARCH, LOUIS XVITH OF FRANCE, WHO WAS BEHEADED, ON THE TWENTY-FIRST OF JANUARY, 1793, CONFORMABLY TO A DECREE OF THE NATIONAL CONVENTION ON SUSPICION OF TREASON.— Which bloody Transaction (it is thought by every true Friend to the American Revolution)

will eternally disgrace the Annals of the French Nation: And may his Death be as sincerely lamented by every *honest* and *grateful* American, as it is by the Majority of the Citizens of *France*—This Narrative, with the Poetry annexed, is published in this Form at the Request of many true Republicans, and recommended to be preserved as a Memorial of that shocking and melancholy Event. [Boston: Printed by Ezekiel Russell and] Sold next the venerable Stump of Liberty-Tree. [Price Two Shillings and Eight per Dozen and Four Pence single.] [1793.] Broadside. Evans 26272. Ford 2701.

At the upper left-hand corner of the title as given above is a comparatively large cut of a man in continental uniform. According to Evans (26271) this is a portrait of Washington. On one side of the General is an angel blowing a horn and on the other a figure holding a spear on which rests a liberty cap. At the upper right-hand corner of the title is a cut of a female soldier holding a musket and powder horn.

Underneath the title, in 2 columns, is a translation from the French Gazette of January 22, 1793, giving details of the execution, and bordered on the left by a cut of a coffin bearing the words, in white line, "Louis Capet King of France Ae. 41." To the right of this extract from the French Gazette, in 2 somewhat narrower columns, are 2 poems. One is entitled "Occasioned by the Death of Louis XVIth" and contains 5 verses of 4 lines each. The other is entitled "On the Decolation of Louis 16."

The title, the translation and the 2 poems take up about half of the broadside. The lower half contains a poem of 17 verses (the final verse misnumbered XVIII) with the title "The Queen's Lamentations For the Death of her Beloved Louis."

The cut of the female soldier stems from the portrait of Hannah Snell used by Isaiah Thomas in his *New England Almanack* for 1775 [Item 72]. We find the cut first in *A New Touch on the Times*, a broadside of about 1779 (see Winslow, No. 90 and Ford, No. 2161). Russell used it in his *Bickerstaff's Genuine Boston Almanack* for 1793 [Item 1361].

· 1794 ·

1368. THE ADVENTURES OF CAPTAIN GULLIVER, IN A VOYAGE TO THE ISLANDS OF LILLIPUT AND BROBDINGNAG. Abridged from the Works of the celebrated Dean Swift. Philadelphia: Printed by W. Young, 1794. With full-page frontispiece and 22 small cuts in the text. 160 pp. A-E^{16}.

This appears to be the only recorded copy of

this edition. It was formerly known only from an advertisement in *Easy Lessons for Young Children*, Philadelphia, W. Young, 1794 (Rosenbach 172). It is either the 3rd or 4th American edition of *Gulliver*, depending on whether it was published before or after Item 148 (the Boston edition of 1794). It might be noted that, in addition to the copies of the 1794 Boston edition noted in Item 148, copies will also be found at Harvard and in the d'Alté A. Welch collection and in the Gillett Griffin collection.

Orig. boards with floreate paper, in cloth case.

1369. BROADSIDE: A worthy Example of a Virtuous Wife, In a most affecting and truly striking Manner exemplified in the remarkably dutiful, humane, benevolent and pious Conduct of a most excellent young Lady, who was Daughter to a very rich and honorable Nobleman, and notwithstanding she had greatly incurred the most cruel and implacable Wrath, and most unrelenting Displeasure of her aged Father, yet she, in the most pious, filial and tender manner, fed him with her own Milk; he being commanded by the Emperor of Rome to be starved to Death, who afterwards pardoned him, and, (for such loyal and dutiful Behavior shewn to her venerable Parent even at the utmost Peril and Hazard of her own Life) she had the highest and most eminent and distinguished Honors of the Kingdom conferred on her by the Emperor.—Never before published in America . . . [There follows a poem of 44 verses, arranged in 3 columns, describing the amazingly filial conduct of this virtuous daughter.] Boston: Printed by E. Russell, near Liberty pole, Octo. 7, 1794—Sold by Jonathan Hallowell, Travelling-trader, in Bridgewater. [Price Four Pence.] Evans 28136.

At the top left-hand corner is a cut of an officer in Continental uniform. This cut was used for the first time, so far as the writer knows, in *Bickerstaff's Boston Almanack, for the Year . . . 1778* [Item 82] which was printed by E. Russell in Danvers. It was intended for a portrait of General Washington and may well have been a genuine attempt to represent Washington. Just what connection the General may have had with the virtuous Roman daughter is not made clear.

In the upper right-hand corner is a cut of a fashionably dressed lady kneeling before what appears to be a desk. This cut will be found on a broadside of 1786 which was "Sold next Liberty-Pole" (see Ford, No. 2432).

The poem is substantially the same as that appearing in Item 1384 and a comparison of the two items is interesting. It has been suggested that the Boston broadside was intended for the Sunday School and the Windsor broadside for the local taverns.

1370. MOTHER GOOSE'S MELODY: OR SONNETS FOR THE CRADLE. IN TWO PARTS. PART I. Contains the most celebrated Songs and Lullabies of the good old Nurses, calculated to amuse Children and to excite them to sleep. PART II. Those of that sweet Songster and Nurse of Wit and Humor, Master William Shakespeare . . . The Second Worcester Edition. Worcester (Massachusetts): Printed by Isaiah Thomas, and sold at his Bookstore, 1794. The greater portion of the title-page is in facsimile. Otherwise this is a perfect copy of the Second American Edition of Mother Goose. Evans 29122. Rosenbach 179. Welch 825.2. Fig. 5.

Contains full-page woodcut frontispiece, pasted to the front wrapper, and 51 other woodcuts which, in their simple directness, do justice to the well-known rhymes.

Of the 1st American edition of Mother Goose, which is now generally accepted to be the edition published by Isaiah Thomas in Worcester about 1785 or 1786, only one imperfect copy is known. It is at the American Antiquarian Society and contains pp. 13-86, but it has been badly mutilated so that large portions of many of its leaves are missing. What purported to be another copy of this edition was listed in the Brinley sale of 1886 (see Vol. IV, No. 7185, of the catalogue of that sale). The whereabouts of this copy is unknown to the writer and, as the title-page was missing, it might possibly have been a copy of a later edition. The copy, lacking a title-page, which is reproduced by W. H. Whitmore in his *The Original Mother Goose's Melody*, Albany, 1889, is actually a copy of the 1794 edition, as a comparison with a perfect copy of that edition has shown.

Of the 1794 edition only 4 perfect copies are recorded, namely, the copies at the American Antiquarian Society, the Free Library of Philadelphia, the Huntington Library, and that in the Edgar S. Oppenheimer collection. In addition, there are the Whitmore copy and the present copy, each lacking the title-page, making in all 6 recorded copies.

While there are typographical differences in Thomas' first and second editions, the cuts used (with the exception of that on p. 34—see Welch 825.2) appear to be identical.

Orig. green paper wrappers, rebacked.

1371. THE PILGRIM'S PROGRESS, FROM THIS WORLD TO THAT WHICH IS TO COME. DELIVERED UNDER THE SIMILITUDE OF A DREAM . . . TO WHICH IS ADDED, THE LIFE AND

DEATH OF THE AUTHOR . . . By John Bunyan. Boston, Printed by Peter Edes, for the Booksellers, 1794. Evans 26717.

Part the First contains a frontispiece and 8 other cuts. Part the Second contains a different frontispiece and 2 other cuts. Part the Third has the same frontispiece as Part the First, but otherwise there are no further cuts.

These are the same cuts as those found in Bumstead's 1800 edition [Item 191]. They were also used in Thomas's edition of 1817 [Item 263], although the latter are so much better printed that the first impression we get is that they are an entirely new set of cuts. The cut on p. 165 in the 1794 edition does not appear in the 1817 edition.

One leaf (pp. 9-10) is missing in this copy of the 1794 edition, but it contains no cuts. The leaf containing pp. 25-26 is misbound after p. 34. Cont. calf, the spine covered with modern cloth.

· 1795 ·

1372. THE HISTORY OF LITTLE KING PIPPIN, WITH AN ACCOUNT OF THE MELANCHOLY DEATH OF FOUR NAUGHTY BOYS. WHO WERE DEVOURED BY WILD BEASTS. LIKEWISE THE WONDERFUL DELIVERY OF MASTER HARRY HARMLESS BY A LITTLE WHITE HORSE. The Second Worcester Edition. Worcester: Printed by Isaiah Thomas, jun. for Isaiah Thomas and Son, 1795. Evans 28834. Welch 515.6.

Contains 22 woodcuts including the frontispiece of "Little King Pippin" and, on p. 9, a view of "the inside" of Mr. Thomas's bookstore. Orig. floreated paper wrappers.

1373. THE NEW-ENGLAND PRIMER IMPROVED, FOR THE MORE EASY ATTAINING THE TRUE READING OF ENGLISH. TO WHICH IS ADDED, THE ASSEMBLY OF DIVINES' CATECHISM. Elizabeth-Town: Printed and Published by Shepard Kollock, 1795. 68 pp.

Contains the small cuts of the alphabet on pp. 10-13 and the cut of the burning of John Rogers on p. 25. In its original floreated wrappers and with its well-designed title-page, this is an attractive little volume. The edition appears to be an unrecorded one.

1374. THE PROTESTANT EPISCOPAL CHURCH CATECHISM; WITH SOME QUESTIONS, TO TRY WHETHER CHILDREN REPEAT IT MERELY BY ROTE; TO ENGAGE THEIR ATTENTION, AND TO IMPRINT THE SENSE OF IT ON THEIR MINDS. New-York: Printed by M. L. & W. A. Davis, No. 151 Water-street, 1795. Evans 29366. The frontispiece is a cut of a clergyman teaching the catechism to the very young. Orig. wrappers.

1375. THE WONDERFUL LIFE AND MOST SURPRISING ADVENTURES OF THAT RENOWNED HERO, ROBINSON CRUSOE, WHO LIVED TWENTY-EIGHT YEARS ON AN UNINHABITED ISLAND. Which he afterwards Colonised. [By Daniel Defoe.] New-York: Printed by Hurtin & Commardinger, for Benjamin Gomez, 1795. See Evans 28555, Rosenbach 190, Welch 260.30.

Contains a full-page frontispiece and 4 smaller cuts (pp. 23, 89, 114, and 139) in the text. Robert W. G. Vail in his article on Benjamin Gomez in *The Colophon*, Part Nine, 1932, says: "Of the half-dozen titles published by Gomez in 1795, two are still famous. *Captain Cook's Third and Last Voyage* has gone through dozens of editions, and the lovely little abridged edition of *Robinson Crusoe*, with its quaint woodcuts, is one of the most charming of the hundreds of editions of this greatest of all boys' books." The copy Mr. Vail examined may have been better printed than the present copy, for it must be confessed that the woodcuts in the latter, quaint though they be, have been so badly printed that they add but little to the charm of the story. Welch 260.29.

Wooden boards with leather back. The boards have been broken so that half of the final leaf, which is pasted to the rear board, is missing. It contained no cut.

· 1796 ·

1376. THE AFFECTING HISTORY OF THE CHILDREN IN THE WOOD. Hartford: Printed by J. Babcock, 1796. Evans 29955, Welch 169.1.

Contains 9 small woodcuts. The first appearance in America of this famous story appears to have been in a broadside printed by Thomas and John Fleet about 1770 (see Rosenbach 64) and reprinted about 1785 (see Rosenbach 101 and Evans 19401). It was a rhymed version. This prose edition of 1796 is apparently the first edition printed in this country with the title *The Affecting History of the Children in the Wood*. Orig. wrappers.

1377. AMERICANISCHER STADT UND LAND CALENDER AUF DAS 1797ste JAHR CHRISTI . . . Philadelphia: Gedruckt und zu haben bey Carl Cist. [1796]. Evans 29980. The woodcut border on the title-page is attractively done, showing the implements of the sea and of the land, and on [E1] recto is a woodcut portrait of Henry Moss, a Virginia negro, who underwent a strange metamorphosis. Sewed.

1378. CAPTAIN COOK'S THIRD AND LAST VOYAGE TO THE PACIFIC OCEAN. IN THE

YEARS 1776, 1777, 1778, 1779 and 1780. Faithfully Abridged from the Quarto Edition. New York: Printed for, and Sold by B. Gomez, 1796.

A woodcut frontispiece, pasted down on the front cover, shows Cook being received by natives.

Mr. R.W.G. Vail in his bibliography of Benjamin Gomez, in *The Colophon*, Part Nine, 1932, lists an earlier edition of this book dated 1795 and locates a copy at the Library of Congress. He fails to list this later edition. Orig. boards.

1378a. THE MOUNTAIN PIPER, OR THE HISTORY OF EDGAR AND MATILDA. [By Arnaud Berquin.] Hartford: Printed by J. Babcock. 1796. Evans 30831. Welch 91.2. With full-page frontispiece and 6 small cuts in the text which follow the narrative closely. Orig. wrappers.

EIN WOHL EINGERICHTETES DEUTSCHES A B C-BUCHSTABIR-UND-LESEBUCH. Germantaun: 179[6]. Contains woodcut frontispiece, 7 cuts in text and printer's mark. [See Item 1904 listed under J. F. Reiche.]

1379. THE PRINCIPLES OF THE CHRISTIAN RELIGION, DIVIDED INTO LESSONS, FOR CHILDREN. By the Rev. P. Doddridge. Hartford: Printed by J. Babcock, 1796. 32 pp., the first and last blank. Evans 30357.

Contains full-page frontispiece and 4 other small cuts. These are considerably worn and do not seem to illustrate any particular religious principles. Perhaps they were intended to soften some of the grim principles of the Lessons such as the first verse of Lesson XXV. "The Judgment past, then down to hell the wicked go, in flames to dwell."

Orig. wrappers, back restored.

1380. THE REMARKABLE HISTORY OF AUGI: OR: A PICTURE OF TRUE HAPPINESS. TOGETHER WITH THE STORY OF THE DREAMER. First American Edition. Worcester: Printed by Isaiah Thomas, Jun., 1796. Evans 31080. Rosenbach 217.

With a woodcut frontispiece intended, no doubt, to portray the impeccable Augi, who earned complete happiness only to lose all, including his life, in the French Revolution. Orig. flowered wrappers.

1380a. TRAVELS OF ROBINSON CRUSOE. Written by Himself. Windham (Connecticut), Printed by John Byrne, 1796. Welch 26.34.

Contains a number of amusing cuts relating to the adventures of Robinson Crusoe. Several leaves are missing but have been replaced by copies taken from a copy of the book in the collection of d'Alté A. Welch who has done a splendid job of repair work, including the covers which were made by him.

Presented by d'Alté A. Welch and with his bookmark.

1381. THE WONDERFUL ESCAPE, OR SAGACITY OUTWITTED. A CURIOUS STORY. Boston: Printed by J. White, 1796. 12 leaves, A-B⁶. The Rosenbach copy of 11 leaves (Rosenbach 226) apparently lacks the frontispiece.

This appears to be a chapbook intended for adult readers, showing love triumphant after many vicissitudes. The frontispiece consists of 2 small cuts and there is an additional cut on p. 12. While these cuts may have been intended to throw light on the story, it is difficult to see just what scenes they were meant to illustrate.

The recto of the frontispiece is blank, and no wrappers are present. It is possible the book was issued without wrappers.

· 1797 ·

1382. THE HOLY BIBLE ABRIDGED; OR, THE HISTORY OF THE OLD AND NEW TESTAMENT. ILLUSTRATED WITH NOTES, AND ADORNED WITH CUTS FOR THE USE OF CHILDREN. Wilmington: Printed and sold by Peter Brynberg, 1797. 136 pp., the last two unnumbered and containing the Tables of Contents. Evans 31809. Rosenbach 228. Welch 560.03.

Contains 7 crude woodcuts, which are probably of an earlier date than the book. Rebound in marbled paper wrappers.

1383. THE NEW-ENGLAND PRIMER; MUCH IMPROVED. CONTAINING, A VARIETY OF EASY LESSONS, FOR ATTAINING THE TRUE READING OF ENGLISH. Philadelphia: Printed by T. Dobson, at the Stone House, No. 41, S. Second Street. 1797. Evans 32530. On B⁸ recto is a small oval cut of the burning of John Rogers, somewhat different in design from the usual cut of this scene. Orig. pink and gold, embossed, flowered wrappers, beautifully preserved.

· 1798 ·

THE CHILD'S SPELLING BOOK. Hartford: 1798. Contains 32 cuts which were probably engraved on wood by Alexander Anderson. [See Item 1398a]

1384. THE GRECIAN DAUGHTER. OR, AN EXAMPLE OF A VIRTUOUS WIFE, WHO FED HER FATHER WITH HER OWN MILK . . . HE BEING CONDEMNED TO BE STARVED TO DEATH BY TIBERIUS CAESAR, EMPEROR OF ROME;

BUT WAS AFTERWARDS PARDONED, AND THE DAUGHTER HIGHLY REWARDED. Fig. 8.

This is a broadside. At the top is a large cut, probably on typemetal, depicting the lactic generosity of the Grecian Daughter. Then follows the title, as given above, and then 5 columns of verse. At the end are the words "Windsor, Printed For The Flying Book-Sellers."

Evans (No. 33815) describes a similar broadside and dates it 1798, but locates no copies. Copies, however, are to be found at the American Antiquarian Society, the Vermont Historical Society, and the Metropolitan Museum of Art in New York City.

There are dated issues of this broadside which have been assumed to be later, viz., Windsor, 1809 (at Harvard), Windsor, 1810 (Windsor Public Library and Vermont Historical Society), and Windsor, 1811 (American Antiquarian Society). The 1809 and 1811 issues (and presumably the 1810 as well) have one peculiar difference in the cut. The large keyhole in the gateway to the left, which is out of all proportion, has been filled in and appears only in outline, and the lines running through this filled in keyhole do not line up accurately with the lines surrounding it. The 1809 issue also shows an additional row of blocks in the floor below the figures and the initials "R.E.S." on one of the floor blocks are no longer visible. The additional row of blocks has disappeared in the 1811 issue.

It can, of course, be argued that the dated issues are the earlier; that for some unexplained reason the keyhole was originally cut merely in outline and later cut out entirely; that, before the undated cut was printed, the plate was shortened and the initials "R.E.S." cut in it. On the other hand we have the Evans date, which indicates an earlier printing for the undated cut, and a comparison of the verses in the undated issue and those in the 1809 and 1811 issues show that some corrections have been made in the latter, for example, column 1, line 10, "knight" has been changed to "night"; column 2, line 4, "Nay" has been changed to "Yea"; column 2, line 3 from the bottom, "brink" has been changed to "bring." It might also be noted that in the undated issue and in the 1809 issue the old form of the letter "s" is used, while this is not true of the 1811 issue. While the situation is not altogether clear, Evans has here been followed and the broadside listed under the year 1798.

In his article on "Isaac Eddy" in *Bibliographical Essays. A Tribute to Wilberforce Eames*, Cambridge, 1924, Harold G. Rugg has pointed out that it has become more or less customary to attribute all unsigned engravings of this general period published at Windsor to Isaac Eddy, of Weathersfield. Eddy was a copperplate engraver and printer who in 1812 engraved some plates for the first Vermont Bible (see Groce and Wallace, p. 205). It is conceivable, therefore, that he made the cut of "The Grecian Daughter." However, in 1798 he was only 22 years of age and it may be doubtful whether he was capable of doing such work. Perhaps Abner Reed of Hartford, who taught engraving to William Mason, the first Philadelphia wood engraver, and who sometimes did work for Windsor publishers, may have been the artist. However, whether the cut is the work of Eddy or Reed or some unknown New England craftsman, it is quite an extraordinary one. It is almost entirely in white line and, if on typemetal, the largest typemetal cut which the writer has seen. It was probably copied from C. van Caukercken's line engraving of the painting of "Cimon and Piro" by Peter Paul Rubens which is now at Amsterdam.

Accompanying this broadside are photostats of the 1809 and 1811 issues.

1385. A HISTORY OF THE LIFE OF AESOP. ACCORDING TO SIR ROGER L'ESTRANGE. TO WHICH IS ADDED, A CHOICE COLLECTION OF FABLES, WITH INSTRUCTIVE MORALS. FOR THE BENEFIT OF YOUTH. Taken from the most eminent mythologists. Philadelphia: Printed at the Southwark Office, No. 289, South Front-Street, 1798. Evans 23273. Rosenbach 238. Welch 20.1.

Contains 20 (not 14 as stated by Evans) cuts illustrating a number of the fables. They are oval in form and would be reasonably attractive had not so many of them been badly printed.

Welch locates 4 copies but of these only the copy in the Rosenbach collection at the Free Library of Philadelphia is complete, the others lacking various leaves. The present copy is complete. Marbled paper over boards with leather spine.

· 1799 ·

1386. THE AFFECTING HISTORY OF THE CHILDREN IN THE WOOD. First Newport Edition. Newport: Printed by H. & O. Farnsworth, 1799. Evans 35086. Welch 169.3.

Contains 9 woodcuts. The first of these, showing the robins covering the two children with leaves, is pasted to the front wrapper and torn across. At the end are two pages containing a number of small cuts which appear to have no relation to the book. In addition to *The Affecting*

History of the Children in the Wood, the book contains *Story of Three Robbers* and a poem, *The Fox, the Cat, and the Spider*.

The first appearance in this country of this prose version of *The Affecting History of the Children in the Wood* appears to be the edition printed in Hartford by J. Babcock in 1796 [Item 1376]. Another edition was issued by Babcock in 1798. Then follows the 1799 Newport edition, here listed. The final appearance of the book in the 18th century, is the edition printed by S. Trumbull in 1800 at Stoningtonport (Evans 36778, Rosenbach 250, and Welch 169.4). Of course, the rhymed version, beginning "Now ponder well, ye parents dear," came earlier, probably about 1770, and was frequently printed (see Rosenbach, Nos. 64, 101, 151, and 222 and Ford, Nos. 3014 *et seq.*). There was also a musical piece in two acts which was issued several times in 1795 (see Evans 29114-29117).

The original front wrapper is present though torn across. What appears to be a portion of the original back wrapper is pinned on.

1387. THE SCHOOLMASTER'S ASSISTANT: BEING A COMPENDIUM OF ARITHMETIC, BOTH PRACTICAL AND THEORETICAL . . . By Thomas Dilworth. Wilmington: Printed and Sold by Bonsal & Niles. Also sold at their Book-Store, No. 173, Market-Street, Baltimore. [1799.] Evans 35411.

The frontispiece portrait of Dilworth is a weak caricature of the author. Doubtless it was derived from some previous portrait of Dilworth, but it would be difficult to determine on which one it is based. Orig. calf.

· 1800 ·

1387a. THE FIRST STEP TO LEARNING: OR, LITTLE CHILDREN'S SPELLING AND READING BOOK . . . By Abner Reed S.M. The Second Edition. East-Windsor: (Connecticut) Printed for the Author, by Luther Pratt, 1800. Evans 38363.

This 2nd edition was published in the same year as the 1st but, as the Preface states, was amended and enlarged. It contains 11 cuts which can hardly be called distinguished. As Abner Reed was an engraver (see Groce and Wallace, p. 528, and Dunlap, Vol. II, p. 176), it would seem likely that he engraved the cuts. William Mason, the early Philadelphia engraver, was a pupil of Reed and, according to Dunlap (Vol. II, p. 383), spoke of Reed's style in woodcutting as "the old typemetal style," a comment which would appear to fit the cuts in this book. Orig. boards, front cover broken.

1388. GREANLEAF'S NEW-YORK, CONNECTICUT, & NEW JERSEY ALMANACK, FOR THE YEAR OF OUR LORD 1801 . . . Brooklyn: printed and sold whole-sale and retail by T. Kirk [1800]. Evans 37543.

On the final page is an "Ode to Gen. Washington" with a woodcut portrait of Washington. There is also a woodcut on the title-page, showing Father Time etc. Sewed.

1389. THE HARVEST HOME. [By Hannah More.] Philadelphia: Printed by B. & J. Johnson, No. 147 High-Street, 1800. Evans 37149. With a cut on the title-page of a hay cart with a merry group sitting on top of the hay. This is No. 22 of the Cheap Repository (see Items 187-88).

At the end are 2 hymns signed "Z" (i.e. Hannah More). See Rosenbach 258 for further facts regarding the *Cheap Repository* tracts and their publishers. Sewed.

1390. THE WONDERFUL LIFE, AND MOST SURPRISING ADVENTURES, OF THAT RENOWNED HERO, ROBINSON CRUSOE; WHO LIVED TWENTY-EIGHT YEARS ON AN UNINHABITED ISLAND, WHICH HE AFTERWARDS COLONIZED. [By Daniel Defoe.] New-York: Printed by John Tiebout, June, 1800. Evans 37306. Welch 260.39.

Contains a frontispiece and 11 cuts in the text. This is the same as No. 42 in Clarence S. Brigham's *Bibliography of American Editions of Robinson Crusoe to 1830*, Worcester, 1958. The word "Adventures" is misspelt "Adventurers" on p. 90 and is correctly spelt on p. 5, which, Mr. Brigham informed the writer, is also true of his No. 42.

Orig. front cover, but back cover and leather back strip supplied.

BY THE HONOURABLE

GEORGE THOMAS, Esq;

Lieutenant Governor and Commander in Chief of the Province of *PENNSYLVANIA,* and Counties of *New-Castle, Kent,* and *Suffex* on *Delaware.*

A PROCLAMATION.

WHEREAS HIS MAJESTY, from a just Resentment of the grossest and most indecent Misrepresentations and Reflections upon His Majesty's Conduct, contained in the *French* King's Declaration against his Majesty, hath by His DECLARATION, dated at St. *James's* the 29th Day of *March* last, declared W A R against the *French* King : A N D W H E R E A S, His Majesty hath signified to me, that It should be proclaimed in the Province under my Government, that His Subjects having this Notice, may take care to prevent any Mischief which they might otherwise suffer from the Enemy, and do their Duty in their several Stations, to distress and annoy the Subjects of the *French* King; and the said Declaration hath been this Day proclaimed accordingly: I DO, with the Advice of the Council, issue this PROCLAMATION, strictly enjoining and requiring all His Majesty's Subjects in this Province, capable of bearing Arms, forthwith to provide themselves with a good Firelock, Bayonet, and Cartouch Box, and with a sufficient Quantity of Powder and Ball ; that they may be prepar'd, not only to defend this His Majesty's Province, and their own Persons, Families, and Estates, but to annoy the Enemy, in case it shall be thought proper to attack them ; and that they do pay due Obedience to such Orders as they shall from time to time receive from me, for these Ends, or from such Officers as have been and shall be by me appointed to command them.

A N D W H E R E A S His Majesty hath been pleased to direct, that I be very rigorous and severe in preventing any Ammunition or Stores of any Kind from being carry'd to the Enemy, I do hereby declare, that in case any of His Majesty's Subjects under my Government, shall be found carrying or transporting any Arms, Powder, Ammunition, or Stores, to, or holding any Correspondence or Communication, with the Subjects of the *French* King, they shall be most rigorously and severely prosecuted and punished for the same. And the Collectors of his Majesty's Customs, Naval Officers, and all other Officers whatsoever, are hereby required to be very diligent and circumspect in their several Stations, in order to prevent or discover such Practices.

A N D W H E R E A S, it is His Majesty's further Pleasure, that I do every thing in my Power to encourage the fitting out Ships to act as Privateers against the Enemy, and that I do take all Opportunities, as far as depends upon me, to distress and annoy the *French*, in their Settlements, Trade and Commerce, His Majesty having already issu'd his Royal Proclamation for the Distribution of Prizes taken by his Ships of War or Privateers, I do invite all His Majesty's Subjects under my Government, to receive the Benefit of this His most gracious Declaration, by fitting out such Privateers, which will not only be greatly for His Majesty's Service, but may bring great Advantages to the Adventurers themselves. And being myself most heartily dispos'd to do every thing that may be for his Majesty's Honour, and the Interest of this Province, I do hereby declare, that I will most readily give all the Encouragement and Assistance that in me lies, to every such Undertaking.

GIVEN under my Hand, and the Great Seal of the Province of Pennsylvania, at Philadelphia, the Eleventh Day of June, in the Eighteenth Year of His Majesty's Reign, and in the Year of our LORD, One Thousand Seven Hundred and Forty-four.

By Command,
RICHARD PETERS, *Secry.*

GEO. THOMAS.

God Save the KING.

1. Broadside announcing war with France, 1744. (Item 1310)

NEW-ENGLAND, Numb. 906.

THE

Bofton Gazette.

Publifhed by *John Boydell.*

2. "I.B." Masthead, *The Boston Gazette*, May 16, 1737. (Item 1308)

Dr. Watts.

3. "N.C." *Divine Songs*,
1775. (Item 1335)

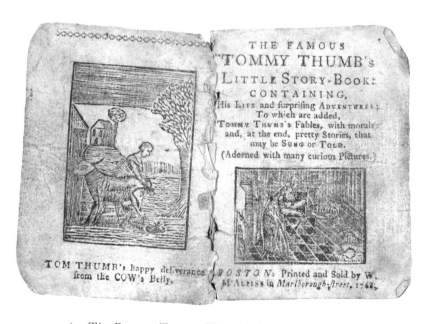

THE FAMOUS
TOMMY THUMB's
LITTLE STORY-BOOK:
CONTAINING,
His Life and furprifing ADVENTURES;
To which are added,
TOMMY THUMB's Fables, with morals:
and, at the end, pretty Stories, that
may be SUNG or TOLD.
(Adorned with many curious Pictures.)

TOM THUMB's happy deliverance
from the COW's Belly.

BOSTON: Printed and Sold by W.
M'ALPINE in *Marlborough-ftreet.* 1768.

4. *The Famous Tommy Thumb's Little Story Book*,
1768. (Item 1317)

HUSH a by Baby
  On the Tree Top,
When the Wind blows
  The Cradle will rock ;
When the Bough breaks
  The Cradle will fall,
Down tumbles Baby,
  Cradle and all.

This may serve as a Warning to the Proud and Ambitious, who climb so high that they generally fall at last.

Maxim.

Content turns all it touches into Gold.

LITTLE

5. *Mother Goose's Melody*, 1794.
    (Item 1370)

6. *Weatherwise's Town and Country Almanack* [1785]. (Item 1351)

7. Parade in Philadelphia after receipt of news of Arnold's treachery. *Americanische Haus- und Wirthschafts-Calender* for 1781. (Item 1343 [1])

GENERAL WASHINGTON'S JACK ASS.

THIS is the true picture of that Celebrated Animal, which his Most Catholick Majesty the King of Spain Bought with his own money and Shipped at his own Expence, for a present to our beloved General.

Hero merit takes, and Gallant Actions shine
Or Mighty Sir, this Ass had ne'er been thine,
Though droll the Gift, yet from a King tis' good ;
Asses, Kings, Ministers are all one blood.

THE GRECIAN DAUGHTER.

Or, an example of a Virtuous WIFE, who fed her father with her own milk---he being condemned to be ftarved to death by
TIBERIUS CÆSAR, Emperor of Rome ; but was afterwards pardoned, and the Daughter highly rewarded.

IN Rome there liv'd a Nobleman
  The Emp'ror to offend,
And for that fault he was adjudg'd
  Unto a cruel end :
That he fhould be in prifon caft
  With irons many a one,
And there be famifh'd unto death
  And brought to fkin and bone :
And more, if any one were known
  By knight or eke by day
To bring him any kind of food
  His hunger to allay,
The Emp'ror fwore a mighty oath,
  Without remorfe, quoth he,
That hould fuftain the hardeft death
  That can be devifed be.
This cruel fentence thus pronounc'd,
  This nobleman was caft
Into a dungeon deep and dark,
  With irons fetter'd faft,
Where, when he had with hunger great
  Remained ten days' fpace,
And tafted neither meat nor drink,
  In a moft woful cafe ;
The tears along his aged face
  Moft piteoufly did fall,
And grievoufly he did begin,
  Complaining, thus to call :
O, Lord, quoth he, what fhall I do ?
  So hungry now am I,
For want of bread, one bit of bread,
  I perifh, ftarve and die.
How precious is one grain of wheat
  Unto a hungry foul ?
One cruft or crumb, or little piece,
  My hunger to controul.

Had I this dungeon heap'd with gold,
  I now would give it all,
To buy and purchafe one fmall loaf,
  Nay, were it e'er fo fmall.
O that I had but every day
  One bit of bread to eat,
Tho' ne'er fo mouldy, black or brown,
  My comfort would be great ;
Yes, though oblig'd to take it up
  Trod down in dirt and mire,
It would be pleafing to my tafte,
  And fweet to my defire.
O Lord, moft happy is the hind
  That labors all the day ;
The drudging mule, the peafant poor,
  That at command do ftay ;
They have their ordinary meals,
  They take no heed at all
Of thofe fmall crums & bits that they
  Do careleffly let fall.
How happy is the little chick,
  Who without fear doth go
And pick up many precious crumbs
  Which they away do throw.
O that fome pretty little moufe
  So much my friend would be,
To bring fome old forfaken crufts
  Into this place to me.
But O, my heart, it is in vain,
  No fuccour can I have ;
No meat, no drink, no water eke,
  My loathed life to fave.
O brink fome bread, for Jefus fake,
  Some bread, fome bread to me ;
I die, I die for want of food,
  None but ftone walls I fee,

Thus night and day he conftant cry'd
  In fuch outrageous fort,
That all the people, far and near,
  Were griev'd at his report,
Though great & many friends he had,
  And daughters in the town,
Yet none durft come to fuccour him,
  Fearing the Emp'ror's frown.
Yet now behold one daughter dear,
  He had, as we do find,
Who liv'd in his difpleafure great,
  Not wedding to his mind :
Altho' fhe liv'd in low eftate,
  She was a virtuous wife,
And for to help her father dear,
  She ventured thus her life :
She quickly to her fifters went,
  And of them did entreat,
That by fome fecret means they woud
  Convey their father meat :
Our Father he doth ftarve, faid fhe,
  The Emp'ror's wrath is fuch,
He dies, alas, for want of food,
  Whereof we have too much.
Pray, fifters, therefore, ufe fome means
  His life for to preferve,
And fuffer not our father dear
  In prifon for to ftarve.
Alas, faid they, what fhall we do,
  His hunger to fuftain ?
You know 'tis death for any one,
  That would his life maintain.
And tho' we wifh him well, faid they,
  We never will agree
To fpoil ourfelves ; we would as foon
  That he fhould die as we ;

And, fifter, if you love yourfelf,
  Let this attempt alone ;
'Tho' you do e'er to fecret work,
  In time it will be known.
O hath our father brought us up,
  And nourifh'd us, quoth fhe,
And fhall we now forfake him quite
  In his extremity ?
No, I will venture life and limb,
  To do my father good ;
The worft that is, I can but die,
  For him I'll fhed my blood.
With that in hafte away fhe flies,
  And to the prifon goes ;
But with her difmal Father dear,
  She might not fpeak, God knows,
Except the Emperor would grant
  Her Father in that cafe,
The keeper would admit no one,
  To enter in that place.
Then fhe unto the Emp'ror hies,
  And falling on her knees,
With wringing hands & bitter cries,
  Thefe words pronounced fhe :
" My haplefs Father, fov'reign Sir,
  Offending of your grace ;
Judg'd to endure a pining death,
  Within a difmal place ;
Which I confefs he has deferv'd,
  Yet, mighty Prince, faid fhe,
Vouchfafe in gracious fort to grant
  One fimple boon to me :
It chanced fo I match'd myfelf
  Againft my father's mind,
Whereby I did procure his wrath,
  As fortune has affigned.

And feeing now the time is come
  He muft refign his breath,
Vouchfafe that I may fpeak to him,
  Before the hour of death ;
And reconcile myfelf to him,
  His favour to obtain,
That when he dies I may not then,
  Under his curfe remain,"
The Emp'ror granted her requeft,
  Conditionally that fhe,
Each day unto her father went,
  Should thoroughly fearched be.
No meat nor drink fhe with her bro't,
  To help him there diftreft,
But every day fhe nourifh'd him
  With milk from her own breaft.
Thus by her milk he was preferv'd
  A twelve month and a day ;
And was fo fair and fat to fee,
  Yet none could tell what way.
The Enpror mufing much thereat,
  At length did underftand,
How he was fed—and not his laws
  Were brake at any hand.
And much admired at the fame,
  And her great virtues fhown,
He pardon'd him and honor'd her
  With great preferments known.
Her Father ever after that,
  Lov'd her as his own life,
And bleft the day that fhe was made
  A virtuous loving wife.

WINDSOR,
PRINTED FOR THE FLYING
BOOK-SELLERS.

8. Broadside, *The Grecian Daughter* [1798]. (Item 1384)

SUPPLEMENT · PART II

AMERICAN BOOK ILLUSTRATION IN

THE NINETEENTH CENTURY

R. A.
[Henry A. Wise?]

A member of the United States Navy, to whom the preface of the Item listed below as 1391 (1) attributes its illustrations.

As noted below there is at least a possibility that Henry A. Wise was himself the illustrator. Wise (May 24, 1819—April 2, 1869) was born in the Brooklyn Navy Yard and, after some training in the Navy, served in the Mexican War, ultimately becoming a lieutenant. He wrote a number of books under the pseudonym "Harry Gringo" and some of his accounts of his naval experiences are of real value. See Stanley J. Kunitz and Howard Haycraft, *American Authors 1600-1900*, New York, 1938, p. 831.

1391. (1) SCAMPAVIAS FROM GIBEL TAREK To STAMBOUL. By Harry Gringo [Henry Augustus Wise] (Lieutenant Wise, United States Navy). New York: Charles Scribner, 1857.

Contains numerous small wood engravings by Roberts regarding which the preface says "The Illustrations have been drawn from sketches taken on the spot, by an accomplished brother bluejacket, whose initials and merit correspond with those of the Royal Academy." Almost all of them are signed "R.A." However, in speaking of an illustration on p. 321 of a girl gathering olives, which bears the R.A. initials, the author says "I made the accompanying flying sketch of one of those damsels in passing. It is not a *chef d'oeuvre* but what can you expect at ten o'clock in the morning?" Could "R.A." have been Wise himself who used the initials "R.A." to disguise the illustrator just as the name Gringo was used to disguise the writer? Or did Wise make the original sketches and "R.A." redraw them for the wood engraver? If Wise had a hand in these illustrations, perhaps he also had something to do with the frontispiece and half title in his better known book, *Tales for the Marines*. Orig. cloth.

(2) TALES FOR THE MARINES. By Harry Gringo [Henry Augustus Wise]. Boston: Phillips, Sampson, & Company . . . 1855. With frontispiece and half title engraved on wood by John Andrew but unsigned by the illustrator. The book is included because of the possibility that Wise might have had a hand in the illustrations. Orig. cloth.

Joseph Alexander Adams
(*See Main Catalogue, p. 45*)

THE CABINET OF INSTRUCTION, LITERATURE, AND AMUSEMENT. New-York: 1829. Contains 2 wood engravings by Adams. That of the N.Y. High School in No. 21 will be found in Item 193. [See Item 1441]

1392. A NEW HIEROGLYPHICAL BIBLE: WITH DEVOTIONAL PIECES FOR YOUTH. Containing Four Hundred Cuts, by Adams. New-York: Harper & Brothers, 1837. This is an earlier edition of Item 200, possibly the first edition as the book was copyrighted in 1836. Unlike Item 200, the borders are not in color. Orig. boards, rebacked, the covers decorated with wood engravings from the book.

1393. THE LIFE OF CHRIST, IN THE WORDS OF THE EVANGELISTS. A COMPLETE HARMONY OF THE GOSPEL HISTORY OF OUR SAVIOUR. For the Use of Young Persons. New-York: Harper & Brothers [n.d., but not later than Dec. 25, 1838, as an inscription with that date appears on the flyleaf].

Contains numerous wood engravings by Adams, many after paintings by old masters. The half title is after a drawing by J. G. Chapman. Orig. cloth.

1394. HISTORIES FROM SCRIPTURE, FOR CHILDREN: EXEMPLIFIED BY APPROPRIATE DOMESTIC TALES. By Miss Graham. New York: John S. Taylor, 1839. With 15 excellent wood engravings by Adams. In original cloth binding, somewhat rubbed, by Colton & Jenkins. On the front cover the bookbinders' names have been nearly obliterated but they are clear enough on the back cover. This is an earlier Colton & Jenkins binding than any Joseph W. Rogers had seen (see p. 180 of "The Rise of American Edition Binding" by Joseph W. Rogers, being Part Two of *Bookbinding in America*, Portland, 1941).

1395. LIVES OF CELEBRATED WOMEN: By the Author of Peter Parley's Tales [S. G. Goodrich]. Boston: Bradbury, Soden & Co., 1844. 2 vols. 1st ed. On the half title is a wood engraving by Adams after a drawing by J. G. Chapman. There are a number of other engravings throughout the book but none of them are signed.

1396. A LETTER from Adams to Benson J. Lossing, dated July 25, the year not given but probably 1871 or 1872, in which Adams writes: "Sometime since I engraved a likeness of Doct. Anderson's father, which was given to Mr. Richardson, wood engraver, in Ann St. to hand to you. I regret very much that I did not succeed much better with it, but the fact is I have been too long out of practice; this cut is only the 15th one that I have done in 28 years, all being small ones. I think that I will not attempt another one as I have lost all confidence in myself; it is impossible for anyone to do justice to anything of that kind without being in constant practice. When you publish your lecture on the Doct. please let me have 2 or 3 copies of it, if convenient . . ."

* The manuscript of this diary, which covers only a few years in the 1790s, will be found in the

This letter refers to the portrait of Alexander Anderson's father which appeared in Lossing's *Memorial of Alexander Anderson*, published in 1872 [Item 357], a portrait which is more particularly referred to on p. 46 of the Main Catalogue. It indicates how little work Adams did after the publication of the Harper's Bible [Item 198].

James Akin
(See Main Catalogue, p. 47)

1397. THE HOUSE THAT JONATHAN BUILT, OR POLITICAL PRIMER FOR 1832. Philadelphia: P. Banks, 1832. A political satire, with 10 wood engravings, all but one signed by Akin. The title-page calls for 12 cuts. Possibly the other 2 appeared on the wrappers which in this copy are not bound in. Modern boards.

Alexander Anderson
(See Main Catalogue, p. 48)

1398. A GOLDEN TREASURY, FOR THE CHILDREN OF GOD, WHOSE TREASURE IS IN HEAVEN; CONSISTING OF SELECT TEXTS OF THE BIBLE, WITH PRACTICAL OBSERVATIONS IN PROSE AND VERSE, FOR EVERY DAY IN THE YEAR. By C.H.V. Bogatzky. With Some Alterations and Improvements by various Hands. New-York: Printed by Wilson & Kirk, 299 Broad-Way, for the New-York Society for promoting Christian Knowledge and Piety, 1797.

Pasted on the front flyleaf is a copper engraving by Anderson, showing two men and a small girl standing in front of a house, with an Indian in the background. One of the men is presenting a book to the other while an angel in the sky unfurls a scroll with the words "The poor have the Gospel preached to them." Underneath are the words "The Gift of the New-York Society for Promoting Christian Knowledge and Piety." Cont. calf.

1398a. THE CHILD'S SPELLING BOOK: CALCULATED TO RENDER READING COMPLETELY EASY TO LITTLE CHILDREN; TO IMPRESS UPON THEIR MINDS THE IMPORTANCE OF RELIGION, AND THE ADVANTAGES OF GOOD MANNERS. Compiled by a Printer. Hartford: Printed by John Babcock, 1798. Evans 33346, who attributes the book to Elisha Babcock.

Contains a frontispiece composed of 4 cuts and 28 other cuts in the text. Anderson in his diary* under the date March 30, 1798, writes:

Columbia University Library. A long-hand copy is at the New York Historical Society.

"This evening I finished Babcock's engravings, amounting to 32 cuts." It seems more than probable that this refers to the 32 cuts of *The Child's Spelling Book*. Furthermore, Rosenbach (No. 274) states without qualification that the cuts in his 4th edition of 1802 (all of which, excepting those in the frontispiece, appeared in this 1798 edition) "are copies by Dr. Alexander Anderson of cuts by Bewick and others."

There was a 2nd edition in 1800 (Evans 37179), a 3rd in 1801 (Shaw & Shoemaker 50203), and a 4th in 1802 (Rosenbach 274). All the cuts of the 1798 edition appear in these later editions except that the frontispieces differ in the 3rd and 4th editions and except that in all three later editions the following 7 cuts are missing, viz.: The Vizard, p. 57, The Serpent, p. 61, The Windmill, p. 63, The Hour Glass, p. 63, The Monkey, p. 75, The Purse, p. 79, and The Egg, p. 79.

At the foot of the final page are the words "The End of Vol. I" and this is also true in the 2nd and 3rd editions but in the 4th edition these words are dropped and in their place appear the words "Copy Right Secured." Apparently no further volumes were ever issued.

In earlier entries in his diary for March 1798, Anderson speaks of sawing out 34 blocks of boxwood, only 2 more than the 32 needed for "Babcock's cuts," which were finished on March 30. It seems likely that these "Babcock cuts" were each engraved on the end of a boxwood block and are genuine and very early examples of American wood engraving.

Orig. boards, leather back.

1399. A Commentary upon the Epistle of Paul the Apostle to the Galatians . . . By Mr. Martin Luther. To which is prefixed, An Account of the Life of the Author. Philadelphia: Printed & Sold by R. Aitken, 1801.

With a frontispiece portrait of Luther after a painting by Dürer engraved by Anderson. It is sometimes difficult to tell whether Anderson's work of this period is on wood or typemetal but this is probably engraved on wood. Cont. calf.

1400. The Farmer's Boy; A Rural Poem. By Robert Bloomfield. The First American Edition. Ornamented with elegant Wood Engravings, by A. Anderson. New York: Printed and Sold by George F. Hopkins, 1801.

This "First American edition" contains the same wood engravings as the "Fifth American edition" of 1803 [Item 221], with some slight differences in arrangement. Both these editions state on the title-page that Anderson is the engraver, although only two of the cuts are signed by him.

None of the cuts of this 1st edition appear in the "Fourth American edition" of 1801 [Item 215], although 2 of them are similar but in reverse. It might be supposed that these 2 cuts had been copied and pirated from the 1st edition. However, while Anderson's name does not appear on either of these 2 cuts in the 1st edition, it does appear on 1 of the 2 reversed cuts. Perhaps Anderson re-engraved them for the 4th edition.

Cont. calf. Presented by Pierce W. Gaines.

1401. The Enchanted Plants; Fables in Verse. Inscribed to Miss Montolieu, and Miss Julia Montolieu. [By Mrs. Montolieu.] New-York: David Longworth, at the Shakespeare-Gallery, 1803.

The frontispiece is a copper engraving by P. Maverick after W. Hamilton R.A. Duyckinck in his *A Brief Catalogue of Books Illustrated with Engravings by Dr. Alexander Anderson*, New York, 1885, lists this book on p. 6 as having "17 tailpieces by Anderson." Actually there are 18 tailpieces. That on p. 34 is signed "A.A." and that on p. 102 is signed "A" and what may be intended for an "A" can be seen on the cut on p. 87. The cuts make the book an attractive little volume. Marbled boards with leather back.

1402. The Poems of Robert Bloomfield. In Two Parts: Part I. The Farmer's Boy. Part II. Rural Tales. Burlington, N.J.: Printed for David Allinson, by Stephen C. Ustick, 1803.

There are 4 wood engravings to illustrate *The Farmer's Boy*, one of which is signed "A." These are the same full-page illustrations, now somewhat worn, which appeared in Item 215, except that the illustration "Summer," which in Item 215 is a copper engraving, has in this edition been re-engraved on wood. There is one unsigned wood engraving in *Rural Tales*, the frontispiece, which it seems fair to assume is also by Anderson. This illustration, re-engraved by Anderson in reverse, will be found in a later edition of *Rural Tales* [Item 271], which is dated 1821. A comparison of the two is interesting as showing the progress Anderson had made, between 1803 and 1821, in the art of wood engraving. Cont. calf with leather back.

1403. The Piligrim's Progress from this World, to That Which is to Come. Delivered under the Similitude of a Dream. In Three Parts . . . By John Bunyan . . . New-York: Printed for John Tiebout, by L. Nichols, 1804.

Contains 22 cuts, which appear to be identical with those found in Bumstead's Boston edition of 1806* [Item 233]. In commenting on the cuts in the 1806 edition, the writer suggested it was strange for Anderson, at this late date, to have reverted to the use of typemetal. Apparently this "reversion" took place at an earlier date than the writer had realized.

As might be expected, the cuts in this 1804 edition are clearer and show less wear than those in the 1806 edition. Cont. calf.

1404. POEMS BY THOMAS ROMNEY ROBINSON, WRITTEN BETWEEN THE AGE OF SEVEN AND THIRTEEN . . . First American, from the Belfast Edition. Brooklyn: Printed by Thomas Kirk, 1808. With a portrait of the boy poet, engraved on wood by Anderson. Orig. boards, rebacked.

1405. DAME PARTLET'S FARM: CONTAINING AN ACCOUNT OF THE GREAT RICHES SHE OBTAINED BY INDUSTRY, THE GOOD LIFE SHE LED, AND ALAS GOOD READER! HER SUDDEN DEATH; TO WHICH IS ADDED, A HYMN, WRITTEN BY DAME PARTLET, JUST BEFORE HER DEATH, AND AN EPITAPH FOR HER TOMB STONE. Philadelphia: Johnson and Warner, 1810.

Contains 18 cuts that look more like typemetal cuts than woodcuts. Anderson's "A" appears on 3, pp. 4, 46 and 47, and many of the others are no doubt his also. Orig. boards.

1406. DIE GEFAHR IN DEN STRASSEN. NEBST EINIGEN ANDERN ERZÄHLUNGEN. Philadelphia: Gedruckt bey Jacob Meyer Für Johnson und Warner, 1810. Rosenbach 418. Welch 398. With a wood engraving by Anderson on the title-page. Orig. boards.

1407. THE JUVENILE LIBRARY: CONTAINING THE HISTORIES OF SANDFORD AND MERTON, MARTIN AND JAMES, AND THE YOUNG ROBBER: DESIGNED FOR THE INSTRUCTION AND AMUSEMENT OF YOUTH. New York: J. C. Totten, 1810. Welch 646.

The frontispiece and all the wood engravings in *The Young Robber* are by Anderson. The cuts in the *Sandford and Merton* and *Martin and James* seem for the most part rather primitive and none are signed, except that on p. 49 of *Martin and James* which is signed "W" and except that the tailpiece on p. 9 of *Sandford and Merton* shows a sailing vessel with the initials H.D. on her stern. It would be pleasant to think that this is an old cut of Henry Dawkins which in some manner had found its way into Totten's printing establishment. Orig. boards with leather back.

* David E. Smith in his "Illustrations of American Editions of *The Pilgrim's Progress* to 1870" in *The*

1408. THE LIFE OF GEORGE WASHINGTON . . . By David Ramsay, M.D. Second Edition. Boston: D. Mallory and Co. . . . 1811. The frontispiece is a wood engraved portrait of Washington, signed "A." Cont. calf.

1409. THE YOUTH'S CABINET OF NATURE, FOR THE YEAR; CONTAINING CURIOUS PARTICULARS CHARACTERISTIC OF EACH MONTH. INTENDED TO DIRECT YOUNG PEOPLE TO THE INNOCENT AND AGREEABLE EMPLOYMENT OF OBSERVING NATURE. New York: S. Wood, 1811.

Exclusive of a few small tailpieces, this book contains 13 wood engravings. They are unsigned and are the same as those which appear in another edition published by Wood the following year. Rosenbach (No. 467), in describing this 1812 edition, says without qualification that the "woodcuts [are] by Anderson," a statement which is lent support by Wood's advertisement on the back cover of the present copy, viz.: "Printed and Sold by Samuel Wood . . . Above 30 Kinds of School and Small Books for Children; With neat cuts engraved by Anderson, and matter carefully selected, calculated not only to amuse, but also to instruct, the infant mind in Morality and Virtue."

This 1811 edition is not listed by Harry B. Weiss in his article on Samuel Wood & Sons in the *Bulletin of the New York Public Library* for September, 1942, Vol. 46, No. 9, nor is it listed by Ralph R. Shaw and Richard H. Shoemaker, *American Bibliography, A Preliminary Checklist for 1811*, New York, 1962. There are copies of it, however, at the New-York Historical Society and the Connecticut Historical Society.

This copy has 52 numbered pages and 1 blank leaf at the end. The first blank leaf, referred to by Rosenbach in describing the 1812 edition, is not present here. Orig. boards, with wood engraving on front cover.

1410. LEISURE HOURS; OR POEMS, MORAL, RELIGIOUS, & DESCRIPTIVE. By Joshua Marsden, Missionary. New-York: Published for the author, and sold by Griffin and Rudd, 1812. Fig. 9.

With frontispiece portrait of Marsden, engraved on wood by Anderson and 3 full-page wood engravings by Anderson in the text. The tailpiece on p. 77 is also by him. Duyckinck in his *A Brief Catalogue of Books Illustrated with Engravings by Dr. Alexander Anderson*, New York, 1885, says of the author (p. 13) "Marsden, an English missionary to North America

Princeton University Library Chronicle, Vol. XXVI, No. 1, at p. 19, found the cuts to be identical.

and the Bermudas, was, at the time of the publication of this book, detained in New York by the embargo." The designs for the illustrations were probably, therefore, of American origin. Duyckinck calls the illustrations "vigorous in design and effective in light and shade. If wholly designed by Anderson, they show his grace and imagination, as in the angel leaving the couch at the death-bed of Voltaire."

Linton (p. 6) says that Anderson was at his best about 1818, but these engravings indicate that he reached maturity as an engraver even earlier. Cont. calf.

1411. THE MINSTREL: OR, THE PROGRESS OF GENIUS. By James Beattie, LL.D. Also, THE SHIPWRECK. By William Falconer. New York: Collins and Co., 1812. The frontispieces of the 2 books are wood engravings by Anderson and a third wood engraving by him is found opposite p. 116. Cont. calf.

1412. FALSE STORIES CORRECTED. New-York: S. Wood, 1813. The date on the front wrapper is 1812. Welch 362.1.

Contains 19 wood engravings, similar to, and apparently printed from the same blocks as, those in Rosenbach (487). This latter is an entirely different edition and is dated 1814. Rosenbach states definitely that the cuts are by Anderson and this is probably so, although none of them bear his name or initials. 44 pages with an additional page of advertising matter identical in content with that in Rosenbach (487). Orig. wrappers, with 2 wood engravings on the back wrapper.

1413. GARDEN AMUSEMENTS, FOR IMPROVING THE MINDS OF LITTLE CHILDREN. New York: Samuel Wood, 1813. Rosenbach (No. 490) describes an edition of this book dated 1814 and Harry B. Weiss in his article on Samuel Wood & Sons in the Bulletin of The New York Public Library for September 1942, Vol. 46, No. 9, lists only the edition of 1814. The 1813 edition probably marks Wood's first issuance of the book. It is not, however, the 1st edition which was published in Boston in 1812 (Welch 397.1).

There is a vignette on the title-page and 10 other wood engravings in the text which are the same cuts as those in the 1814 edition except that in the latter edition two tailpieces are omitted. Rosenbach says that all of the engravings are by Anderson and he is probably right. That on p. 19 is signed "A" and what looks like the same initial can be dimly discerned in the cut on p. 15.

The type of the two editions differs. The title-page of the earlier edition states that it is "Published" by Samuel Wood, while the later edition uses the words "Printed and Sold." The printers of the 1813 edition, as the final leaf shows, were Pelsue & Gould of 9 Wall Street.

Orig. wrappers with a wood engraving on the front wrapper.

1414. THE ADVENTURES OF GIL BLAS OF SANTILLANE. Translated from the French of Monsieur LeSage, by Tobias Smollett, M.D., to which is prefixed, A Life of the Author. New York: Richard Scott, 1814. 4 vols.

Each volume contains a full-page wood engraving by Anderson as a frontispiece. On each half title there is a smaller wood engraving. These are almost certainly by Anderson also. In fact the one in Vol. IV is signed "A." Orig. boards with morocco backs.

1415. THE BEAUTIES OF SHAKSPEARE: REGULARLY SELECTED FROM EACH PLAY, WITH A GENERAL INDEX, DIGESTING THEM UNDER PROPER HEADS. By the Late Rev. William Dodd, LL.D. New York: R. M'Dermut & D. D. Arden, 1814. The frontispiece is a scene from Midsummer-Night's Dream, engraved on wood by Anderson in his best style. Cont. calf. From the estate of Henry N. Paul.

1416. THE PLEASURES OF HOPE, AND OTHER POEMS, By Thomas Campbell. And THE PLEASURES OF MEMORY, By Samuel Rogers. Albany: D. Steele, 1814. The frontispiece was engraved on wood by Anderson. Orig. boards.

1417. THE BIRTH-DAY PRESENT. By Miss [Maria] Edgeworth. Boston: Wells and Lilly, 1815. Welch 291.1. With a full-page frontispiece, repeated on the front wrapper, engraved on wood by Anderson. Orig. wrappers.

1418. A YEAR OF THE LIFE OF THE EMPEROR NAPOLEON; OR AN HISTORICAL ACCOUNT OF ALL THAT HAPPENED FROM THE 1ST OF APRIL, 1814, TO THE 20TH OF MARCH, 1815 . . . Translated from the French of A.D.B.M. . . . Lieutenant of Grenadiers [A.D.B. Monier]. New-York: David Longworth, 1815. With a portrait of Napoleon, after a painting by David, engraved by Anderson. Orig. boards.

1419. CHRYSAL; OR, THE ADVENTURES OF A GUINEA: WHEREIN ARE EXHIBITED VIEWS OF SEVERAL STRIKING SCENES, WITH CURIOUS AND INTERESTING ANECDOTES OF THE MOST NOTED PERSONS IN EVERY RANK OF LIFE, WHOSE HANDS IT PASSED THROUGH, IN AMERICA, ENGLAND, HOLLAND, GERMANY AND PORTUGAL. By an Adept [Charles Johnstone]. From the second enlarged and corrected edition.

New-York: D. Huntington, 1816. 4 vols. Vol. I has a frontispiece engraved on wood by Anderson. It shows him at his best. Orig. printed boards, uncut.

1420. DOCUMENT dated December 15, 1817, signed by James Monroe as President of the United States, granting land in the Territory of Illinois to Elijah Birge, a veteran of the War of 1812. It is on vellum and in the upper left-hand corner is a wood engraving by Anderson showing a female figure, perhaps meant to represent Columbia, presenting a bounty deed to a soldier while his wife and child stand beside him, the wife pointing to the distant prairies.

1421. ESSAY ON THE THEORY OF THE EARTH. By M. Cuvier . . . WITH MINERALOGICAL NOTES . . . By Professor Jamessen. TO WHICH ARE NOW ADDED, OBSERVATIONS ON THE GEOLOGY OF NORTH AMERICA . . . By Samuel L. Mitchell. New-York: Kirk & Mercein, 1818. Contains 8 plates. The frontispiece and Plate I are wood engravings by Anderson. Plates II, IV, VI, VII, and VIII are copper engravings by Anderson. Plate III is not signed. Cont. boards with calf back.

1421a. RETURNING FROM THE BOAR HUNT. A wood engraving by Anderson after Ridinger. According to Linton, p. 6, this was done about 1818. Linton reproduces the cut in a double-page folding frontispiece to his History of Wood-Engraving in America and says of it "No more vigorous piece of pure white line work has been done outside of the Bewick circle" [see also Item 268].

On the bottom of the white mat is written in pencil: "Wood-engraving from two blocks by Alexander Anderson. This impression is one of the proofs printed by Anderson himself. From the collection of his grandson."

ALBUM containing over 1000 wood engravings probably used in books published by the American Sunday School Union in Philadelphia during the 1820s. One engraving signed "A." [See Item 1674]

1422. EARLY INSTRUCTION, RECOMMENDED IN A NARRATIVE OF THE LIFE OF CATHERINE HALDANE; WITH AN ADDRESS TO PARENTS ON THE IMPORTANCE OF RELIGION. [By James Alexander Haldane.] New Haven: J. Babcock & Son, 1820. Welch 442.8. On the verso of the front wrapper is a wood engraving by Anderson. The wood engraving on the recto of the front wrapper may be his also. Orig. wrappers.

1423. LONDON; A DESCRIPTIVE POEM. New York: Samuel Wood and Sons, No. 261 Pearl-Street; And Samuel S. Wood & Co. No. 212, Market-St. Baltimore [ca. 1820]. Contains 6 full-page wood engravings of London views, that of St. Paul's Cathedral on p. 15 bearing Anderson's initial.

Harry B. Weiss in his article on Samuel Wood & Sons in the Bulletin of the New York Public Library for September 1942, lists this book but fails to locate a copy. Welch (730a) lists a copy substantially similar to the above, except that it is dated 1820 and, on the title-page, "New-York" is misspelled "Nerv York." This would appear to be a somewhat earlier issue than the copy here listed. Orig. boards.

1424. THE PROGRESS OF THE DAIRY; DESCRIPTIVE OF THE METHOD OF MAKING BUTTER AND CHEESE; FOR THE INFORMATION OF YOUTH. New-York: Samuel Wood and Sons, No. 261, Pearl-Street; and Samuel S. Wood & Co. No. 212 Market-St., Baltimore [ca. 1820]. With 7 delightful wood engravings by Anderson depicting various phases of dairy work, all but two carefully colored by hand. Orig. wrappers.

1425. THREE ENGRAVED WOOD BLOCKS, undated, but probably executed about 1820-1830, as follows:

(1) Block signed "Anderson," apparently a New England Puritan scene with people on shore among trees and a ship close by.

(2) Block unsigned but marked by a former owner as the work of Anderson. It shows the graveside monument of Col. John Brown, an officer in the Revolutionary Army, killed in battle October 19, 1780.

(3) Block unsigned but marked by a former owner as the work of Anderson. It was intended to advertise "Purified Windsor Soap."

1426. VERSES FOR LITTLE CHILDREN. New York: Samuel Wood & Sons, No. 261, Pearl-street; and Samuel S. Wood & Co., No. 212 Market-street, Baltimore, 1820. Contains 6 wood engravings by Anderson. Anderson was then at the height of his power and the engravings are excellent. Orig. wrappers.

1427. THE BEAUTIES OF SHAKSPEARE. By the Late Rev. William Dodd, LL.D. New York: Evert Duyckinck, 1821.

There are wood engravings on the title-page and at the head of the first, second, and third parts. Two are signed "A" and the others are probably by him also. Duyckinck in his A Brief Catalogue of Books Illustrated with Engravings by Dr. Alexander Anderson, New York, 1885, at p. 4, lists this book but calls for only 3

Anderson engravings, apparently overlooking the engraving at the head of Part III, although, since this is not signed, it is possible that Anderson was not the engraver of it. The cut used in the earlier edition of this book [Item 1415] does not appear in this later edition. Cont. calf. From the estate of Henry N. Paul.

1427a. THE HISTORY OF JACOB; A SCRIPTURE NARRATIVE, IN VERSE. New York: Samuel Wood and Sons, No. 261, Pearl-Street; and Samuel S. Wood & Co. No. 212, Market-St., Baltimore, 1822.

With 7 round wood engravings by Anderson. Harry B. Weiss in his article on Samuel Wood & Sons in the *Bulletin of the New York Public Library* for September 1942, lists an edition of 1820 but fails to list this later edition. Probably both editions contain the same cuts. Orig. stiff covers.

1428. THE LIFE OF JOSEPH, A SCRIPTURE NARRATIVE. By E. Miller. New York: Mahlon Day, 1823. With 7 wood engravings. The well-engraved frontispiece is signed "A" and the cuts on pp. 8 and 11 might well be his work. One hesitates to attribute the remaining cuts to him. Orig. wrappers.

1429. A GROUP OF 30 TRACTS, bound in one volume, all but one published by the New-York Religious Tract Society. One tract, *The Ship-wreck*, was published in New York by the American Religious Tract Society. 6 of them are dated 1824 and the rest are probably about that time. Most of them appear to be children's tracts.

The tracts contain numerous wood engravings. Many of these will be found in the 1807 edition of *The Looking-Glass for the Mind* [Item 237], the cuts in which are probably all by Anderson and follow generally his cuts in the 1795 edition of the same book [Item 210]. Some of the cuts in the present volume bear his initials.* Indeed it seems likely that Anderson was responsible for the majority of the engravings in these 30 tracts.

The New-York Religious Tract Society was founded in 1812 and in 1825 merged with the American Tract Society of Boston (formerly the New England Religious Tract Society) to form the national American Tract Society. It began to issue its children's tracts in 1824, the series being largely reprinted from the illustrated children's tracts issued by the Religious Tract Society established in London. Many of the Eng-

lish engravings were copied for the New York series. The New-York Religious Tract Society issued some 75 children's books before the merger with the American Tract Society of Boston. (See Lawrance Thompson, *The Printing and Publishing Activities of The American Tract Society from 1825 to 1850*, New York, 1941, at p. 4 *et seq.*, and Sinclair H. Hitchings, "Some American Wood Engravers 1820-1840," *PAGA*, Vol. IX, No. 4.)
Orig. boards with calf back.

1430. REFLECTIONS ON THE WORKS OF GOD IN NATURE AND PROVIDENCE, FOR EVERY DAY IN THE YEAR. By Christopher C. Sturm. Translated by Adam Clarke, LL.D. F.A.S. New York: Abraham Paul, 1824. With frontispiece portrait of Sturm and 4 full-page cuts of the seasons, all engraved on wood by Anderson. Cont. calf.

1431. TALES TO MY DAUGHTER: MORAL AND INTERESTING. CONTAINING, THE BUNCH OF CHERRIES, OR, JOYS OF PARTICIPATION: THE STRAW HAT: THE STARLING: AND THE GREEN SHOES. Translated from the French. New-Haven: J. Babcock and Son . . . 1824. 3 full-page wood engravings, of which 2 bear Anderson's initial.

This is bound with the following juveniles:

a. EMILY AND HENRIETTA; OR, A CURE FOR IDLENESS. AN IMPROVING TALE FOR YOUTH. Translated from the French, by W. F. Sullivan, A.M. New-Haven: J. Babcock and Son . . . 1824. 3 full-page unsigned wood engravings.

b. PLEASANT STORIES; OR, THE HISTORIES OF BEN THE SAILOR AND NED THE SOLDIER. CONTAINING, NUMEROUS ENTERTAINING ANECDOTES AND ADVENTURES OF REAL LIFE; VOUCHED AS GENUINE AND AUTHENTIC. By W. F. Sullivan, A.M. New-Haven: J. Babcock and Son . . . 1824. 2 full-page wood engravings bearing Anderson's initial.

c. EMULATION; OR, THE BENEFIT OF GOOD EXAMPLE. AN INTERESTING NARRATIVE, FOR THE ATTENTIVE PERUSAL OF YOUNG PERSONS. By W. F. Sullivan, A.M. New-Haven: J. Babcock and Son . . . 1824. 3 full-page wood engravings bearing Anderson's initial.

The unsigned engravings are probably by Anderson also (see Duyckinck, *A Brief Catalogue of Books Illustrated with Engravings by Dr. Alexander Anderson*, New York, 1885, p. 29).
Orig. boards.

* It is interesting to note that the signed cut on p. 6 of *Address to a Child* (which is another copy of Item 276), while of the same subject as that on p. 1

of the 1795 *Looking Glass*, differs not only from the latter cut but also from the corresponding cut in the 1807 edition.

1432. THE TRANSMIGRATIONS OF INDUR. New Haven: J. Babcock and Son ... 1824. With full-page frontispiece and 7 other wood engravings in the text. The frontispiece is signed "A" and the other cuts are probably his also. There is an unsigned wood engraving on the front wrapper. Orig. wrappers.

1433. A CHECK drawn on the Schuylkill Bank in the City of Philadelphia and dated December 10, 1825. In the upper left-hand corner is a neat little wood engraving signed "A" which probably depicts a view on the Schuylkill River.

THE COLUMBIAN PRIMER. Newark: 1825. Full-page frontispiece engraved on wood by Anderson. [See Item 1793]

1434. THE CHILD'S MAGAZINE, October, 1827. Vol. I [No. 4]. Published for the Sunday School Union, Methodist Episcopal Church. [New York]: N. Bangs & J. Emory [1827]. The wood engraving on p. 61 is by Anderson. Presented by Sinclair H. Hitchings.

1435. THE COTTAGE MINSTREL; OR, VERSES ON VARIOUS SUBJECTS. By a Female of this City [Sarah Wharton]. Affectionately addressed to the youthful part of her own sex. Philadelphia: Printed for the Authoress, by Joseph Rakestraw, 1827. With a frontispiece engraved on wood by Anderson. Orig. boards, with leather back.

1436. THE PUBLICATIONS OF THE AMERICAN TRACT SOCIETY. Vols. I-IV, and Vols. VII and VIII. Vol. I has on its title-page the address of "87 Nassau-Street, near the City Hall, New York" which was the Society's address from 1825 to 1827, but wherever an address appears on the tracts themselves it is 144 Nassau St. (to which the Society moved in 1827), with the exception of Tract 18 where the old 87 Nassau St. address is retained. It would appear, therefore, that these early tracts had been exhausted and were reprinted, somewhere between 1827 and 1833, when the Society moved to 150 Nassau St. In Vols. II and III the address on the title-pages and on all tracts containing an address is 87 Nassau St. In Vol. IV the title-page address is 87 Nassau St. but that on the tracts is 144 Nassau St., while in Vols. VII and VIII the address on the title-pages and on the tracts is 144 Nassau St.

A great many of the wood engravings are probably by Anderson, but his name or initial appears only on certain of them. One engraving (Tract 92 in Vol. III) is signed "P" (could this be Page?) and one engraving (Tract 93 in Vol. III) is signed "C" (early work of Childs?).

In Vol. I there are 23 wood engravings. Anderson's name or initial will be found on 12 [Tracts 1, 3, 8, 9 (the name is undecipherable, but is reasonably clear on the same cut at p. 85 in Item 311), 10, 14, 18, 19, 22, 24, 26, and 28].

In Vol. II there are 23 wood engravings, 12 bearing Anderson's initial (Tracts 34, 35, 36, 39, 41, 51, 55, 57, 58, 59, 63, and 66).

In Vol. III there are 22 wood engravings, 7 bearing Anderson's initial (Tracts 72, 73, 77, 80, 82, 83, and 89).

In Vol. IV there are 23 wood engravings, 11 bearing Anderson's initial (Tracts 94, 99, 103, 104, 107, 108, 114, 116, 118, 120, and 122).

In Vol. VII there are 17 wood engravings, 5 bearing Anderson's name or initial (Tracts 199, 203, 208, 210, and 222).

In Vol. VIII there are 9 wood engravings, 4 bearing Anderson's initial (Tracts 235, 239, 245, and 250).

In addition to the wood engravings listed above, which occur at the heads of the tracts, there are a number of small unsigned tailpieces.

Item 311, published some years later, is also Vol. I of *The Publications of the American Tract Society*. It contains the same tracts (reset for the most part and sometimes with different titles) with the exception of Tracts 13, 14, 25, 28, and 31, where different tracts have been substituted. Many of the same cuts will be found in this later edition, although in some instances the blocks, if not completely recut, have had slight alterations made in them. Cuts which are entirely different appear at the heads of the following numbered tracts in Item 311: 1 (a cut by A. J. Mason in place of one by Anderson), 5, 6, 11, 27 (a cut signed "A" in place of an unsigned cut), 28 (here the tract itself is different), and 29.

Uniformly bound in cont. calf.

1437. RELIGIOSE AUFSÄTZE, . . . Erster Band. Herausgeben Von der Americanischen Tractat-Gesellschaft, und zu haben an ihrem Verlage, Nro. 144, Nassaustrasse, Neu-York . . . [n.d., but between 1827 and 1833, the years when the American Tract Society was located at 144 Nassau St. in New York City].

Contains 30 tracts, each separately paginated. Most of them contain a wood engraving. Anderson's initial appears on the engravings which head Tracts 2, 5, 9, 15, 17, 21, 26, and 30, but others are no doubt by him. The cut on Tract 18 is signed with a "P" and that on Tract 20 with a "C." Many of the cuts will be found in Item 1436. Cont. calf.

1438. TEN DIALOGUES ON THE EFFECTS OF ARDENT SPIRITS. New York: The American

Tract Society, 144 Nassau-street [between 1827 and 1833]. This is No. 17 of Series III. With 4 full-page wood engravings, 3 of which bear Anderson's name or initial. There are also 7 vignettes, those on pp. 16 and 26 carrying Anderson's initials. Orig. wrappers.

1439. BOOK OF CUTS, DESIGNED FOR THE AMUSEMENT & INSTRUCTION OF YOUNG PEO-PLE. New York: Mahlon Day, 1828. With 21 wood engravings. 3 of these (pp. 9, 10, and 20) bear Anderson's initial, but many more are certainly his work. Orig. wrappers, with wood engravings.

1439a. A PRESENT TO CHILDREN, BY THE AUTHOR OF "DITTIES FOR CHILDREN, POETIC TALES, GOOD GIRL'S SOLILOQUY." &c &c [Nancy Sproat*]. New-York: Samuel Wood and Sons, No. 261, Pearl Street; and Samuel S. Wood & Co., No. 212, Market Street, Baltimore [ca. 1830]. Rosenbach, 748. With 8 wood engravings by Anderson. Orig. wrappers.

1440. THE AMERICAN TRACT MAGAZINE. Group of 29 issues of this rather scarce little monthly, viz.: Vol. IV, Nos. 6, 8, 9; Vol. V, Nos. 2-5, 7-9, 11; Vol. VI, Nos. 6, 7, 11; Vol. VII, No. 5; Vol. IX, Nos. 6-9; Vol. X, Nos. 1, 6, 10; Vol. XI, Nos. 8-10; Vol. XIII, Nos. 8-10; Vol. XIV, No. 6; Vol. 15, No. 6. New York: American Tract Society, June 1829-June 1840.

13 wood engravings are to be found in this miscellaneous lot, together with 3 different wrapper wood engravings which appear several times. Anderson's initial is on the cut in No. 4 of Vol. V and possibly on the cut in No. 5 of that Vol. also, but many of the other cuts are well enough done to be his work. One cut (No. 3 of Vol. V) is signed "Mason," probably A. J. Mason.

No. 11 of Vol. VI (November 1831) contains a "Sketch of the Origin and Character of the Principal Series of Tracts of The American Tract Society." This gives a list of 255 consecutively numbered tracts, together with 11 "Occasional Tracts," showing the name of the author in most cases, the number of pages in the tract and whether it is a reprint from the publications of the Religious Tract Society in London.

Of these 29 nos., 15 are in the original wrappers. The others lack wrappers.

1441. THE CABINET OF INSTRUCTION, LITERATURE, AND AMUSEMENT . . . Vol. I. New-York: Theodore Burling, 1829. H. R. Piercy, Printer, 265 Bowery.

* See Alice Sproat Emery, "Nancy Sproat and her Little Books for Good Children" in the Bulletin of

This periodical was at first published semimonthly on the 1st and 16th of each month by Piercy & Burling. Its first number was that for September 16, 1828. With the number for April 16, 1829, Burling became sole publisher with Piercy as printer, and with the number for May 9, 1829, it was made a weekly. Vol. I contains 24 numbers, Sept. 16, 1828—June 27, 1829.

At the head of each number is a wood engraving. Anderson's name or initial will be found on those in Nos. 1, 4, 5, 8, 9, 10, 11, 12, 13, 15, and 18. No indication is given of the draftsman except that the cut in No. 15 was designed by Alexander J. Davis, the architect. John H. Hall of Albany was the engraver of the cut in No. 14 and J. A. Adams engraved those in Nos. 21 and 23.

Cont. calf with the name of Samuel Newton Rudkin stamped in gold on the front cover.

1442. TALES FOR THOMAS. CONTAINING, THE SOLDIER, THE PRESENT, THE RETURN, THE HOUSE, THE DOG, LITTLE HARRY, THE GARDEN, STRAWBERRIES, THE KITE, THE BLACK MAN. By A.C.H. of Newport, R.I. New-York: Mahlon Day, 1829. The frontispiece bears Anderson's initials. Some of the small cuts in the text may be his also. Orig. wrappers, covered with floreated paper.

1443. A BOOK FULL OF PICTURES. WITH INTERESTING EXPLANATIONS TO EACH. New-Haven: S. Babcock . . . 1830.

The frontispiece, a wood engraving signed "A," dramatically portrays "The Landlord discovered in his attempt to poison three French Officers, by introducing arsenic into a tumbler of Punch," an incident about which, unfortunately, the text says not a word. There are smaller wood engravings on both wrappers and 20 throughout the text, all of which may well be Anderson's work. A few of them are crudely colored. Orig. wrappers.

1444. FOX'S BOOK OF MARTYRS. A UNIVERSAL HISTORY OF CHRISTIAN MARTYRDOM: FROM THE BIRTH OF OUR BLESSED SAVIOUR TO THE LATEST PERIODS OF PERSECUTION. Originally Composed by the Rev. John Fox, A.M., and now Corrected Throughout, with Copious and Important Additions Relative to the Recent Persecutions in the South of France. In Two Volumes. New Edition: Embellished with Sixty Fine Engravings. Philadelphia: Key, Mielke & Biddle, 1832.

As appears from the list of engravings in each

The New York Public Library, August 1951.

volume, there are only 55 engravings. Nothing is missing. All are wood engravings. The frontispiece, a portrait of Fox, is signed by A. J. Mason, as are a number of the other engravings. Anderson's name or initials appear on the following Plates: V, VI, VIII, X, XIII, XIV, XV, XVII, XVIII, XXII, XXVII, XXXI, XXXII, XLV, and LIII. In addition to the frontispiece, Mason's name appears on the following Plates: XVI, XIX, XXI, XXVIII, XXX, XXXVIII, XLI, XLIV, and LI. No doubt many, if not all, the unsigned Plates were engraved by either Anderson or Mason. Cont. calf.

HISTORY OF THE UNITED STATES. New Haven: 1832. Frontispiece engraved on wood by Anderson. [See Item 1481]

EVENING READINGS IN HISTORY. Springfield: 1833. The cut on p. 89 is by Anderson. [See Item 1482]

1445. LIVES OF THE APOSTLES AND EARLY MARTYRS OF THE CHURCH. By the author of "The Trial of Skill." New York: J. & J. Harper, 1833. This is No. I of the Boy's and Girl's Library. With a view of Jerusalem engraved on wood by Anderson. Orig. boards with a wood engraving of "The Bay and Harbour of New York" on the front cover.

1446. THE PICTURE READER; DESIGNED AS A FIRST READING BOOK, FOR YOUNG MASTERS AND MISSES. By a Friend to Youth. New Haven: S. Babcock, 1833. Contains numerous wood engravings. The frontispiece and those on pp. 12, 16, 20, 22, 24, 26, 28, 38, 40, 42, 44, and 46 bear Anderson's name or initials. Orig. wrappers.

1447. RHODE ISLAND TALES. By a Friend to Youth, of Newport, R.I. [Miss A. Howland]. New York: Mahlon Day, 1833. This is the first edition of the book and, with a few unimportant differences in the tailpieces, contains the same wood engravings which appeared in the edition to be found in Item 324. Orig. boards.

1448. THE HISTORY OF PETER THOMPSON. IN TWO PARTS. By the author of Noonday and Evening; Cottage Friends; Shepherd's Son &c. New York: The American Tract Society, 150 Nassau-street [after 1833]. This is No. 9 of Series IV. Of the 3 full-page wood engravings, 2 bear Anderson's initial. The third, and the small vignettes throughout the book, may well be his also. Orig. wrappers.

1449. HONESTY THE BEST POLICY. New York: American Tract Society [after 1833]. The address on the front wrapper is 144 Nassau-st.

but that on the title-page is 150 Nassau-street. It is tract No. 1 of Series III. The cut on p. 29 was engraved on wood by Anderson and some of the other engravings in the tract may be his also. Orig. wrappers.

1450. THE PUBLIC SCHOOLS, PUBLIC BLESSINGS. By a Father. New York: Mahlon Day, 1837. In the text are two full-page wood engravings by Anderson. On the cover is a wood engraving by Hooper which is probably after a drawing by G. L. Brown. Orig. wrappers.

1451. PLAIN THINGS FOR LITTLE FOLKS; SEASONED WITH INSTRUCTION, BOTH FOR THE MIND AND THE EYE. [By Mary (Belson) Elliott.] New Haven: S. Babcock, 1838. Contains 6 full-page wood engravings all but one of which bear Anderson's name or initials. There is an unsigned wood engraving on the front wrapper and a number of small engravings throughout the text. Orig. wrappers.

1452. INFANTINE KNOWLEDGE: A SPELLING AND READING BOOK, ON A POPULAR PLAN. New York: Charles S. Francis & Co., 252 Broadway. [By Eleanor (Frere) Fenn?] Boston: Joseph H. Francis, 128 Washington St. [ca. 1840].

Contains numerous wood engravings. The frontispiece to Part First is by Anderson and in this part there are also 13 full-page engravings by him, each containing four views of different objects. The smaller cut on p. 75 is also by Anderson. The only cut in Part Second with Anderson's initials is that on p. 44. It is likely, however, that all the engravings are his. Orig. cloth.

1453. LITTLE RICHARD: A STORY FOR LITTLE BOYS. Northampton: E. Turner [ca. 1840]. With 4 full-page wood engravings by Anderson. Orig. wrappers.

1453a. THE LU LU MULTIPLIER. New York: Samuel Raynor [ca. 1840].

Contains 32 wood engravings, which are printed on one side of a leaf only, the other side being left blank. That on p. 3 is signed with Anderson's initials. Other engravers whose names or initials appear are John C. Crossman, Gordon, Butler and Hart. Karpinski in his *Bibliography of Mathematical Works printed in America through 1850*, Ann Arbor, 1940, at p. 417, calls this book "an attempt at popularizing the multiplication table." The rhymes which appear under the cuts could hardly have had this effect but the cuts make the book a delightful juvenile.

In orig. wrappers.

1454. FAMILIAR TALES FOR CHILDREN. By Mrs. Sarah L. Griffin. Macon: Benjamin F. Griffin, 1841. Contains 6 wood engravings. That at p. 26 is signed "Anderson" and that at p. 152 is signed "A." The engraving at p. 132 looks very much like Anderson's work. The illustrations do not seem to have been made for the book and may have been used previously in other books. This is a scarce Georgia juvenile. Orig. cloth.

1455. NATURAL HISTORY OF QUADRUPEDS; FOR THE EDIFICATION & AMUSEMENT OF YOUTH. Cooperstown: H. & E. Phinney, 1841. The date on the front wrapper is 1840.

Contains numerous wood engravings. Those on pp. 7, 13, 17 (repeated on the front wrapper), and 25 (repeated on the title-page) are signed "A." Several are by John H. Hall. Orig. wrappers with wood engravings. Presented by Seven Gables Bookshop.

1456. STORY OF A WREN, AND HIS FAMILY. Northampton: A. R. Merrifield, 1841. With 11 wood engravings, only 2 or 3 of which have anything to do with the reading matter. That on p. 14, which is probably intended to depict the landing of the Pilgrims, carries the Anderson "A." Others may well be his also. Orig. wrappers.

1457. IU PITABUN . . . THE PEEP OF DAY; OR, A SERIES OF THE EARLIEST RELIGIOUS INSTRUCTION THE INFANT MIND IS CAPABLE OF RECEIVING. [By Favell Lee (Bevon) Mortimer.] Boston: Printed for The American Board of Commissioners for Foreign Missions, by T. R. Marvin, 1844.

This is a translation of The Peep of Day into the language of the Ojibwa Indians. It contains 10 wood engravings. That facing p. 85 is signed "AA." The one facing p. 19 is signed "Munson," possibly S. B. Munson, although he is supposed to have moved to Cincinnati about 1830. The engraving of "The Crucifixion," facing p. 102, is an interesting one in its attempt to create a background of mystery and increasing darkness. Orig. boards, with leather back.

1458. THE WELL-SPRING. Edited by Rev. Asa Bullard. Boston: The Massachusetts Sabbath School Society, 1844. The Well-Spring was a weekly and this is No. 31 of Vol. I, issued August 2, 1844. It contains a number of wood engravings and on the first page will be found an excellent impression of one by Anderson, showing David playing his harp.

ILLUSTRATIVE ANECDOTES OF THE ANIMAL KINGDOM. Boston: 1845. On the half title is a wood engraving by Anderson. [See Item 1579]

1459. (1) MOTHER GOOSE'S MELODIES. The only Pure Edition. Containing all that have ever come to light of her Memorable Writings, together with those which have been discovered among the mss. of Herculaneum. Likewise every one recently found in the same stone box which hold the golden plates of the Book of Mormon. The Whole Compared, Revised, and Sanctioned, by one of the Annotators of the Goose Family. With many new engravings. Entered, according to Act of Congress, in the year 1833, by Munroe & Francis, in the Clerk's Office, of the District Court of Massachusetts. Boston: Printed and Published by Munroe and Francis [ca. 1845].

This title-page is identical with that of Rosenbach 784 except for the imprint, the latter's imprint reading "New York and Boston: C. S. Francis and Company." Rosenbach in his Erratum dates his edition as not earlier than 1842. On the last page of the edition here listed is an advertisement of Chimes, Rhymes & Jingles [see Item 401], which was copyrighted in 1845. Hence it has been entered as about that date.

This Munroe and Francis edition of Mother Goose is later than Item 690, the date of which is probably 1835. The later edition contains most of the cuts which appeared in the earlier edition although a few of the earlier cuts were not used again. The later edition, however, contains 12 comparatively large wood engravings which are not to be found in the 1835 edition. Half of these (pp. 15, 21, 22, 31, 41, and 45) bear Anderson's initials and also appear in (2) below. The other 6 (pp. 4, 14, 73, 76, 77, and 79), while unsigned, are reprinted in (2) below, where they are attributed to Anderson. 4 cuts which appear in (2) and also in this item (pp. 34, 51, 59, and 62), are to be found in Item 690. While attributed to Anderson in (2), their appearance in Item 690 casts at least some doubt on this attribution. The same engravings by Dearborn, Bowen, Hartwell, and Childs, which are found in Item 690, appear in this edition also.

Orig. green wrappers with woodcuts. The front wrapper has the Munroe and Francis imprint but the back wrapper has the imprint "Boston: Joseph H. Francis, and C. S. Francis, New York."

(2) ILLUSTRATIONS OF MOTHER GOOSE'S MELODIES. Designed and Engraved on Wood by Alexander Anderson, M.D., with an Introductory Notice by Evert A. Duyckinck. Privately printed by Charles L. Moreau. New York: 1873.

Duyckinck, in his introduction, after speaking of the "Only Pure" edition of Mother Goose's Melodies printed by Munroe and Francis, says "Her [Mother Goose's] Boston publishers after their careful edition of the work took care to strengthen their labours by calling in the aid of the Father of Wood Engraving in America, the already distinguished A.A. or Dr. Alexander Anderson of New York. He cheerfully employed his genius on the task, producing the series of wood engravings which by the kindness of Mr. Charles S. Francis we are now at liberty to include in this brochure. It is not difficult to detect in them something of the artist's characteristic tastes and powers, particularly in such specimens as the old woman sailing against the wind in that aerial broomstick navigation beyond the 'reaches of the moon' [see engraving 5 and p. 22 in (1) above] . . . while we may fancy the wood engraver adding authorship to his art, as he describes in verses which we do not remember to have seen in any other edition, his own favorite longing for the fiddle [see engraving 14 and p. 76 of (1) above] in performing upon which instrument he was an acknowledged adept."

There are 17 wood engravings. Of these Nos. 3, 4, 5, 6, 8, and 9 bear Anderson's initials and, in view of Duyckinck's statement and the wording of the title-page, it would seem plausible to attribute all the others to Anderson also, especially as we find them in the edition of Munroe and Francis listed under (1) above. However 4 of them (nos. 7, 10, 11, and 12) appeared also in a much earlier Munroe and Francis edition [Item 690] and Anderson may not have been working that early for the Boston publishers. That Duyckinck was not too careful in his statements is shown by the fact that the final engraving, which is also to be found in (1) and in Item 690, bears Bowen's initials.

Only 10 copies were printed on large paper of which this is No. 8. It is inscribed by Moreau, under date of June 12, 1873, to Henry T. Drowne. Orig. cloth.

1460. A Supplement to the Plays of William Shakespeare: comprising the Seven Dramas . . . The Two Noble Kinsmen, The London Prodigal, Thomas Lord Cromwell, Sir John Oldcastle, The Puritan, or The Widow of Watling Street, The Yorkshire Tragedy, The Tragedy of Locrine. Edited . . . by William Gilmore Simms, Esq. The First American Edition. New York: George F. Cooledge & Brother, 1848. Contains 2 full-page and 7 smaller wood engravings by Anderson. Orig. cloth.

1461. The Christmas Tree and Other Stories, for the Young. By Mrs. Lovechild [Eleanor F. Fenn?]. Philadelphia: John Ball, 1850. Contains 5 full-page and a number of smaller wood engravings. The full-page engraving facing p. 42 is signed "AA." Orig. cloth.

1462. Proof of Wood Engraving by Anderson of the "Mansion of Belmead," together with receipt, dated Jan. 30, 1850, signed by Anderson, acknowledging payment by Philip St. George Cocke, Esq. of the sum of $20 for the engraving. It shows a very stately mansion and was drawn by Alexander J. Davis who, no doubt, was the architect. Accompanying the engraving is an impression of Anderson's trade card with his 279 Broome St. address.

The Pleasant Journey. New Haven [ca. 1850]. 8 wood engravings by Anderson. [See Item 1901]

1463. Allen Crane, the Gold Seeker. Troy, N.Y.: Merriam, Moore & Co. [ca. 1851-1856]. This is one of "The Sherwood Juveniles" and contains a collection of short stories and anecdotes for children, many of which are not paginated.

Anderson's initial will be found on wood engravings on pp. 4 and 6 of *Allen Crane*, on pp. 2, 5 and 7 of *Wicked Willie*, at the head of *The Reward*, on the second page of *Cruelty*, and at the head of *Dangers of the Sea*. Work of George L. Brown, Alonzo Hartwell and J. W. Barber will also be found. Orig. boards.

1463a. The Child's Cabinet of Stories. Troy, N.Y.: Merriam, Moore & Co. [ca. 1851-1856]. Contains 3 stories and some additional material. Wood engravings by Anderson will be found on pp. 2, 3 and 9 of "Louis Bond," pp. 3 and 5 of "George Bell, the Farmer's Boy" and pp. 9 and 11 of "John White and his Lottery Ticket." Orig. boards with a wood engraving on the front cover.

1464. Doctor Bolus and his Patients. Troy, N.Y.: Merriam, Moore & Co. [ca. 1851-1856]. Following *Doctor Bolus and his Patients* are a number of other stories and poems, including *Doctor Bolus after Dinner*; *John and Jane, the Two Orphans*; *George Denton, the Truant*; *Long Jake, the English Beggar*; *The Drunkard*; *Young Richard* and others.

This is an attractive children's book full of wood engravings, many of which bear Anderson's initials. The final cut advertising a new series of globes is signed "N. F. White Sc." Orig. cloth.

1465. A series of 5 juveniles published at Troy, N.Y., by Merriam, Moore & Co. None bears a date but Merriam & Moore were printing in Troy between 1851 and 1856. The front cover carries the title "The Child's Casket." The 5 juveniles are as follows:

(1) NORAH DEAN. The first leaf of this carries the title "My Uncle Timothy." There are 13 wood engravings, those on pp. 3 and 5 bearing Anderson's initials and that on p. 10 bearing the initials of Abel Bowen.

(2) JAMES BROWN AND THE HORSES. With 16 small wood engravings, unsigned.

(3) EDNA JANE, THE CARELESS CHILD. With 13 wood engravings, that on p. 3 bearing Anderson's initials.

(4) RHODA GREEN, THE SAILOR'S WIDOW. With 14 wood engravings, those on pp. 5 and 7 bearing the initial "M."

(5) THE CHILD'S GEM. With 8 wood engravings, unsigned.

Orig. boards with a wood engraving on front cover.

FORM LETTER OR BROADSIDE issued July 2, 1855, by George F. Cooledge of New York, a Business-Note Shaver, with a wood engraving by Anderson. [See Item 1862]

1466. YOUNG BIBLE READER. Cincinnati: Truman & Spofford [ca. 1855]. Contains 22 small Bible cuts, which are not badly done and all appear to be by the same hand. Those on pp. 9 and 11 bear Anderson's initials. Orig. wrappers.

HUTCHINGS' ILLUSTRATED CALIFORNIA MAGAZINE. San Francisco: 1857-1861. On p. 240 of Vol. V there is an illustration by Mc-Lenan which also carries the initials "A.A." [See Item 1874]

1467. SKETCH OF ST. ANTHONY AND MINNEAPOLIS, MINNESOTA TERRITORY. St. Anthony: William W. Wales, Minneapolis: Tho's Hale Williams, 1857.

Contains a number of views in and about St. Anthony and Minneapolis. Those on pp. 8, 11, 17, and 20 were engraved on wood by Anderson. J. Wells made the drawing for the illustration on p. 8, and 2 others (front. and p. 13), engraved by S. F. Baker, are also signed by Wells. He may have been responsible for all of the illustrations. Several of these engravings, showing signs of wear, will be found in *Minnesota; Then and Now* published in 1869 [Item 356]. Orig. wrappers.

1468. SINGLE SHEET ADVERTISEMENT with the heading "For Sale on Moderate Terms: The Block of Dwelling Houses upon Murray Hill, Fifth Avenue, Opposite the Croton Reservoir. Designed by Alex'r J. Davis, and erected by Geo. Higgins, Esq." It was probably printed about 1858-1859.

At the top is a wood engraving of the build-ings offered for sale (eleven independent dwellings "combined as in one palace"), which is signed "Anderson." It shows the "palace," the northeast corner of the reservoir and Fifth Avenue with its horse drawn omnibus, a horseback rider, etc. The wood engraving was apparently copied, much reduced, from a lithograph of the property made by Hatch & Co. which is reproduced (Plate 148b) in Vol. III of *The Iconography of Manhattan Island*, by I. N. Phelps Stokes, New York, 1918. Stokes, at pp. 721-22, mentions the reduced advertisement. The cut has been touched rather delicately with color.

1469. ITEMS RELATING TO ANDERSON found among the Papers of Benson J. Lossing. They all probably date from between 1862 and 1868.

(1) WASH DRAWING of Anderson drawn from life almost certainly by Lossing. It is a sensitive piece of work and portrays admirably the benign old gentleman.

(2) PROOF IMPRESSION of the portrait of Anderson which appears opposite p. 84 in Lossing's *Memorial of Alexander Anderson* [Item 357]. It was drawn by Browere and expressly engraved for the book by Thomas Sugden. It shows Anderson, aged 44, seated at a table working on a wood block.

(3) DOCUMENT, signed by Anderson, dated June 5, 1862, acknowledging receipt from Lossing of $6.00 for engraving a reduced copy of the caricature—Ograbme. This cartoon of "The Embargo" appears, unreduced, in Lossing's *Memorial of Alexander Anderson* (see p. 161 of Main Catalogue), where the drawing is attributed to John Wesley Jarvis. This appears to have been a mistake. Anderson both drew and engraved the cartoon. The reduced cut will be found at p. 785 in Lossing's *Pictorial Field-Book of the War of 1812*, New York, 1869 [Item 989]. It was, no doubt, ordered by Lossing for this purpose. A proof impression of the wood engraving is attached to the receipt.

(4) RECEIPT, dated January 1864, signed by Anderson, for $5 covering the engraving of the caricature—death of snapping turtle. This cartoon, inspired by the repeal of the Embargo Act, was originally designed by Jarvis and engraved on wood by Anderson about 1814. Murrell (Vol. I, p. 74) calls it "the first cartoon for newspaper reproduction in America." It appeared in the *New York Evening Post*. Anderson's reduced cut of 1864 will be found at p. 787 of Lossing's *Pictorial Field-Book of the War of 1812*. A proof impression of the wood engraving is attached to the receipt. Although the receipt is dated January 1864, Anderson has written opposite his signature the date of April 21, 1864

(his birthday) and, under his signature, the words "aged 89 years."

(5) SEVERAL WOOD ENGRAVINGS by Anderson, on some of which he has written his name and address. On the back of one Lossing has written: "This was drawn, engraved and printed in October, 1868. Dr. Anderson (who was born in April, 1775) wrote his name and address on this card on Sunday, the 18th of Oct. 1868, and presented it to me."

HISTORICAL COLLECTIONS OF NEW JERSEY. New Haven: 1868. The wood engravings on pp. 188 and 534 are by Anderson. [See Item 1485(2)]

1470. EARLY AMERICAN WOOD ENGRAVINGS BY DR. ALEXANDER ANDERSON AND OTHERS. With an Introductory Preface by Evert A. Duyckinck. New York: Burr & Boyd, 1877.

The Preface states: "This little volume contains impressions from a series of Wood Blocks engraved for tracts and juvenile books published in the early part of the present century by the eminent Quaker publisher in New York, Samuel Wood. In a brief memoir of himself written by the late Dr. Anderson he speaks of Mr. Wood as 'one of my most constant employers. I did an infinity of cuts for his excellent set of small books.'"

Of the 65 wood engravings contained in the book, 20 carry Anderson's initials. For the dates of Samuel Wood and his firms, see Harry B. Weiss, "Samuel Wood & Sons, Early New York Publishers of Children's Books" in the *Bulletin of The New York Public Library*, September 1942, Vol. 46, No. 9. Orig. cloth.

1471. LIFE AND WORKS OF ALEXANDER ANDERSON, M.D., THE FIRST AMERICAN WOOD ENGRAVER. By Frederic M. Burr. New York: Burr Brothers, 1893.

Contains over 30 illustrations engraved on wood by Anderson. There is also a portrait of Anderson at the age of 92, drawn by August Will and engraved by E. J. Whitney, and a portrait of Anderson at the age of 44, drawn by John H. I. Browere and engraved by T. Sugden. The book, of which 725 copies were printed, is signed by the author. Cloth.

John Andrew

1815-1875

Born in England, Andrew came to Boston sometime prior to 1851, where he became one of the leading wood engravers of this country. He was a partner in the firms of Baker, Smith & Andrew and Baker & Andrew in 1853-1854 and in Andrew & Filmer in 1858-1860 and after. Later he apparently formed a partnership with his son, for many engravings signed John Andrew-Son are to be found in the late 1860s and 1870s. In his advertisement in *History of Boston*, Boston, 1856 [Item 1763], he described himself as "Designer and Engraver on Wood," although it is interesting to note that the advertisement itself was designed by Hyde. However, it is probable that Andrew did from time to time act as draftsman as well as engraver. See Groce and Wallace, pp. 10, 21, and 22.

1472. THREE ALBUMS, described below, containing proofs of wood engravings by Andrew and his firms. Most of them do not disclose the name of the draftsman and it is possible that in many cases Andrew himself made the drawing. At any rate they constitute an interesting cross-section of the work of one of the important engravers of his time. For purposes of identification the proofs in each album have been numbered.

(1) ALBUM containing over 275 proofs, the great majority bearing John Andrew's name but a few (see Nos. 7, 32, 71, 80, 87, 88, 95, 97, 172, 185, 186, 187, 192, 193, 237, 260, and 278) with the names of Andrew-Filmer, and at least one (see No. 190) with the names of Baker-Andrew. The dates are probably in the 1850s and 1860s.

Proofs will be found of the half title (No. 65) for Horatio Alger's *Bertha's Christmas Vision*, published in Boston in 1856, of the frontispiece and half title (Nos. 80 and 278) for Oliver Optic's *Poor and Proud*, published in Boston in 1854, of the frontispiece and half title (Nos. 87 and 235) for Oliver Optic's *Little by Little*, published in Cincinnati by Rickey, Mallory & Co., and of the half title (No. 157) for Joseph W. Jenks' *The Rural Poetry of the English Language*, published in Boston in 1856.

Only a few of the illustrators can be determined. These are:

Charles A. Barry, Nos. 147, 148, 173, 189, and 191.

Carl E. Doepler, Nos. 140-146 and 149. All of these will be found in Jacob Abbot's *Rollo on the Rhine* [Item 704], published in Boston in 1855 (see frontispiece and pp. 12, 51, 63, 74, 114, 132, and 190).

J. N. Hyde, No. 186.

Samuel W. Rowse, No. 107.

Samuel Wallin, No. 178.

At the beginning of the Album are 6 wash drawings, probably made in connection with intended book illustrations, the last two of which are signed "Field." This might be Mrs. P. G. Field (wife of the painter Erastus Salisbury Field) to whom, in the Main Catalogue, are attributed the illustrations of several books, or it might be Edward R. Field, an artist and designer on wood, who lived in Brooklyn (see Groce and Wallace, p. 224).

Orig. leather.

(2) ALBUM containing some 340 proofs of wood engravings, executed by John Andrew, Andrew-Filmer, John Andrew-Son, and George T. Andrew. The dates are probably from about 1855 to about 1875. A number of the proofs have notes of instruction from the illustrator to the engraver, which add to their interest. Most of them do not disclose the name of the illustrator but a few of them do.

The illustrator who appears most frequently is Frank Merrill. There are 20 proofs after his drawings, viz.: Nos. 84, 86-90, 94-97, 99, 100, 104, 107-109, 122, 194, 195, and 199. No. 96 is dated 1873. Other illustrators whose work appears are:

James C. Beard, Nos. 235 and 236.

Hammatt Billings, with a number of engravings after his drawings which later appeared in some of the volumes of Mrs. Follen's *Twilight Stories*, published in Boston by Whittemore, Niles & Hall in 1856 [Item 1508], viz.: Nos. 145 and 150 in *The Pedler of Dust Sticks*, at pp. 17 and 30; Nos. 196, 223, and 288 in *Made Up Stories*, at pp. 5, 30, and 58; No. 283 in *Old Garret, Part Second*, at p. 5, together with No. 147 which is the engraved title-page for that book; and Nos. 263, 264, 265, and 292 in *Old Garret, Part Third*, at pp. 18, 30, 91, and 73, together with No. 144 which is the engraved title-page for that book.

C. Bush, Nos. 60, 63, 74, 75, 121, 124, and 125.

F.O.C. Darley, Nos. 127, 128, 166, 168, and 273. Nos. 166 and 168 appeared in *The Drummer Boy* [Item 658], at pp. 20 and 259.

Harry Fenn, Nos. 19-21.

A. Fredericks, No. 190.

Thomas Hogan, No. 16.

J. A. Hows, No. 270, with a note from Andrew, for Hows' consideration.

Jervis McEntee, No. 197.

Marsden, No. 230.

G. Perkins, Nos. 7, 34, 36, 40, 43, and 160.

H. L. Stephens, No. 216.

A. C. Warren, No. 314.

W. Waud, No. 207.

G. G. White, Nos. 114, 115, 117-119. These will be found in *The Young Crusoe*, Boston, 1864 [Item 1279].

½ morocco, spine defective.

(3) ALBUM containing over 100 proofs of wood engravings by John Andrew, Andrew-Filmer, and George T. Andrew. The dates for the most part are probably in the 1860s and 1870s. It is interesting to note that one or two are marked "Personal work of John Andrew" (see Nos. 76 and 77), which may indicate how little of the engraved work which bears his name or the name of one of his firms he may have been personally responsible for.

At least 50 of the proofs are after drawings by Wheelock (probably Merrill G. Wheelock) for *The White Hills*, Boston, 1860 [Item 1272]. One (No. 12) is marked "First proof for Mr. Wheelock to touch" and another (No. 31) "First Proof Franconia Notch."

The work of the following illustrators will also be found—John Henry Hill (Nos. 76 and 77); J. N. Hyde (Nos. 94, 114, and 117); Thomas Nast (No. 92); A. C. Warren (No. 88); A. R. Waud (No. 84).

Wrappers.

George Washington Appleton
1805-1831

A portrait painter and engraver of Boston. See Groce and Wallace, p. 12.

In the Main Catalogue some books are listed with cuts signed "Appleton" [see Items 296, 469, and 530], and the writer suggested [Item 469] that these might be early works of Thomas Gold Appleton. Perhaps it would be more plausible, however, to attribute them to George Washington Appleton. While some of the cuts signed with his name are in books published later than 1831, the supposed date of his death, these cuts may have been made earlier. Furthermore there may be some question whether he did not live beyond 1831, the last year in which his name appears in Boston directories.

1473. BOSTON TWO HUNDRED YEARS AGO, OR THE ROMANTIC STORY OF MISS ANN CARTER (DAUGHTER OF ONE OF THE FIRST SETTLERS) AND THE CELEBRATED INDIAN CHIEF, THUNDERSQUALL; WITH MANY HUMOROUS REMINISCENCES AND EVENTS OF OLDEN TIME. Boston: 1830. Wright I (337).

The frontispiece, which is signed "Appleton" shows Miss Carter and Thundersquall plighting their troth. Behind them is a distant view of Boston in 1630 with what is probably intended to represent Beacon Hill looking more like the Matterhorn. Under the cut appear the words, "The young Indian and Miss Carter stood before the altar, and plighted their mutual vows. Oh, it was a strange, and almost an unholy sight, to see a young and innocent creature, in the very morning of her life, thus throw herself away upon one whose home, from infancy, had been the forest and the cave." Orig. wrappers.

George Holbrook Baker

1827-1906

Born in Massachusetts, Baker lived during his younger days in Dedham and Boston. As he had inherited some artistic talent from his mother, he was apprenticed to a commercial artist named Smith, in New York City, and, after working for him some three years, he became a student at the National Academy where he won many prizes. During his stay in New York he did much sketching and painting, particularly in the White Mountains. Becoming infected with the Gold Rush fever, he joined a party of 12 men and started for the West by way of Vera Cruz. After a battle with a band of Mexicans, in which one of their party was killed, Baker reached San Francisco in May 1849. He headed for the gold mines, but soon grew discouraged and returned to San Francisco where he tried one business venture after another, traveling extensively and doing much sketching of the mining towns. In 1852 he moved to Sacramento. He went into business with E. L. Barber, and Baker and Barber are said to have turned out many woodcut views of California, Baker being the artist and Barber the woodcutter. Later Baker set up independently as a lithographer in Sacramento. In 1862 he carried his lithographing business to San Francisco and there he lived until his death. His work, says Peters, is extremely good and of relatively large volume. See Harry T. Peters, *California on Stone*, Garden City, 1935, p. 14 and p. 47; Groce and Wallace, p. 22.

1474. CROSSING THE PLAINS. Views Drawn from Nature, in 1853, by George H. Baker. Published by Barber & Baker, Sacramento [1853]. Fig. 11.

This is a sheet or broadside containing 13 views drawn by Baker showing scenes of the route across the plains, such as "Emigrant Train Passing Wind River Mountains," "Indians Chasing Buffaloes, Scott's Bluffs," "First Night on the Plains," and "Driving Stock Across the Plains." It is an interesting record of what the Crossing meant in those days. The views were, no doubt, engraved on wood by Barber.

This broadside was bought in Sacramento in 1853 by Oliver Hazard Perry Ayres and was acquired from his great-great-grandson.

1475. SAN FRANCISCO PAST AND PRESENT. Published by Barber & Baker of San Francisco, M. Ullman, Agent, San Francisco. Printed at the Sun office [1854].

This is a large sheet or broadside containing 2 wood engravings, one entitled "San Francisco as it was, 1849," which was "Taken from Rincon Point, by G. H. Baker, June 1, 1849," and the other entitled "San Francisco as it is, 1354 [*sic*]," which is stated to be "From Nature, by G. H. Baker, Dec. 1854." No doubt the engraver of the two views was Barber. There is also a wood engraved inset map of the vicinity of San Francisco. The text surrounding the engravings gives an account of the growth of the city.

One of George H. Baker's lithographs, as listed by Peters, is "Port of San Francisco, June 1, 1849. From the original drawing by George H. Baker made at date expressly for the New York Tribune and published in that paper's issue of Aug. 28, 1849." The view is from Rincon Hill (see Harry T. Peters, *California on Stone*, Garden City, 1935, p. 53). This view, engraved on wood by J. F. Badeau of New York, was actually published in *The New York Daily Tribune* on August 30, 1849. It differs considerably from the view in the broadside but it is obviously taken from about the same position. Either Baker made two drawings on June 1, 1849, or else that published in 1854 was based on the New York Tribune's drawing or on the subsequent lithograph.

John Warner Barber

(*See Main Catalogue, p. 67*)

ALBUM containing over 1000 wood engravings probably used in books published by the American Sunday School Union in Philadelphia during the 1820s. One engraving signed "J.W.B." [See Item 1674]

1476. THE HISTORY OF GOOD CHILDREN, WITH AN ACCOUNT OF A GALLERY OF PICTURES AND MUSEUM. Hartford: George Goodwin & Sons, 1820. Welch 496. With 5 wood engravings by Barber, very early work of this engraver. Orig. wrappers.

1477. YOUTHFUL RELIGION EXEMPLIFIED; OR A BRIEF NARRATIVE OF THE LIFE AND HAPPY DEATH OF ELIZA THORNTON. By John Dodington. From the Fourth London Edition. Hartford: George Goodwin & Sons, 1821. Contains 2 wood engravings, that on the title-page being repeated on the front wrapper. The engraving on p. 11 is signed "B" and resembles Barber's work. Orig. wrappers.

1478. THE DRUNKARD'S PROGRESS, OR THE DIRECT ROAD TO POVERTY, WRETCHEDNESS & RUIN. Broadside designed and published by J. W. Barber, New Haven, Con., [*sic*] Sept., 1826. Fig. 10.

Contains 4 large wood engravings by Barber

showing "The Morning Dram" which is "The Beginning of Sorrow," "The Grog Shop" with its "Bad Company," "The Confirmed Drunkard" in a state of "Beastly Intoxication," and the "Concluding Scene" with the family being driven off to the alms house. It is an interesting set of cuts, faintly reminiscent of Hogarth.

1479. MEMOIR OF ANN ELIZA STARR, OF CONNECTICUT. Revised by the Committee of Publication. Philadelphia: American Sunday School Union, 1827. The frontispiece is signed "J.W.B." The small cut on the title-page and front wrapper may be also by Barber. Orig. wrappers.

1480. A STANDARD SPELLING BOOK; OR, THE SCHOLAR'S GUIDE TO AN ACCURATE PRONUNCIATION OF THE ENGLISH LANGUAGE . . . By James H. Sears. The Revised Edition. Rochester: E. Peck & Co., 1827. With 5 wood engravings by Barber (pp. 34, 41, 53, 62, and 76). Orig. boards with leather back.

1481. HISTORY OF THE UNITED STATES; TO WHICH IS PREFIXED A BRIEF HISTORICAL ACCOUNT OF OUR ENGLISH ANCESTORS, FROM THE DISPERSION AT BABEL, TO THEIR MIGRATION TO AMERICA; AND OF THE CONQUEST OF SOUTH AMERICA BY THE SPANIARDS. By Noah Webster, LL.D. New-Haven: Durrie & Peck, 1832. First Ed.

Contains 22 small wood engravings in the text, 3 of which bear Barber's name or initials (pp. 16, 64, and 69). Many of the others are, no doubt, also by him. That on p. 203 is signed "E.L.B." (probably E. L. Barber of New Haven [see Item 375]). The full-page frontispiece of the Capitol at Washington is by Anderson. Orig. boards, with leather back and with a notation on flyleaf of the purchase of the book on September 25, 1832 for .50.

1482. EVENING READINGS IN HISTORY . . . Springfield: G. and C. Merriam, 1833. Contains a number of wood engravings. The frontispiece bears Barber's initials and that on p. 67 might well be his also. The cut on p. 89 is signed "A." Orig. boards.

1483. THE MARINER'S CHRONICLE: CONTAINING NARRATIVES OF THE MOST REMARKABLE DISASTERS AT SEA . . . New Haven: Durrie and Peck, 1834. The frontispiece, a full-page wood engraving, is signed "J. W. Barber Sc." In the text are 24 smaller unsigned wood engravings which are in Barber's style. Cont. calf.

1484. BUNYAN'S PILGRIM'S PROGRESS, FROM THIS WORLD TO THAT WHICH IS TO COME: EXHIBITED IN A METAMORPHOSIS, OR A

TRANSFORMATION OF PICTURES. Fifth Edition, Improved. New Haven, Ct.: E. Barber, n.d. [ca. 1835-1845].

This is a later edition of Item 360. The cuts have been redrawn and re-engraved. While J. W. Barber's name appears only in the copyright notice, the style of the cuts is his and it seems safe to attribute them to him. The drawings in this edition, while somewhat more vigorous than those in the earlier edition, show no marked improvement, but the engraving is surer and shows greater experience.

Presented by Christian A. Zabriskie.

1485. (1) HISTORICAL COLLECTIONS OF THE STATE OF NEW JERSEY . . . By John W. Barber and Henry Howe. New York: Published for the Authors, by S. Tuttle, 1844. 1st ed.

Contains numerous wood engravings of places in New Jersey. The preface states that the drawings were, with two or three exceptions, taken on the spot by the authors. Barber was probably responsible for most of the work, although Howe's name appears on the illustration on p. 508. Sanborn's initials appear on the cut on p. 245. A view of Nassau Hall at Princeton will be found facing p. 266. Cont. calf.

Accompanying this book is Barber's wood block from which the illustration on p. 257 of the "Central View in Hightstown" was printed.

(2) HISTORICAL COLLECTIONS OF NEW JERSEY . . . By John W. Barber, assisted by Henry Howe. New Haven, Conn.: Published by Subscription, by John W. Barber, 1868.

This is a later edition in which, while most of the cuts from the 1st edition are retained, numerous changes have been made. The preface gives a list of the "Additions," but states that, besides this list, "new engravings have been taken of nearly all the prominent places in the State . . ." An examination shows that in a number of instances new cuts have been substituted for those in the first edition or else the old cut has been re-engraved, while in a few cases new cuts have been added with some detriment to the text (see pp. 81, 87, 113, 127, 137, 148, 150, 159, 176, 185, 187, 188,* 206, 207, 219, 224, 225, 232, 241, 251, 266, 280, 286, 288, 312, 330, 376, 385, 407, 410, 433, 449, 471, 483, and 502). It is interesting to compare some of the old and the new engravings and note the changes which have taken place between the dates of the two editions. Thus, for example, the view of Nassau Hall at p. 266 has been re-engraved, to reflect the numerous changes in reconstruction necessitated by the fire which occurred in 1855.

---

* New cut engraved by Anderson at the age of 93.

The text following p. 512 is new and contains a number of additional engravings, including one by Anderson (p. 534) made in his 93rd year.

Orig. cloth.

1486. ORIGINAL WOOD BLOCK cut by Barber for the view of Charlestown in Jefferson County, Va., which appears at p. 342 of Howe's *Historical Collections of Virginia* [Item 922], published in Charleston in 1845.

1487. (1) HISTORICAL, POETICAL AND PICTORIAL AMERICAN SCENES; PRINCIPALLY MORAL AND RELIGIOUS . . . By John W. Barber and Elizabeth G. Barber. New Haven, Ct.: J. H. Bradley [cop. 1850]. Contains more than 100 wood engravings. While unsigned, most of them are undoubtedly the work of Barber. Orig. cloth.

(2) HISTORICAL, POETICAL AND PICTORIAL AMERICAN SCENES; PRINCIPALLY MORAL AND RELIGIOUS; BEING A SELECTION OF INTERESTING INCIDENTS IN AMERICAN HISTORY: TO WHICH IS ADDED A CHRONOLOGICAL TABLE OF IMPORTANT EVENTS, IN THE SECESSION WAR. By John W. Barber . . . and Elizabeth G. Barber. New Haven, Conn.: Published by J. W. & J. Barber for J. H. Bradley. It is undated but the last event of the Secession War is given under date of April 14, 1863, so that it must have been published some time after that date.

This edition, considerably later than (1) above and with some additions and some eliminations, has the same illustrations as in (1) with the following exceptions:

   a. A different half title cut is used.
   b. The wood engravings of the State seals, which begin at p. 109 of (1), have been eliminated.
   c. Beginning with p. 168, the contents of (2) are new as are also a number of wood engravings relating chiefly to the Civil War.

This later edition is on heavy paper with good impressions of the cuts. ½ morocco.

ALLEN CRANE. Troy, N.Y.: [*ca.* 1851]. Barber's initials appear on the wood engraving on the second page of *About Being Rich*. [See Item 1463]

1488. ORIGINAL WOOD BLOCK from which the portrait of J. W. Barber in the frontispiece to *The Picture Preacher* [Item 382a] was printed. In the book the caption under this portrait reads, "The above engraving in the opinion of my friends is a correct portrait of myself at this time, Feb. 2nd, 1880, my eighty-second birthday." The portrait as it appears in the book is signed with the initials "L.S." in the lower left-hand corner so that this apparently was not a self-portrait. There has been some slight retouching of the block since its use in Item 382a and the corners have been eliminated, converting an almost square wood engraving into an oval one. In the process the letters "L.S." have disappeared.

Charles A. Barry
(*See Main Catalogue, p. 70*)

THE ILLUSTRATED AMERICAN BIOGRAPHY. New York: 1854. Barry designed the advertisement for Barker's Cheveux Tonique (the only article that will Positively Restore Hair on Bald Heads) which appears on p. 233. [See Item 1964]

ALBUM OF WOOD ENGRAVINGS by John Andrew, etc. [*ca.* 1855-1865]. 5 engravings after Barry. [See Item 1472(1)]

THE COMPLETE MANUAL FOR YOUNG SPORTSMEN. New York: 1856. The half title is designed by Barry and engraved on wood by N. Orr—Co. [See Item 1705]

1489. THE KIDNAPPED AND THE RANSOMED. BEING THE PERSONAL RECOLLECTIONS OF PETER STILL AND HIS WIFE "VINA," AFTER FORTY YEARS OF SLAVERY. By Mrs. Kate E. R. Pickard. Syracuse: William T. Hamilton, 1856. 3 full-page illustrations by Barry, engraved on wood by N. Orr & Co. The half title may also be Barry's work. Cont. ¾ morocco.

THE WEEKLY NOVELETTE. Boston: 1857-1862. Illustrations by Barry will be found in Vol. I, p. 17; Vol. II, pp. 265, 272, 352, 384, and 409; and Vol. IV, p. 9. The engravers whose names appear are John Andrew, Baker, Bricher, and Peirce. [See Item 1545]

James Carter Beard
(*See Main Catalogue, p. 70*)

MARTYRIA. Boston: 1866. The illustrations are, for the most part, from sketches made by the author, A. C. Hamlin, but the figures in them are by Barry. [See Item 1695]

ALBUM OF WOOD ENGRAVINGS by John Andrew, etc. [*ca.* 1855-1875]. 2 engravings after Beard. [See Item 1472(2)]

OUT OF TOWN. New York: 1866. At p. 307 is a wood engraving by J. P. Davis-Speer after a design by Beard. No initials are given and it is possible that this is the work of another Beard. [See Item 1673]

My Opinions and Betsey Bobbet's. Hartford: 1873. The full-page illustrations at pp. 53, 141, and 162 and the smaller illustrations on pp. 211 and 213 are by Beard. Some of the other illustrations resemble his work. [See Item 1750]

William Holbrook Beard
1824-1900

Brother of James Henry Beard and uncle of James C. Beard, Thomas F. Beard, and Daniel C. Beard. He was a portrait and animal painter. After working a short time in Ohio, he moved to New York City in 1845. Except for some eight years in Buffalo and two years in Europe, he spent his life in New York. See Groce and Wallace, p. 38.

Harper's Bazaar. Vols. I-III. New York: 1867-1870. Illustrations by Beard will be found in Vol. III, pp. 13 and 169. [See Item 1729]

Emile F. Beaulieu
(See Main Catalogue, p. 71)

Pebbles and Pearls for the Young Folks. Hartford: 1868. Contains a view of Printing-House Square, New York, drawn by Beaulieu. [See Item 1939]

George P. Belden

George P. Belden was born in Ohio, ran away from home and lived for some time with the Indians in the West, acquiring two squaws and doing many extraordinary deeds. He later joined the U.S. Army, but in 1870 found he could no longer stand army life and returned to the trapping and hunting grounds. He left his diaries and manuscripts with General James S. Brisbin. According to the latter, Belden's career was "more varied and remarkable than that of any paleface west of the Missouri." Brisbin rewrote Belden's manuscript but "only made such changes as would enable me to place it in a connected form, and in most cases have allowed the manuscript to retain the exact words of the adventurous chief, soldier, hunter, trapper and guide."

1490. Belden, The White Chief; or, Twelve Years among the Wild Indians of the Plains. From the Diaries and Manuscripts of George P. Belden, the Adventurous White Chief, Soldier, Hunter, Trapper, and Guide. Edited by Gen. James S. Brisbin, U.S.A. Cincinnati and New York: C. F. Vent . . . 1870. First edition.

Contains numerous illustrations, engraved on wood by the New York Bureau of Illustration. The preface states "The illustrations are from original designs, many of them made in outline by Mr. Belden himself, and others by Mr. Inman, formerly of New York, but now of the Regular Army." Orig. cloth.

Frank Henry Temple Bellew
(See Main Catalogue, p. 71)

The Illustrated News. Vol. I. New York: 1853. Work by Bellew will be found on pp. 112 and 160. [See Item 1836]

1491. Harry Lee; or, Hope for the Poor. New York: Harper & Brothers, 1859. With 8 full-page illustrations by Bellew, the name of the wood engraver not appearing. Orig. cloth.

Harper's Bazaar. Vols. I-III. New York: 1867-1870. "Comicalities" by Bellew appear at p. 976 (2) of Vol. I, and pp. 16, 124, 125, 140, 160 (2), 176, 192, 332 (2), and 336 (3) of Vol. II. [See Item 1729]

Widow Spriggins, Mary Elmer, and Other Sketches. New York: 1867. The frontispiece is after a drawing by Bellew. [See Item 1756]

Spectacles for Young Eyes. New York: 1869. Facing p. 142 is an illustration signed with Bellew's mark of a triangle. It is engraved on wood by Anthony-Davis. [See Item 1713]

Alfred F. Bellows
(See Main Catalogue, p. 72)

1492. A Description of the New York Central Park [By Clarence C. Cook]. New York: F. J. Huntington and Co., 1869.

Contains some 100 wood engravings of scenes in Central Park. The Publisher's Note says "One of our most popular artists, Mr. A. F. Bellows, has spent many months making the drawings . . . our best engravers have employed their skill in cutting them on the wood." The names of Kingdon-Boyd appear on the full-page illustration on p. 97 and on the smaller cuts on pp. 126, 147, and 173, but the writer was unable to find the names of any other engravers. Orig. cloth.

Charles M. Bennett

1493. Old Nurse's Book of Rhymes, Jingles, and Ditties, as Written by Mother Goose. Philadelphia: Willis P. Hazard,

1859. Hazard's cheapest edition of Mother Goose's Melodies. Contains 30 original designs by Charles M. Bennett, not badly drawn. The only wood engraver's name to appear is that of Bunn on p. 4. On the back wrapper is a cut designed by Stephens. Orig. wrappers.

E. B. Bensell

(See Main Catalogue, p. 73)

1494. BARBARA ST. JOHN. By P. B. [Parthene Ballard] Chamberlain. Philadelphia: J. C. Garrigues & Co., 1869. Wright II (484) fails to locate a copy except one "withdrawn from circulation."

Contains 4 full-page illustrations engraved on wood by Lauderbach. The frontispiece is signed with Bensell's initials and probably all are after his designs. Presentation copy from the author. Orig. cloth.

1495. THE MERMAN AND THE FIGUREHEAD. A CHRISTMAS STORY. By Clara F. Guernsey. Philadelphia: J. B. Lippincott & Co., 1871. Wright II (1042), who ascribes the book to Lucy Ellen Guernsey. Contains frontispiece and 4 other full-page illustrations by Bensell, engraved on wood by Van Ingen-Snyder. Orig. cloth.

1496. ORANGE BLOSSOMS. FRESH AND FADED. By T. S. Arthur. Philadelphia: J. M. Stoddart & Co. . . . 1871. 3 illustrations by Bensell and 1 by C. Schussele, all engraved on wood by Lauderbach. The frontispiece is a steel engraved portrait of T. S. Arthur. Orig. cloth.

1497. THREE YEARS IN A MAN-TRAP. By the Author of "Ten Nights in a Bar-Room" [T. S. Arthur]. Philadelphia: J. M. Stoddart & Co., 1872. This is the 1st edition of Item 400 and contains the same illustrations. Orig. cloth.

1498. WAS IT AN INHERITANCE? OR, NANNIE GRANT. A NARRATIVE. By Mrs. H.N.K. Goff [Harriet Newell (Kneeland) Goff.] Philadelphia: Claxton, Remsen & Haffelfinger, 1876. Wright III (2200). With 4 full-page illustrations by Bensell, engraved on wood by J. Dalziel of Philadelphia. Orig. cloth.

THE BODLEYS TELLING STORIES. New York: 1878. The frontispiece is an illustration by Bensell, engraved on wood by Lauderbach, which first appeared at p. 49 of Vol. IV of *The Riverside Magazine for Young People*. [See Item 1732]

1499. THE BOY'S PERCY, BEING OLD BALLADS OF WAR, ADVENTURE AND LOVE FROM BISHOP THOMAS PERCY'S RELIQUES OF ANCIENT ENGLISH POETRY . . . Edited for Boys with an Introduction by Sidney Lanier. New York: Charles Scribner's Sons, 1882. With 50 illustrations from original designs by Bensell. Orig. cloth.

Edward Beyer

1820-1865

A German by birth, Beyer came to America about 1848 and returned to Germany about 1857. In 1850 he was living in Philadelphia. He was a painter of landscapes and panoramas and his Virginia views were lithographed in Germany after his return and published in Richmond in 1858. See Groce and Wallace, p. 47.

1500. PICTORIAL FOR THE MILLION, A SUPPLEMENT TO THE COMMERCIAL INTELLIGENCER. Philadelphia: Wm. F. Miskey and Co., January, 1851. Fig. 12.

This unwieldy supplement consists of 2 huge leaves about 29¾ inches high and 21½ inches wide. They are full of wood engravings, most of them the work of W. B. Gihon, the Philadelphia engraver. On the first page is a view of the "Friends' Meeting House at Jordans, and the Grave of William Penn" signed "E. Beyer." It is a well designed landscape and Gihon was the engraver. The view of Penn's house on Second Street, Philadelphia, has a signature which also may be that of Beyer. In fact it is quite possible that all 13 engravings printed on the first page under the heading of "Scenes in the Life of William Penn" are after Beyer's drawings.

On the second and third pages are 12 Western views which are signed with an intricate monogram in which the letters B and Y and possibly R and E can be discerned. This may be Beyer's monogram, but the views differ considerably in style from those on page 1.

On the fourth page is a wood engraving by Gihon illustrating Wordsworth's "We are Seven" and signed "R. W. Hulme, Del."

Hammatt Billings

(See Main Catalogue, p. 74)

1501. THE AMERICAN CRUISER; OR, THE TWO MESSMATES. A TALE OF THE LAST WAR. By the author of "Life on the Ocean" [George Little]. Boston: Waite, Peirce and Company, 1846. Wright I (1699).

This is the 1st edition. It contains 8 full-page illustrations. They are not signed by the draftsman but the title-page of the 2nd edition [Item

402], which contains all 8 of these illustrations, states that they are by Billings. The 2nd edition has 4 additional full-page illustrations (front. and pp. 180, 312, and 324) and a title-page vignette.

The frontispiece of the 1st edition carries the legend "Illustrations by Brown and Worcester, Washington Street." This illustration appears at p. 16 of the later edition without the legend. Brown and Worcester were a Boston firm of wood engravers, the partners being Samuel E. Brown and Fernando E. Worcester (see Groce and Wallace, pp. 90 and 702). The legend, therefore, refers to the engravers of the illustrations, not the draftsman. 2 of the additional illustrations in the 2nd edition were engraved by a different Brown. Orig. cloth.

1502. POEMS. By Oliver Wendell Holmes. New and Enlarged Edition. Boston: William D. Ticknor & Company, 1849.

Contains a view of Cambridge on p. 1, and 5 other rather slight wood engravings, one on the title-page and the others on pp. 253, 258, 263, and 272. Thomas F. Currier in his A Bibliography of Oliver Wendell Holmes, New York, 1953 (pp. 44-45), assigns the vignette on p. 1 to Billings and reproduces it facing p. 45. He describes the cut at some length. The other cuts he attributes to Billings as draftsman are the old punch bowl on p. 253 and the head- and tail-pieces to "The Stethoscope Song." He attributes the cuts on the title-page and on p. 272 to Brown (probably Nathan Brown) as the draftsman and Hartwell as the engraver. The Cost Books of Ticknor and Fields edited by Tryon and Charvat, New York, 1949 (A 139, p. 129), show that Billings received $12 for his designs and Brown $4.50, while Hartwell received $10 and an unidentified engraver (N. Gookin?) $20 for their work as engravers.

This is the first issue of this edition, in which 8 poems appear for the first time. Orig. chocolate cloth.

1503. LITTLE EVA SONG. UNCLE TOM'S GUARDIAN ANGEL. Words by John G. Whittier. Music by Manuel Emilio [Boston]: John P. Jewett & Co. [cop. 1852].

This is a broadside printed on cotton cloth. Under the title is Billings' illustration of "Little Eva Reading the Bible to Uncle Tom in the Arbor" which appears opposite p. 68 in Vol. II of the 1st edition of Uncle Tom's Cabin [Item 408]. There follow 2 bars of music and the words of Whittier's poem which contains that ingenious rhyme

"Weep no more for happy Eva
Wrong and sin no more shall grieve her."

Surrounding the whole is a printer's ornamental frame through which runs a ribbon with the words "Uncle Tom's Cabin, by Harriet Beecher Stowe, is a Picture of American Slavery, not overdrawn, since Southern Publications themselves give as facts accounts of characters and incidents fully matching anything this work presents—115,000 copies or 230,000 vols. have been sold in 6 months. Jewett & Co. Publishers."

Whittier's poem first appeared in The Villager, a publication circulated principally in Amesbury and Salisbury Mills, Mass. Its first printing in the form of sheet music (a 4-page leaflet) was copyrighted on June 16, 1852, and no doubt published shortly thereafter. It is comparatively common. The present broadside on cotton cloth, which was copyrighted on September 27, 1852, appears to be rare. Carroll Wilson (Thirteen Author Collections of the Nineteenth Century, New York, 1950) locates copies at Yale, Harvard, and Haverhill Public Library. See also Thomas Franklin Currier, A Bibliography of John Greenleaf Whittier, Cambridge, 1937, p. 576.

1504. MEMOIRS OF A LONDON DOLL, WRITTEN BY HERSELF [Richard H. Horne]. Edited by Mrs. Fairstar. Boston: Ticknor, Reed, and Fields, 1852. With 4 wood engravings which the title-page states are "by Baker from designs by Billings." Billings received $20 for the designs and Baker $50 for the engravings. Orig. cloth.

THE ILLUSTRATED NEWS. Vol. I. New York: 1853. The title-page to Vol. I is designed by Billings and engraved by Frank Leslie. [See Item 1836]

1505. MARTIN MERRIVALE: HIS X MARK. By Paul Creyton [John Townsend Trowbridge]. Boston: Phillips, Sampson and Company . . . 1854. Wright II (2552).

Contains 16 full-page wood engravings (including the half title) by Baker-Andrew and W. J. Baker* and also small vignettes at the chapter headings, most of which are by the same engravers. No draftsman's name appears but an advertisement by Phillips, Sampson and Company in Norton's Literary Gazette and Publishers' Circular, New Series, Vol. I, Number VII (p. 180), states that the illustrations are "from original designs by Billings and other Artists." Most of the full-page illustrations sufficiently resemble Billings' work to warrant attributing them to him. Some of the small vi-

* One (p. 145) was engraved by Smith & Pierson.

gnettes might be his also, but it is difficult to assign them to any particular artist. Orig. cloth.

1506. THE WORTH OF THE WORTHLESS; A CHRISTMAS AND NEW YEAR'S STORY. By John Ross Dix. Boston: Published under the Direction of the Shakspeare Division of Sons of Temperance, No. 46, 1854. With an illustration on half title and 3 headpieces, all after designs by Billings and engraved on wood by Baker, Smith, and Andrew. Orig. cloth.

ALBUM OF WOOD ENGRAVINGS by John Andrew, etc. [ca. 1855-1875]. At least 12 engravings after Billings. [See Item 1472(2)]

1507. THE MAGICIAN'S SHOW BOX, AND OTHER STORIES. By the Author of "Rainbows for Children" [Mrs. Caroline Tappan]. Boston: Ticknor and Fields, 1856.
Contains 7 wood engravings by John Andrew. The name of the designer does not appear, but *The Cost Books of Ticknor and Fields*, edited by Warren S. Tryon and William Charvat, New York, 1949, states at p. 343 that H.B. was the designer. Billings received $35 for the 7 illustrations and Andrew received $105 for the engravings. With respect to the authorship of the book, see B.A.L. 3161. Orig. cloth.

1508. MRS. FOLLEN'S TWILIGHT STORIES. Each of the following juveniles was written by Eliza Lee (Cabot) Follen, each is dated 1856 and copyrighted 1855, each contains a frontispiece and 4 smaller illustrations in the text by Billings, engraved on wood by John Andrew, each is in its original cloth binding, and each bears the imprint "Boston: Whittemore, Niles & Hall. Milwaukee: A. Whittemore & Co." except Nos. 3 and 4 which do not carry the Milwaukee imprint.
1. TRUE STORIES ABOUT DOGS AND CATS.
2. MADE-UP STORIES.
3. THE PEDLER OF DUST STICKS.
4. THE OLD GARRET. PART FIRST.
5. THE OLD GARRET. PART SECOND.
6. THE OLD GARRET. PART THIRD. This No. 6 was, in 1856, the last of *Mrs. Follen's Twilight Stories*. However, at the foot of the list of the 6 stories, the publishers announce their intention of adding 6 more to the series. This was apparently done in 1858 and we find Nos. 7, 8, and 9 each bearing that date and each with a frontispiece by Winslow Homer [see Items 1724, 1725, and 1723]. There were 3 other numbers, which the writer has not seen, viz.: No. 10, *Conscience*; No. 11, *Piccolissima*; and No. 12, *Little Songs*. See, however, Item 1722a.

THE WEEKLY NOVELETTE. Boston: 1857-1862. An illustration by Billings, engraved on wood by Peirce, will be found in Vol. X, p. 288. [See Item 1545]

GLEASON'S WEEKLY LINE-OF-BATTLE SHIP. Boston: 1859. In the No. for August 6 is an article about Billings, together with his portrait drawn by A. Hill. The design of Billings' Pilgrim Monument appears on the final page. [See Item 1961]

1509. STORIES FROM FAMOUS BALLADS. FOR CHILDREN. By Grace Greenwood [Sara J. Lippincott]. Boston: Ticknor and Fields, 1859. With a steel engraved frontispiece after a drawing by G. H. Cushman, and 4 full-page illustrations by Billings, engraved on wood by Andrew-Filmer. Orig. cloth.

1510. THE ILLUSTRATED PILGRIM ALMANAC [for] 1861. Boston: Office of the National Monument to the Forefathers [1860].
Contains numerous wood engravings which the introductory notice on p. (2) states "are from drawings made by Mr. Hammatt Billings, of Boston, a gentleman well known for his versatile genius, and also for his enthusiastic zeal for raising an enduring memorial in honor of the Plymouth fathers. . . . The descriptions of a large part of the illustrations are from the pen of the same distinguished artist." In fact, Billings and George Coolidge took out the copyright. The names of Andrew-Filmer appear on many of the cuts and they probably did most of the engraving. An advertisement of theirs, announcing the opening of a New York office, appears in the "Advertising Department" at the end of the almanac.
Beginning on p. (41) is a list of the members of The Pilgrim Society and it is probable that each member received a copy of the almanac. Henry W. Longfellow was a member and this is his copy, with his signature on the front wrapper. The first issue of this almanac appears to have been for the year 1860. Nathaniel B. Shurtleff was General Editor. Orig. wrappers.

1511. LITTLE FRANKIE AT SCHOOL. By Mrs. Madeline Leslie [Harriette Newell (Woods) Baker]. Boston: Crosby and Nichols [cop. 1860]. The frontispiece is by Billings, engraved on wood by Nichols. The illustration on p. 35 is probably by Billings also. Orig. cloth.

1512. LITTLE FRANKIE ON A JOURNEY. By Mrs. Madeline Leslie [Harriette Newell (Woods) Baker]. Boston: Crosby and Nichols [cop. 1860]. Contains a frontispiece engraved on wood by Nichols after an unusually bad drawing by Billings. Orig. cloth.

1513. STORIES OF FRONTIER ADVENTURE IN THE SOUTH AND EAST. By William T. Coggeshall. New York: Follett, Foster and Company. J. Bradburn (successor to M. Doolady), 1863. It was first published in Columbus by Follett, Foster and Co. in 1860 under the title *Frontier Life and Character in the South and West*, a 2nd Columbus edition being issued in 1861 under the same title as that of this Item 1513. Wright II (595) locates only one copy of each of these earlier editions, neither of which appear to have been illustrated.

Contains 7 illustrations by Billings, engraved on wood by Andrew-Filmer. That facing p. 70 is in facsimile. Modern cloth.

1514. THE DESERTED VILLAGE. By Oliver Goldsmith. Boston: J. E. Tilton and Company, 1866.

Contains 15 full-page and 17 half-page illustrations by Billings, engraved on wood by Andrew. Billings evidently liked his task. Goldsmith's poetry and Billings' illustrations combine to make a delightful little book. Orig. cloth. Presented by Seven Gables Bookshop.

1515. PROOF OF WOOD ENGRAVING after a drawing by Billings which Billings intended as the frontispiece to the Second Part of *Little Women*. Louisa Alcott disliked it intensely, as is made evident by her letter to Elizabeth B. Greene which is quoted in full in Item 206 of the Main Catalogue and with Fig. 15 in this Supplement. Fig. 14.

The drawing shows Amy, looking somewhat mature, sitting on a terrace with a view over water to what might be a lighthouse which she appears to be sketching. Teddy, mustacheless and not too close by, is lying on his stomach in the grass sticking flowers in the ribbons of Amy's hat. At the top is a pencilled note from the publishers: "If Miss A. will return this Friday A.M. Mr. Niles will be obliged." Under this, in ink, in Miss Alcott's handwriting is written "Oh, please change em!" and, on the sides of the engraving, also in her handwriting, are the words: "Amy too old & no curls. Amy is 17, slender & picturesque. Teddy *much* too young and no mustache. He is 21 in the story & very handsome." At the bottom of the engraving Miss Alcott has written "Lazy Laurence."

This then is the proof on which Miss Alcott expressed her criticisms of Billings' first attempt to illustrate Amy and Teddy, criticisms which led to an entirely different frontispiece. The second attempt of Billings at a frontispiece was also rather unsuccessful, as Miss Alcott makes clear in her letter to Elizabeth Greene referred to above.

THE SUN-SHINE SERIES. Boston: 1870.

Billings designed the Series title and did it well. [See Item 1780]

1516. THE STORY OF THE GREAT FIRE, BOSTON, NOVEMBER 9-10, 1872. By "Carleton," an Eye-witness [Charles Carleton Coffin]. Illustrated by Billings, from Sketches Taken on the Spot. Boston: Shepard and Gill, 1872.

The book describes the great Boston fire of 1872. There are 8 illustrations (one repeated on the front wrapper) of which the author says in his preface "Mr. Billings's . . . pictures are accurate representations, and being such, are therefore historic. They are far more effectual than any words of mine can be to portray the indescribable grandeur of the conflagration." In the advertisements at the end are 2 drawings by A. C. Warren. Orig. wrappers.

Hiram Bingham
(*See Main Catalogue, p. 77*)

1517. A RESIDENCE OF TWENTY-ONE YEARS IN THE SANDWICH ISLANDS; OR THE CIVIL, RELIGIOUS, AND POLITICAL HISTORY OF THOSE ISLANDS . . . By Hiram Bingham, A.M. Second Edition. Hartford: Hezekiah Huntington . . . 1848.

Contains 6 full-page illustrations of Hawaiian scenes. A note on p. XIII says of these: "The well-executed engravings on wood, by Mr. B. F. Childs, are, excepting the 6th, from sketches taken by the writer, on the ground." Bingham's work as a draftsman was much superior to his work as an engraver, if we judge the latter from the cuts in Item 432. However, in the present Item he may have had some professional assistance, as the illustration at p. 35 is signed "Herrick." Modern buckram.

Henry Collins Bispham
1841-1882

A Philadelphian by birth, Bispham was a pupil of William T. Richards. Later he studied with Otto Weber in Paris. His "The Lion Sultan," after being exhibited at the Salon and the Royal Academy, was presented, in the year following the artist's death, to the Pennsylvania Academy of Fine Arts. See Fielding, p. 30.

1518. THE WONDERFUL STORIES OF FUZBUZ THE FLY AND MOTHER GRABEM THE SPIDER. [By S. Weir Mitchell.] Philadelphia: J. B. Lippincott & Co., 1867. Contains 9 full-page illustrations and 1 small illustration at p. 15. From their style it would seem likely that all are by the same hand. Those facing pp. 24

and 62 are signed "H. C. Bispham fecit." Orig. cloth.

Abel Bowen

(See Main Catalogue, p. 78)

1519. A Compilation of Biographical Sketches of Distinguished Officers in The American Navy, with other Interesting Matter. By Benjamin Folsom. Newburyport: Published by the Compiler, Horatio G. Allen, Printer, 1814. With a folding frontispiece showing the Constitution and Guerriere, engraved on wood by Bowen. It is difficult to find work of Bowen of so early a date as this, done within two years after the opening of his engraving office in Boston. Modern ¾ calf. Fig. 13.

1520. The Idiot, or, Invisable Rambler. By Samuel Simpleton, Boston, Saturday, April 25, 1818. This is No. 16 of Vol. I of *The Idiot,* a weekly magazine published every Saturday.

It consists of 4 pages and on the verso of the first page is a cut signed A.B. It shows two men on horseback. One, a well-fed man on a very fat horse, is saying "I am going to Ohio." The other, an ill-fed man on a famished and dejected horse, is replying "I have been." There are a few other wood engravings. The masthead, with its portrait of *The Idiot,* is worthy of J. Downes. Presented by the Swann Galleries.

1521. A Reward of Merit certificate issued by the Lemuel Capen Coolidge School to Phineas H. Glover. The date is somewhat difficult to decipher but is probably August 26, 1819. At the top of the certificate is a charming landscape with boys rolling hoops and a hay cart in the distance. It is engraved on wood and signed "A. Bowen Sc." At the bottom appear the words "Published by Henry Bowen, Congress-street, Boston."

1522. Low's Almanac, for the Year of our Lord and Saviour Jesus Christ, 1822 . . . By Nathanael Low, South Berwick. Boston: Munroe & Francis [1821].

Contains 12 wood engravings showing the occupations of the months, cuts of considerable nostalgic charm. On that for January appear the initials "A.B.," while those for March, August and November are signed merely "B." It seems probable that Bowen did them all. Sewed.

1523. A Survey of Boston and its Vicinity . . . By John G. Hales. Boston: Printed by Ezra Lincoln, 1821. The frontispiece is "A

View of the Old State-House" engraved on wood by Bowen. It first appeared at p. 225 in Item 436. Among other statistics, the book gives the length in yards of the principal streets in Boston. Orig. boards.

1524. A Book for New-Hampshire Children, in Familiar Letters from a Father. Exeter: Francis Grant, 1823. With a frontispiece map of New Hampshire and 2 wood engravings by Bowen, one showing Phillips Exeter Academy and the other the State House at Concord. Orig. boards, leather back.

1525. The History of the Adventures, Love, and Constancy, of Paul and Virginia. Plymouth: H. E. Moore, 1824. With a frontispiece engraved on wood by Bowen. This illustration will also be found in an edition of the book published in Concord in 1831 [Item 451]. Orig. boards with leather back.

1526. History of Boston . . . By Caleb H. Snow, D.D. Boston: Abel Bowen, 1825. This is another copy of Item 440. It is a presentation copy from Bowen to his prize pupil, Alonzo Hartwell.

On the wood engraving of the "Liberty Tree, 1774," facing p. 266, is written in pencil "A.H.Sc." This may well have been written by Hartwell and may mean that Bowen, whose initials appear in the cut, made the drawing on the block but allowed Hartwell, who was about 20 years of age at the time of the book's publication, to do the engraving. ½ morocco.

1527. The Worcester Talisman, A Literary and Miscellaneous Journal . . . Worcester, Mass.: Dorr & Howland, 1828. Vol. 1, containing 26 numbers, published every other week, April 5, 1828—March 21, 1829.

The frontispiece is a copper engraving of the "East View of Faneuil Hall Market," showing Faneuil Hall in the background and in the distance the dome of the New State House. Bowen was both draftsman and engraver. At the end is the "Village Register" dated January 24, 1829, giving, among others, the names of 19 lawyers, 4 physicians, 2 dentists, and 1 gravestone maker. Worcester appears to have been a healthy but litigious community in 1829. Orig. boards.

Tales of Travels West of the Mississippi. Boston: 1830. The middle cut on p. 17 bears Bowen's initials. [See Item 1538]

A Present from Peter Parley to all his Little Friends. Philadelphia: 1831. Toward the end of the book there are several wood engravings signed "B" (see pp. 140, 142, 143,

146, 147, and 150) which may be by Bowen. [See Item 1539]

1528. YOUTH'S KEEPSAKE; A CHRISTMAS AND NEW YEAR'S GIFT FOR YOUNG PEOPLE. Boston: Carter and Hendee, 1831. The small cut on p. 14 is by Bowen. The cuts on pp. 12 and 209 may be his also. There are 3 cuts on which Hartwell's characteristic "H." appears. The book's principal illustrations, however, are a number of line engravings after paintings by various artists.

On p. 207 appears "The Fairy World," a poem by Oliver Wendell Holmes. This marks its first and only appearance. A letter written by Holmes on September 11, 1830, forwarding the manuscript of the poem for publication in *Youth's Keepsake*, indicates that this was a school boy's effort (see Thomas Franklin Currier and Eleanor M. Tilton, *A Bibliography of Oliver Wendell Holmes*, New York, 1953, at p. 303, where this letter is given). Orig. boards.

1529. WHIG AGAINST TORY: OR, THE MILITARY ADVENTURES OF A SHOEMAKER. A TALE OF THE REVOLUTION. FOR CHILDREN. Hartford: Silas Andrus. Cincinnati: Roff and Young, 1832. With 13 small wood engravings. That on p. 18 is signed "B" and all look like the work of Bowen. Orig. boards with leather back.

THE PEOPLE'S MAGAZINE. Vol. I. Boston: 1834. With 1 wood engraving by Bowen. [See Item 1785]

A PORTFOLIO FOR YOUTH. Philadelphia: 1835. The cut on p. 170 bears Bowen's initials. [See Item 1825]

1530. TRAVELS INTO SEVERAL REMOTE NATIONS OF THE WORLD; BY LEMUEL GULLIVER, FIRST A SURGEON, AND THEN A CAPTAIN OF SEVERAL SHIPS. By Dean Swift. Boston: Charles Gaylord, 1835. Contains 5 wood engravings of which 3 bear Bowen's initials. Orig. boards.

1531. THE SEASONS. Northampton: A. R. Merrifield, 1841. A small juvenile with a number of wood engravings. That on p. 16 was engraved by Bowen. On the back wrapper is an engraving signed "Childs." Orig. wrappers.

1532. THE ADVENTURES OF ORPHAN HENRY; OR, THE SURE ROAD TO WEALTH AND HAPPINESS. By Elizabeth Anne Smythe. Boston: Munroe and Francis, 128 Washington Street; Charles S. Francis, New-York [n.d., but before 1842 when the firm of C. S. Francis was formed into a Company]. With 8 wood engravings of which 4 are signed either "B" or "A.B."

Probably Bowen engraved them all. The frontispiece is repeated on the front wrapper. Back wrapper missing.

1533. ENDLESS AMUSEMENTS: OR THE ART OF LEGERDEMAIN MADE EASY TO YOUNG PERSONS. First Edition. Boston: Theodore Abbot, 1842. Full-page frontispiece engraved on wood by Bowen, which is repeated on the front cover, and numerous unsigned wood engravings in the text. Most of these cuts are to be found in Item 459, a later edition. Orig. boards.

MOTHER GOOSE'S MELODIES. Boston [ca. 1845]. Contains at least 6 wood engravings by Bowen (pp. 2, 7, 9, 53, 56, and 64). All of these appeared in Item 690, but the 2 final ones, the initials being difficult to decipher, were not mentioned in the Main Catalogue. They will be found at pp. 44 and 64 of Item 690. [See Item 1459(1)]

TORREY'S NARRATIVE. Boston: 1848. The tailpiece on p. 32 is signed A.B. [See Item 1957]

1534. BIRDS OF THE WOODLAND AND THE SHORE. Boston: Brown, Bazin & Co., 1855. With numerous wood engravings. Those on pp. 15 and 19 were engraved by Bowen. Some of John H. Hall's work will also be found. Orig. cloth.

Theodore C. Boyd
(See Main Catalogue, p. 83)

1535. THE FORTUNES OF A YOUNG WIDOW. A NARRATIVE OF FONDNESS, FASHION, FINANCE—OF SIMPLICITY, CREDULITY, ROGUERY AND CUNNING—RELATING TO RICH OLD HUSBANDS, YOUNG WIVES, PENNILESS ADVENTURERS, MODERN FINANCIERS—THE PHILOSOPHY OF KEEPING UP APPEARANCES, OF LIVING WITHOUT MEANS, WITHIN MEANS AND BEYOND MEANS. A VERITABLE REVELATION OF NEW YORK LIFE IN THE NINETEENTH CENTURY. By an Old Inhabitant. New York: Stearns & Company, 1850. Not in Wright.

Contains 23 wood engravings (one repeated on title-page) signed "T. C. Boyd." It seems probable from the quality of the drawings that Boyd was both draftsman and engraver. They include a view of a den of infamy (p. 43), a cock fight (p. 62), and other interesting scenes of New York Life.

This novel was published in 1850 in the *Sunday Dispatch* which claimed that it was "Written expressly for this Paper." A copy of the *Sunday Dispatch* for May 12, 1850, containing Chapters 30 and 31 and one illustration by Boyd, accompanies the book. The *Dispatch* was published in New York by Williamson & Burns. For further information regarding it see Mott, Vol. II, p. 37. Modern cloth.

1536. FRESH LEAVES FROM THE DIARY OF A BROADWAY DANDY. Edited by John D[enison] Vose, Esq. New York: Bunnell & Price, 1852. Wright II (2599). Fig. 18.

With numerous small wood engravings of a comic nature, drawn by Boyd and engraved by Avery. The author in his preface says, "Much credit devolves upon the artists, (Mr. Boyd, the designer, and Mr. Avery, the engraver,) for their masterly performances of the illustrations." It might be noted, however, that occasional initials appear which might raise a question as to whether all of the illustrations are the work of Boyd and Avery. Modern cloth.

Thomas C. Boyd

Boyd was working in San Francisco in 1856-1860. He was a wood engraver of portraits and views. The view of the waterfront at Sacramento City, designed by Boyd and drawn on stone by Victor Hoffman (reproduced in the *Old Print Shop Portfolio* for November 1948, at p. 61) shows that Boyd was a designer as well as an engraver.

1537. CALIFORNIA ILLUSTRATED FAMILY MEDICAL ALMANAC FOR THE YEAR OF OUR LORD AND SAVIOUR JESUS CHRIST, 1860 . . . ASTRONOMICAL CALCULATIONS IN MEAN OR CLOCK TIME, by Warren Mix. San Francisco: Park & White, 1860. Park & White were agents for "family medicines" and this almanac was evidently used as a means of advertising some of their remedies.

Contains a number of illustrations intended to be humorous all of which seem to have had the same designer. That on p. 47 is signed "Boyd." It seems probable that Boyd drew and engraved them all. His name also appears on an illustrated advertisement on p. 48. The front wrapper, which contains 4 somewhat more sophisticated drawings, is signed "Boyd, Sc."

Cowan lists this almanac in Vol. I, p. 12, of his *Bibliography of the History of California*, San Francisco, 1933, and, judging from the details he gives, must have seen a copy. Neither Drake (No. 96) nor Greenwood (see his *California Imprints*, Los Gatos, California, 1961, No. 1206) appear to have seen a copy and merely cite Cowan, Greenwood adding that the Cowan copy had not been located. It would appear, therefore, that the present copy and the Cowan copy (unless they are one and the same) are the only copies of record. Orig. wrappers.

Joseph H. Brightly
(*See Main Catalogue, p. 83*)

THE ILLUSTRATED NEWS. Vol. I. New York: 1853. A drawing of Girard College, Philadelphia, by Brightly, engraved by Louderback & Hoffmann, appears on p. 261, and on p. 332 are 2 small Philadelphia views by Brightly, engraved by R. Telfer and Hoffmann respectively. [See Item 1836]

John Henri Isaac Browere
1790-1834

After two years of study in Europe, Browere made New York City his headquarters. He was both a sculptor and a painter but was best known as a taker of life masks. His collection of life masks included those of Jefferson and Lafayette. See Groce and Wallace, p. 84.

LIFE AND WORKS OF ALEXANDER ANDERSON, M.D.: New York: 1893. With a portrait of Anderson drawn by Browere. [See Item 1471]

George Loring Brown
(*See Main Catalogue, p. 84*)

1538. TALES OF TRAVELS WEST OF THE MISSISSIPPI. By Solomon Bell [William J. Snelling]. Boston: Gray and Bowen, 1830.

Contains 42 wood engravings of which 5 are signed "G.L.B. Sc." (front., title-page, and pp. 7, 10, and 38), 9 are signed "G.L.B." (pp. 7, 9, 25, 26, 30, 32, 48, 88, and 118), 6 bear the initials of John Downes, 1 those of Abel Bowen, and 1 the name of Hartwell. The others are unsigned. The frontispiece is repeated on p. 21. Brown's illustrations are the earliest of his work which the writer has seen. If the date of his birth, February 2, 1814, given by Groce and Wallace is correct, he was only 16 when this book was published. Whether at so early an age he could have been designer as well as engraver of these illustrations seems doubtful, although his failure in many cases to add the letters "Sc." after his initials may possibly be an indication that, in those cases, he was both draftsman and engraver.

Howes (S739) says that this is the "First American juvenile book on the trans-Mississippi region." This copy once belonged to James Russell Lowell and was presented by him to his mother. On the front cover is a pen and ink inscription "H.B.S. Lowell from Jamie" probably in her hand, and on the fly-leaf in his hand is written in pencil "Mrs. H. B. Lowell from her affectionate son James R. Lowell April 12th, 1834." Orig. boards with cloth back.

1539. A PRESENT FROM PETER PARLEY TO ALL HIS LITTLE FRIENDS. Philadelphia: Thomas Holden, 1831. Contains over 200 wood engravings. The frontispiece bears Brown's initials. Several engravings are signed "B" and, while these also might be by Brown, they seem more likely to have been the work of Bowen. The final engraving in the book is by Hartwell. Orig. boards with leather back. Presented by Seven Gables Bookshop.

THE PEOPLE'S MAGAZINE. Vol. I. Boston: 1834. The wood engraving on p. 28 is after a drawing by Brown. [See Item 1785]

THE PUBLIC SCHOOLS, PUBLIC BLESSINGS. New York: 1837. On the cover is an illustration which, while the draftsman's name is hard to decipher, appears to be after a drawing by Brown. It is engraved on wood by Hooper. [See Item 1450]

RECOLLECTIONS OF THE UNITED STATES ARMY. Boston: 1845. With 1 cut engraved by Brown. It is the best drawn and most effective cut in the book. Possibly Brown was also its draftsman. [See Item 1702]

ALLEN CRANE. Troy, N.Y.: [ca. 1851]. Brown engraved the cut on p. 7 of *Gold Hunting* and also that at the head of *The Old Schoolmaster*. [See Item 1463]

John G. Brown
(See Main Catalogue, p. 86)

OUT OF TOWN. New York: 1866. At p. 121 is an illustration by J. G. Brown, the name of the wood engraver not appearing. [See Item 1673]

McGUFFEY'S SECOND ECLECTIC READER. Cincinnati and New York [cop. 1879]. On p. 121 is an excellent illustration by Brown, engraved on wood by Juengling. [See Item 1907a(2)]

Nathan Brown
(See Main Catalogue, p. 86)

POEMS. By Oliver Wendell Holmes. Boston: 1849. 2 illustrations by Brown, probably engraved on wood by Hartwell. [See Item 1502]

PLYMOUTH AND THE PILGRIMS. Boston: 1851. Contains 1 cut signed "N. Brown." [See Item 1720]

Samuel E. Brown
(See Main Catalogue, p. 86)

1540. AUTOBIOGRAPHY OF DAVID RUSSELL, A BOSTON BOY AND TRUE AMERICAN. . . . Written by Request. Boston: Printed for the Author, 1857. Wright II (2141). Contains 5 full-page wood engravings. That facing p. 212 depicts a horrifying shipwreck and is signed "S. E. Brown, Del." He was probably the engraver also. The rest are unsigned. Orig. cloth.

J. Ross Browne
(See Main Catalogue, p. 86)

1541. YUSEF; OR THE JOURNEY OF THE FRANGI. A CRUSADE IN THE EAST. By J. Ross Browne. New York: Harper & Brothers, 1853. Contains some 50 wood engravings which the List of Illustrations states are "from sketches by the author." However, at least 3 of them (pp. 260, 363, and 391) were drawn by F. A. Chapman. Many of them are signed "Lossing-Barritt" and that firm probably engraved them all. Orig. cloth.

Charles (or C.) Burton

It is not certain when Burton came from England to America, but it may have been as early as 1800. He was a landscape and portrait painter, but is best known for his miniature views of New York City and Philadelphia, published in 1831. He is listed in New York City directories from 1828 to 1831. Although he is supposed to have gone South in 1831, it seems likely that he was the Burton who made the drawings for some of the illustrations in the item listed below. See Groce and Wallace, p. 98.

THE PANORAMA OF PROFESSIONS AND TRADES. Philadelphia: 1836. The preface states that Burton was one of the illustrators and the initials C.B. appear on 4 of the cuts (pp. 180, 185, 189, and 195). They were engraved on wood by A. J. Mason. [See Item 1866]

Charles G. Bush

Bush drew for *Appleton's Journal* and also for the Harpers. According to Murrell (Vol. II, p. 15), Bush made his debut as a humorous artist in June 1869, with his drawing in *Harper's Weekly* of the Boston Peace Jubilee. "No description," says Murrell "can do justice to the gay irreverence and irrelevance with which the youthful Bush has charged his drawing." Murrell reproduces this cartoon. Later Bush became one of the pioneers of the daily newspaper cartoon and did excellent work for the *World*. See Murrell, p. 130; Weitenkampf, pp. 219 and 284.

ALBUM OF WOOD ENGRAVINGS by John Andrew, etc. [*ca.* 1855-1875]. At least 7 engravings after Bush. [See Item 1472(2)]

HARPER'S BAZAAR. Vols. I-III. New York: 1867-1870. Full-page drawings by Bush will be found in Vol. III at pp. 8, 312, 441, 472 and 777, the most interesting showing "Fifth Avenue After Church" on p. 312. What are probably his initials appear on a few of the illustrations for James DeMille's *Cord and Creese* which began in the first number of November 2, 1867. He was one of the illustrators of Fritz Hugh Ludlow's *The Household Angel*, which began in the number for May 30, 1868, and also illustrated *The Sacristan's Household*, which began in the number for August 8, 1868. Other work of his will be found at pp. 400 and 460 of Vol. II and p. 796 of Vol. III. [See Item 1729]

THE MOONSTONE. New York: 1868. The initials "C.G.B." appear on the illustration on p. 147, while the illustrations on pp. 24, 41, 48, 58, 62, 71, 74, 85, 91, 98, 101, 114, 133, 152, and 198 are signed "B" or "C.B." [See Item 1783]

CORD AND CREESE. New York: 1869. Some of the illustrations are signed "B." or "C.B." These are probably the work of Bush. [See Item 1894]

1542. THE LADY OF THE ICE. A NOVEL. By James DeMille. New York: D. Appleton and Company, 1870. With 12 full-page illustrations by Bush, engraved on wood by John Filmer. Orig. cloth.

George W. Carleton
(See Main Catalogue, p. 88)

NEW YORK IN SLICES. New York: 1849. Contains several illustrations probably by Carleton. [See Item 1833 and Item 1030]

VANITY FAIR. Vols. 1-6. New York: 1859-1862. The drawing on p. 243 of Vol. 3 is probably by Carleton. [See Item 1933]

1543. OUR ARTIST IN PERU . . . By Geo. W. Carleton. New York: Carleton . . . 1866. 50 humorous drawings by Carleton, each introducing his little bird (see Weitenkampf, p. 266) whose antics are sometimes more amusing

than the drawing itself. It is similar in form to Carleton's *Our Artist in Cuba* (Item 479), which appeared in 1865. Orig. cloth. Presented by Howard C. Rice.

1544. COLLEGE TRAMPS. A NARRATIVE OF THE ADVENTURES OF A PARTY OF YALE STUDENTS DURING A SUMMER VACATION IN EUROPE, WITH KNAPSACK AND ALPENSTOCK, AND THE INCIDENTS OF A VOYAGE TO ROTTERDAM AND RETURN, TAKEN IN THE STEERAGE. By Frederick A. Stokes. New York: G. W. Carleton & Co., 1880.
Contains numerous small illustrations. On those on pp. 19, 138, 187, 224, and 241 appears Carleton's rambunctious little bird. Probably many more are Carleton's also. That on p. 23 bears McLenan's initials. Orig. cloth.

William de la Montagne Cary
(See Main Catalogue, p. 88)

THE ILLUSTRATED CHRISTIAN WEEKLY. New York: 1871. The illustration on p. 216 is signed "Cary," although the letters have not been reversed when the block was cut. It is engraved on wood by A. Harral. [See Item 1627]

THE BODLEYS TELLING STORIES. New York: 1878. On p. 132 is an illustration by Cary which first appeared on p. 312 of Vol. IV of *The Riverside Magazine for Young People*. [See Item 1732]

W. L. Champney
(See Main Catalogue, p. 89)

1545. THE WEEKLY NOVELETTE. Boston: M. M. Ballou, 1857-1862. The first 10 volumes of this publication with the exception of Nos. 15-26 of Vol. IV, and including, in Vol. III, 4 extra novelettes for April, May, June, and July 1858, making in all 66 novelettes. Bound in 6 vols. Also an additional vol. containing all the nos. of Vol. II except Nos. 25 and 26.
These volumes contain the novelettes listed below under the names of their authors. For the most part they are reprints of previously published books. Following each title are the volume and page number of *The Weekly* where the novelette is to be found. If the title is in Wright, the Wright number is given and also the date which Wright assigns to the book's first appearance and the number of copies of the 1st edition which Wright locates. Where a title appears in Wright, the alternate title and words of description which follow have been omitted, except in some cases where there are substan-

tial changes in the title or changes in the order in which the title and alternate title are given.

Averill, Charles E.
1. THE SECRET SERVICE SHIP. Vol. VIII, p. 289. Wright I (209), 1848. 3 cop.

Ballou, Maturin Murray.
2. THE ADVENTURER. Vol. VIII, p. 33. Wright I (226), 1848. 4 cop.
3. THE ARKANSAS RANGER: OR, DINGLE THE BACKWOODSMAN. A STORY OF EAST AND WEST. By Lieutenant Murray [pseud.]. Vol. III, extra novelette for April 1858. Not in Wright.
4. THE CABIN BOY. Vol. III, p. 65. Wright I (232), [cop. 1848]. 2 cop.
5. THE GIPSY DAUGHTER. Vol. II, p. 225. Wright II (204), 1851. 1 cop.
6. THE HEART'S SECRET. Vol. II, p. 97. Wright II (205), 1852. 1 cop.
7. THE HIGHWAYMAN: OR, THE NEAPOLITAN BANDITTI. A TALE OF LOVE AND PRIDE. By Lieutenant Murray [pseud.]. Vol. IX, p. 65. Possibly Wright I (239), 1847. 3 cop.
8. THE SEA LARK: OR, THE QUADROON OF LOUISIANA. A THRILLING TALE OF THE LAND AND SEA. By Lieutenant Murray [pseud.]. Vol. V, p. 1. Wright I (2522) lists this under Albert W. Sumner, dates it 1850, and locates 2 cop.
9. THE TURKISH SLAVE. Vol. V, p. 65. Wright I (256), 1850. 2 cop.
10. THE UNKNOWN MASK: OR, THE BELLE OF MADRID. A TALE OF SPAIN AND THE SPANISH. Vol. VI, p. 33. Wright I (230), 1849. 2 cop.

Cheever, Henry P.
11. THE WITCH OF THE WAVE. Vol. III, p. 321. Wright I (510), 1847. 2 cop.

Cobb, Sylvanus, Jr.
12. ALICE, THE FISHER GIRL. Vol. IX, p. 385. Wright II (563), [185?]. 1 cop.
13. THE ARMORER OF TYRE: OR, THE ORACLE AND ITS PRIEST. AN EASTERN ROMANCE. Vol. I, p. 385. Not in Wright.
14. THE BRAVO'S SECRET. Vol. I, p. 65. Wright II (564), 1851. 2 cop.
15. THE CHILD OF THE BAY. Vol. VI, p. 162. Wright II (565), 1852. 2 cop.
16. THE CHINESE JUGGLER: OR, THE GRANDEE'S PLOT. A TALE OF THE CELESTIAL EMPIRE. Vol. VII, p. 321. Wright II (571), [185?]. 3 cop.
17. THE GOLDEN EAGLE. Vol. I, p. 2. Wright I (556), 1850. 2 cop.
18. HENRY LA NUIT: OR, THE FOUNDLING OF ESTELLA. A TALE OF NAVARRE, IN

THE OLDEN TIME. Vol. X, p. 161. Not in Wright.
19. HILDEBRAND: OR, THE BUCCANEER AND THE CARDINAL. A SICILIAN STORY OF SEA AND SHORE. By Austin C. Burdick [pseud.]. Vol. VII, p. 65. Not in Wright.
20. IVAN THE SERF. Vol. IV, p. 33. Wright II (570), [185?]. 2 cop.
21. THE KING'S TALISMAN. Vol. I, p. 257. Wright II (573), 1851. 1 cop.
22. THE KNIGHT OF LEON. Vol. VIII, p. 161. Wright II (574), 1853. 1 cop.
23. THE LOST HEIR. Vol. III, p. 1. Wright II (575), 1853. 2 cop.
24. THE MOUNTAINEER: OR, THE WILD CHIEFTAIN. A MORAVIAN TALE. Vol. VII, p. 129. Probably Wright I (555), [1850?]. 1 cop.
25. THE OCEAN MARTYR. Vol. III, extra novelette for June 1858. Wright II (578), n.d. 1 cop.
26. ORLANDO CHESTER. Vol. II, p. 161. Wright II (580), 1852. 1 cop.
27. PAUL LAROON. Vol. III, p. 385. Wright II (581), [185?]. 3 cop.
28. THE ROYAL YACHT. Vol. VII, p. 1. Wright II (583), [185?]. 3 cop.
29. THE SEA LION. Vol. III, p. 193. Wright II (584), 1853. 3 cop.
30. THE STORM CHILDREN. Vol. II, p. 289. Wright II (585), 1853. 1 cop.
31. THE VENETIAN BUCCANEER. Vol. V, p. 193. Wright I (558), 1850. 1 cop.
32. THE WANDERING GUERRILLA. Vol. IX, p. 129. Wright II (586), [185?]. 1 cop.
33. THE YANKEE CHAMPION: OR, THE TORY AND HIS LEAGUE. A REVOLUTIONARY TALE OF LAND AND SEA. Vol. I, p. 129. Not in Wright.

Duganne, Augustine Joseph Hickey.
34. THE PRINCE CORSAIR. Vol. IX, p. 257. WRIGHT II (797), [185?]. 1 cop.

Durivage, Francis Alexander.
35. THE DOOMED KING: OR, THE CROWN AND THE SWORD. A ROMANCE OF THE THRONE, THE ALTAR, AND THE CAMP. Vol. II, p. 97. Not in Wright.
36. THE PHANTOM OF THE SEA: OR, THE RED CROSS AND THE CRESCENT. A STORY OF BOSTON BAY AND THE MEDITERRANEAN. Vol. III, extra novelette for May 1858. Not in Wright.

Hill, George Canning.
37. ESMERELDA. Vol. X, p. 225. Wright II (1208), 1852. 2 cop.

Hunter, Major F. C.
38. THE BEGGAR OF LYONS: OR, THE RES-

TORATION. A ROMANCE OF FRANCE
AND SPAIN. Vol. VII, p. 385. Not in
Wright.

39. THE CHILD OF THE WRECK. Vol. IX,
p. 1. Wright I (1247), [cop. 1848]. 3
cop.

40. THE FOUNDLING: OR, HERMIONE OF
ST. ANTOINE. A ROMANCE OF THE
CONTINENT. Vol. V, p. 385. Wright I
(1248), 1849. 2 cop.

41. THE WRECKERS: A STORY OF THE SEA
AND THE SHORE. Vol. X, p. 353. Not in
Wright.

Ingraham, Joseph Holt.
42. THE ARROW OF GOLD. Vol. X, p. 289.
Wright II (81), [185?]. 1 cop. Wright
does not list it under Ingraham.

43. THE DANCING STAR: OR, THE SMUG-
GLER OF THE CHESAPEAKE. A STORY OF
THE COAST AND SEA. Vol. I, p. 321.
Not in Wright.

44. THE LADY IMOGEN: OR, THE WRECK
AND THE CHASE. A TALE OF BLOCK
ISLAND AND THE SOUND. Vol. VIII, p.
353. Not in Wright.

Judson, Edward Zane Carroll (Ned Buntline).
45. THE BLACK AVENGER. Vol. VI, p. 97.
Wright I (1515), 1847. 3 cop. A book
made famous by Tom Sawyer.

46. THE KING OF THE SEA. Vol. VI, p. 289.
Wright I (1521), 1847. 1 cop.

47. THE QUEEN OF THE SEA. Vol. V, p.
129. Wright I (1531), 1848. 4 cop.

48. THE RED REVENGER. Vol. VII, p. 193.
Wright I (1532), 1848. 3 cop.

49. THE VOLUNTEER. Vol. VIII, p. 225.
Wright I (1537), 1847. 3 cop.

Orne, Mrs. Caroline (Chaplin)
50. LIONEL AINSWORTH. Vol. IX, p. 321.
Wright II (1823), [185?]. 1 cop.

Piper, A. G.
51. THE BEL ISABEL: OR, THE CONSPIRA-
TORS OF CUBA. A STORY OF THE GREEN
LAND AND BLUE SEA. By F. Clinton
Barrington [pseud.]. Vol. V, p. 257. Not
in Wright.

52. BLACKLOCK: OR, THE WANDERER OF
THE SEA. A STORY OF RIVER, MAIN
AND OCEAN. By F. Clinton Barrington
[pseud.]. Vol. X, p. 97. Not in Wright.

53. CAPTAIN BELT: OR, THE BUCCANEER
OF THE GULF. A ROMANTIC STORY OF
THE SEA AND SHORE. Vol. IV, p. 161.
Wright II (1910), 1851. 3 cop.

54. RED HAND: OR, THE CRUISER OF THE
ENGLISH CHANNEL. A STORY OF THE
OLDEN TIME. By F. Clinton Barrington

[pseud.]. Vol. III, p. 129. Probably
Wright II (1911), 1851. 1 cop.

Poore, Benjamin Perley.
55. THE SCOUT: OR, SHARPSHOOTERS OF
THE REVOLUTION. Vol. VI, p. 353.
Probably Wright II (1926), [185?]. 1
cop.

Robinson, John Hovey.
56. THE BLACK KNIGHT. Vol. IV, p. 97.
Wright I (2129), 1849. 2 cop.

57. THE BRIGAND: OR, THE CONVENT OF
SANTA CLARA. A TALE OF PORTUGAL.
Vol. IX, p. 193. Probably Wright I
(2128), [1850?]. 1 cop.

58. THE GIPSEY BRIGAND: OR, THE CHILD
OF THE SIERRA. A ROMANCE OF SUNNY
SPAIN. Vol. V, p. 321. Wright I (2131),
[cop. 1848]. 1 cop.

59. THE MAID OF THE RANCHE. Vol. III,
p. 257. Wright II (2072), [186?]. 1
cop.

60. MARION'S BRIGADE. Vol. II, p. 353.
Wright II (2073), 1852. 4 cop.

61. THE PIONEER: OR, THE ADVENTURERS
OF THE BORDER. A TALE OF WESTERN
LIFE. Vol. II, p. 33. Not in Wright.

62. THE REBEL SPY. Vol. VI, p. 227.
Wright II (2079), 1852. 1 cop.

63. REDPATH. Vol. X, p. 33. Wright II
(2080), [185?]. 2 cop.

64. THE ROYAL GREENS. Vol. III, extra
novelette for July 1858. Wright II
(2083), [185?]. 3 cop.

65. THE RUINED ABBEY: OR, THE GIPSEYS
OF FOREST HILL. A ROMANCE OF OLD
ENGLAND. Vol. VII, p. 257. Not in
Wright.

66. THE WHITE ROVER. Vol. I, p. 193.
Wright II (2087), 1852. 3 cop.

Each of the above novelettes has 4 illustrations, with the exception of No. 1, which is unillustrated, Nos. 25 and 64, which have 3 illustrations, and Nos. 3 and 36, which have 6. Nos. 14
and 33 were probably illustrated by A. Hill
whose signature appears. In the case of Nos. 25
and 36 Alfred Waud was the illustrator. As to
the illustrations of the remaining novelettes,
Champney's name frequently appears and for
the most part the drawings resemble his work.
It seems probable that the bulk of the work
was his. W. J. Peirce was the principal wood
engraver.

In addition to his illustrations for the novelettes other illustrations by Champney will be
found—see Vol. III, p. 48; Vol. VI, pp. 160 and
224; Vol. VII, pp. 297, 376, and 377; Vol.
VIII, p. 368; and Vol. X, p. 185. The only en-

gravers whose names appear are Bricher and Peirce.

There are various miscellaneous illustrations scattered through the periodical. The illustrators include Charles A. Barry, A. C. Warren, A. Hill, Samuel Wallin, S. S. Kilburn, John R. Chapin, George T. Devereux, W. R. Miller, A. Waud, W. Waud, Winslow Homer, William Wade, J. H. Manning, and Hammatt Billings. It is probable that most of these miscellaneous illustrations had previously appeared in other Ballou publications. Cloth and half leather.

GLEASON'S WEEKLY LINE-OF-BATTLE SHIP. Boston: 1859. With an illustration by Champney in the number for November 26. [See Item 1961]

1546. THE NOVELETTE. Boston: Office American Union, Flag of our Union, and Dollar Monthly. 30 non-consecutive numbers of this publication which appears to be a rare serial. It is not mentioned by Mott in his *History of American Magazines*, nor is it listed in the *Union List of Serials*.

According to the publishers' advertisement, there were 13 issues of *The Novelette* each year, or one for every 4 weeks, each number containing some short stories and miscellaneous reading matter in addition to a complete novel. It was closely related to *The Weekly Novelette* which was devoted principally to the publication of complete novels in 4 weekly installments. Some issues of *The Novelette* appear to comprise 4 numbers of *The Weekly Novelette* issued with new wrappers. The publishers were Elliott, Thomes & Talbot. Each of the 30 numbers is in its original wrappers.

It is difficult to arrive at the approximate dates of publication of these numbers. 2 of them bear the date April 1863, but these are widely separated numbers, viz., Nos. 12 and 80, so that this date is not very helpful. However, between No. 104 and No. 106 Messrs. Elliott, Thomes & Talbot changed their address from 118 Washington Street to 63 Congress Street. This new address appears in the Boston Directory for 1865. On the other hand, until No. 106 the 118 Washington Street address appears throughout and yet this address is not given in the Boston Directory until 1863. Before that the address is 100 Washington Street. It is hard to reconcile these dates with the statement that 13 numbers were issued in a year. No intensive search has been made to solve this problem. The best that can be said at present is that the serial was published during the decade of the sixties.

Following the method adopted in describing Item 1545, the 30 novelettes contained in these 30 numbers are listed below under the names of their authors. Following each title is the number of the issue of *The Novelette* in which it is to be found and the copyright date, if given. Where the title is in Wright, the Wright number is given and also the date which Wright assigns to the book's first appearance and the number of copies of the 1st edition which Wright locates. It might be noted, however, that only 7 of the 30 novelettes are to be found in Wright.

All 30 novelettes are illustrated and the illustrations resemble Champney's work. In a few instances his name actually appears. Accordingly, it is believed that most, if not all, the novelette illustrations are his and the Item has been listed under his name. The work of other illustrators occasionally appears in the miscellaneous matter and this is noted below.

Aiken, George L.
1. CYNTHIA. THE PEARL OF POINTS. A TALE OF NEW YORK. No. 91. 6 illustrations, engraved on wood by Peirce. A drawing of Trenton's State House by J. R. Chapin will also be found on p. 50 in this number.
2. ORPHA'S HUSBAND: OR, THE PATH OF ERROR. A ROMANCE OF EVERYDAY LIFE. No. 104. Copyrighted, 1864. 7 illustrations, 2 of which are signed by Champney as draftsman and 3 by N. Brown as engraver. A drawing of "Class Day at Harvard University," by Winslow Homer will be found on p. 50. It first appeared in *Ballou's Pictorial Drawing-Room Companion* on July 3, 1858.

Ballou, Maturin Murray.
3. THE GIPSEY DAUGHTER: OR, THE FORTUNES OF A SPANISH CAVALIER. A STORY OF THE ROVING TRIBES OF SPAIN. By Lieutenant Murray [pseud.]. No. 116. Wright II (204), 1851. 1 cop. This novel will also be found in Item 1545. 4 illustrations, the first signed by Champney, all engraved on wood by Peirce.
4. THE GREEK ADVENTURER! OR, THE SOLDIER AND THE SPY. A TALE OF THE SIEGE OF SEBASTOPOL. By Lieutenant Murray [pseud.]. No. 85. 4 illustrations, engraved on wood by Peirce. A drawing by Kilburn of Tufts College will be found on p. 42 and a drawing by Nast of Norwalk, Conn., engraved on wood by John Andrew, on p. 46.
5. THE HEART'S SECRET: OR, THE FORTUNES OF A SOLDIER. A TALE OF LOVE AND THE LOW LATITUDES. By Lieutenant Murray [pseud.]. No. 9. Wright II

(205), 1852. 1 cop. This novel will also be found in Item 1545. 4 illustrations, engraved on wood by Peirce. An illustration by Wade, appears on p. 35 and one by A. Hill on p. 43, both engraved on wood by Peirce.

6. THE OUTLAW: OR, THE FEMALE BANDIT. A STORY OF THE ROBBERS OF THE APENNINES. By Lieutenant Murray [pseud.]. No. 107. Copyrighted, 1859. Wright II (206), 187?. 1 cop. 6 illustrations, all probably engraved on wood by Peirce.

7. THE SCARLET FLAG: OR, THE CARIBBEAN ROVER. A STORY OF THE EARLY BUCCANEERS. By Lieutenant Murray [pseud.]. No. 90. Copyrighted, 1857. 5 illustrations, engraved on wood by Peirce. A drawing by Devereux will be found at p. 42, one by Kilburn at p. 46, and one by Wade at p. 47.

Clarence, Walter.
8. THE FREEBOOTER: OR, THE SCOURGE OF THE CARIBBEAN SEA. No. 120. Copyrighted, 1859. 8 illustrations, one of which is signed by Hayes, as the engraver.

9. THE SEA GULL: OR, THE WITCH OF THE NORTH SEA. A ROMANCE OF THE SEVENTEENTH CENTURY. No. 111. Copyrighted, 1859. 9 illustrations, engraved on wood by Peirce.

Cobb, Darius.
10. ADELINE DESMOND: OR, THE SPY OF NEWBERN. A STORY OF THE WAR. No. 94. Copyrighted, 1863. 5 illustrations, engraved on wood by Peirce.

Cobb, Sylvanus, Jr.
11. THE LOST HEIR: OR, THE DUKE AND THE LAZZARONE. A ROMANCE OF NAPLES. No. 14. Wright II (575), 1853. 2 cop. This novel will also be found in Item 1545. 4 illustrations, that on p. 39 signed "Champney," engraved on wood by Peirce. A drawing by A. Waud, engraved on wood by Hayes, is on p. 38 and another drawing by Waud, engraved by Fox, on p. 50.

12. THE STORM CHILDREN: OR, THE LIGHT-KEEPER OF THE CHANNEL. A STORY OF SEA AND LAND ADVENTURE. No. 12. Dated April 1863 at the top of p. 3. Wright II (585), 1853. 1 cop. This novel will also be found in Item 1545. 4 illustrations, engraved on wood by Peirce. A drawing of Col. Samuel Jaques, drawn by Winslow Homer from a photograph and engraved by Peirce,

will be found on p. 26. It originally appeared in *Ballou's Pictorial Drawing-Room Companion* on May 7, 1859.

13. THE TEXAN CRUISER: OR, CALYPSO THE WANDERER. A TALE OF THE MEXICAN WAR. No. 84. 4 illustrations, engraved on wood by Peirce. An illustration by Champney of the vestibule of the Boston Theatre is on p. 38 and another by him of the Worcester Railroad Depot is on p. 47.

14. THE VISCONTI: OR, BARBARIGO THE STRANGER. A TALE OF MILAN DURING THE MIDDLE AGES. By Austin C. Burdick [pseud.]. No. 97. 4 illustrations, unsigned by the engraver. A drawing by Champney, engraved on wood by John Andrew, is on p. 42.

Duganne, Augustine Joseph Hickey.
15. BIANCA: OR, THE STAR OF THE VALLEY. A ROMANCE OF THE ALPS. No. 80. Dated April, 1863 at the top of p. 3. Wright II (796), 185?. 2 cop. 4 illustrations, engraved on wood by Peirce.

Durivage, Francis Alexander.
16. THE BRIDE OF THE ATLANTIC: OR, THE SECRET OF THE SEA. No. 121. Copyrighted, 1860. 6 illustrations, engraved on wood by Peirce.

17. MARIAN MALVERN: OR, THE HEIRESS OF GLENDALE. A ROMANCE OF THE DAYS WE LIVE IN. No. 102, copyrighted, 1864. 7 illustrations, of which 3 are signed by Champney (pp. 22, 27, and 30). N. Brown was the wood engraver. On the final page is a portrait of Jefferson and a view of Monticello, drawn by Kilburn.

18. THE POLICE SPY: OR, THE SECRET CRIMES OF PARIS. A ROMANCE OF THE SEVENTEENTH CENTURY. No. 117. Copyrighted, 1860. 6 illustrations, 2 of which are signed "Champney," engraved on wood by Peirce. Views of "Partridge Shooting" and "Bison Hunting" signed "W.C." (probably William Croome) will be found on pp. 42 and 46. A view in Portland, Me., drawn by W. Waud and engraved on wood by Fox appears on p. 47.

19. SIR RASHLEIGH'S SECRET: OR, THE MYSTERY OF SYBIL'S CLIFF. A ROMANCE OF CRIME AND RETRIBUTION. No. 96. Copyrighted, 1863. 6 illustrations, the first signed by Champney, all engraved on wood by Peirce. 2 drawings by A. Waud will be found on pp. 14 and 50, the wood engravers being Hayes and Tarbell.

9. Anderson, "Death of Voltaire," *Leisure Hours*, 1812. (Item 1410)

The CONFIRMED DRUNKARD.

Beastly Intoxication, Loss of Character, Loss of Natural Affection, Family Suf-fering, Brutality, Misery, Disease, Mortgages, Sheriffs, Writs &c.

10. Barber. From broadside, *The Drunkard's Progress*, 1826. (Item 1478)

EMIGRANT TRAIN PASSING WIND RIVER MOUNTAINS.

11. Baker. From broadside, *Crossing the Plains* [1853]. (Item 1474)

12. Beyer. *Pictorial for the Million*, 1851. (Item 1500)

13. Bowen. "Constitution and Guerriere," *A Compilation of Biographical Sketches of Distinguished Officers in the American Navy*, 1814. (Item 1519)

"Oh, Betsy! such trials as I have had with that Billings no mortal creter knows! He went & drew Amy a fat girl with a pug of hair, sitting among weedy shrubbery with a lighthouse under her nose, & a mile or two off a scrubby little boy on his stomach in the grass looking cross, towzly, & about 14 years old! It was a blow, for that picture was to be the gem of the lot. I bundled it right back & blew Niles [of Roberts Brothers] up to such an extent that I thought he'd never come down again. But he did, oh bless you, yes, as brisk & bland as ever, & set Billings to work again. You will shout when you see the new one for the man followed my directions & made (or tried to) Laurie 'a mixture of Apollo, Byron, Tito & Will Greene,' Such a baa Lamb! hair parted in the middle, big eyes, sweet nose, lovely moustache & cunning hands; straight out of a band-box & no more like the real Teddy than Ben Franklin. I wailed but let go for the girls are clamoring & the book can't be delayed. Amy is pretty & the scenery good but—my Teddy, oh my Teddy!"

15. Billings. *Little Women, Part Second*, 1869 (Item 206[2]), and text of letter from Louisa May Alcott to Elizabeth B. Greene, April 1, with kind permission of The Clifton Waller Barrett Library of the University of Virginia.

14. Billings. Proof of first attempt at frontispiece for *Little Women* with Louisa May Alcott's notations. (Item 1515)

AMY AND LAURIE.

" I'm all ready for the secrets." said Laurie, looking up with a decided expression of interest in his eyes. — PAGE 239.

"Here comes 'Hole in the Day.'" See page 50.

16. Close. *White and Red*, 1869. (Item 1560)

"Coward!" cried I, "would you shoot a dying man?" Page 124.

17. Champney. Larry Lockwell [1864].
(Item 1547)

18. Boyd. "Here we are—so look, wonder,
and laugh, at juvenile love scenes."
*Fresh Leaves from the Diary of a Broadway
Dandy*, 1852. (Item 1536)

20. THE SPANISH TROOPER: OR, THE MISER OF MADRID. A ROMANCE OF THE OLD AND NEW WORLD. No. 110. Copyrighted, 1858. 9 illustrations, 2 of which are signed by Peirce as the engraver.

21. STEEL AND GOLD: OR, THE HEIR OF GLENVILLE. A TALE OF THE REVOLUTION. No. 82. 4 illustrations, engraved on wood by Peirce. A view of the city of St. Paul drawn by W. Waud will be found on p. 47.

22. THE VENDETTA: OR, THE SECRET OF CONFESSION. A STORY OF CORSICA. No. 106. Copyrighted, 1858. 6 illustrations, engraved on wood by Peirce. A drawing by Hill of the interior of King's Chapel, Boston, engraved on wood by Peirce, will be found on p. 35.

Orne, Mrs. Caroline (Chaplin).

23. THE SECRET LEAGUE: OR, THE MYSTERIES OF ALBURN HALL. A STORY OF OLD ENGLAND. No. 95. Copyrighted, 1858. 6 illustrations, engraved on wood by Peirce.

Robinson, John Hovey.

24. DISINHERITED: OR, THE HEIR OF MOTCOMBE. A TALE OF ENGLAND. No. 88. 4 illustrations, engraved on wood by Peirce. Other work by Champney will be found on pp. 26 and 38. On p. 50 is Winslow Homer's portrait of Captain Robert B. Forbes, drawn from a photograph and engraved by Peirce, which had first appeared in *Ballou's Pictorial Drawing-Room Companion* on August 20, 1859.

25. HALF-WITTED NAT: OR, THE MISER OF PATUXET. A STORY OF PROVINCIAL TIMES. No. 93. Copyrighted, 1857. 8 illustrations, that on p. 35 signed by Champney. Peirce was the wood engraver.

26. MARION'S BRIGADE: OR, THE LIGHT DRAGOONS. A TALE OF THE REVOLUTION. No. 13. Wright II (2073), 1852. 4 cop. This novel will also be found in Item 1545. 4 illustrations, engraved on wood by Peirce. Work by A. Waud will be found on pp. 38 and 50, the first of these being engraved on wood by Hayes.

27. THE MOUNTAIN OF GOLD: OR, THE PRIESTESS OF THE SUN. A STORY OF WILD ADVENTURE IN MEXICO. No. 89. Copyrighted, 1857. 6 illustrations of which 4 are signed by Champney (pp. 3, 14, 18, and 22). Peirce was the wood engraver.

28. THE UNKNOWN: OR, THE SECRET HELPER. A TALE OF WRONG AND RETRIBUTION. No. 92. Copyrighted, 1858. 8 illustrations, engraved on wood by Peirce.

Vinton, Matthew S.

29. JIG POTTER: OR, RALPH SINGLETON'S PROTÉGÉ. A TALE OF CRIME AND RETRIBUTION. No. 98. Copyrighted, 1864. 7 illustrations. The first is signed "Champney del" but is unsigned by the wood engraver. Of the rest 2 are engraved by Peirce and 4 by N. Brown.

Williams, John B.

30. THE BLACK MENDICANT: OR, THE MYSTERIOUS PROTECTOR. A STORY OF PLOT AND PASSION. No. 99. Copyrighted, 1858. 4 illustrations of which 1 is signed by Peirce as the engraver. On p. 50 is an illustration by A. Hill showing the "Return of Soldiers at Charlestown, Mass., from the Seat of War."

Accompanying the above 30 numbers is the following: THE NOVELETTE. No. 1. CONTAINING THE STORY COMPLETE OF THE ARKANSAS RANGER: OR, DINGLE THE BACKWOODSMAN. A STORY OF EAST AND WEST. By Lieutenant Murray [Maturin Murray Ballou]. Boston: Office American Union and Ballou's Monthly Magazine. No. 23 Hawley Street.

It contains 3 unsigned illustrations and Thomes & Talbot of 23 Hawley Street were the publishers. On the recto of the back wrapper appears the publisher's "Announcement for 1876." Thomes & Talbot was a later partnership than that of Elliott, Thomes & Talbot, the publishers of the 30 numbers above listed. This No. 1 must be either the beginning of a new series or else a reprint of the original No. 1.

1547. LARRY LOCKWELL; OR, I WILL BE A SAILOR. A BOOK FOR BOYS. By Mrs. L. C. Tuthill [Mrs. Louisa Caroline (Huggins) Tuthill]. Philadelphia: Perkinpine & Higgins [cop. 1864]. Fig. 17.

Contains 3 full-page illustrations by Champney. The wood engraver may be N. Brown but the name is difficult to decipher. At the end is a catalogue of books published by Perkinpine & Higgins and another Champney illustration (one for the "Soldier Boy's Library" engraved on wood by N. Brown[?]) appears here. There are also illustrations in this catalogue by E. J. Whitney and G. G. White. Orig. cloth.

1548. ROMANTIC BELINDA. A BOOK FOR GIRLS. By Mrs. L. C. Tuthill [Mrs. Louisa Caroline (Huggins) Tuthill]. Boston: Crosby and Ainsworth [cop. 1864 by Crosby & Nichols]. 4 illustrations by Champney, definitely 2, and probably all, engraved on wood by N. Brown. Orig. cloth.

1549. THE BUSHRANGERS. A YANKEE'S AD-
VENTURES DURING HIS SECOND VISIT TO
AUSTRALIA. By William H. Thomes. Boston:
Lee and Shepard, 1866. Wright (2463) locates
only one copy, that of the New York Public
Library. Another copy, however, is to be found
at the American Antiquarian Society.

Contains 4 full-page illustrations, all of which
appear to be by the same artist. One is signed
"W.L.C." The only engraver's name to appear
is that of N. Brown. Orig. cloth.

1550. BOTH SIDES OF THE STREET. By
Mary Spring Walker. Boston: Henry Hoyt [cop.
1870].

The frontispiece and the illustrations at pp.
133 and 206 are by Champney. Those at pp.
90 and 156, while unsigned, are probably his
also. All are engraved on wood by Kilburn.
There is one illustration by Close.

This was a prize book. Out of over 300
manuscripts presented in competition, it was
awarded the first prize of $600. Orig. cloth.

1551. MOTH AND RUST. A VERY PLAIN
TALE. [By Mrs. Julia (McNair) Wright.] Boston [cop. 1870]. Wright II (2811).

Contains 2 full-page illustrations by Champney (front. and p. 286) and 2 other illustrations,
1 by J. N. Hyde and 1 by A. P. Close, the latter signed by Kilburn who may have engraved
them all. Orig. cloth.

1552. TOM BENTLEY; OR, THE STORY OF A
PRODIGAL. Boston: Henry Hoyt [cop. 1870].
At p. 147 is a full-page illustration by Champney, engraved on wood by Kilburn. There is one
illustration by Close. The frontispiece is signed
"Kilburn" but whether as draftsman or engraver or both does not appear. Orig. cloth.

1553. THE WHALEMAN'S ADVENTURES IN
THE SANDWICH ISLANDS AND CALIFORNIA. By
Wm. H[enry] Thomes. Boston: Lee and Shepard . . . 1872. Wright II (2469). This is one
of "The Ocean Life Series." With 4 full-page
illustrations by Champney. That facing p. 72
was engraved on wood by John Andrew-Son
who probably engraved them all. Orig. cloth.

1554. LIFE IN THE EAST INDIES. By W[il-
liam] H[enry] Thomes. Boston: Lee and Shepard . . . 1873.

Contains 4 full-page illustrations by Champney. The name of John Andrew-Son appears
on the frontispiece and this firm probably engraved all of them. At the end are advertisements of some of Thomes' books, viz.: *The
Whaleman's Adventures, A Slaver's Adventures,
The Gold Hunters' Adventures, The Bushrangers*, and *The Gold Hunters in Europe*. Of

the 5 illustrations accompanying these advertisements, 3 bear Champney's name or initials
and probably all are his.

This is one of "The Ocean Life Series."
Wright II (2466) locates only 2 copies. Orig.
cloth.

John R. Chapin
(*See Main Catalogue, p. 89*)

1555. RICHES AND HONOR. A NEW ENG-
LAND STORY, FOUNDED ON FACT. By the Author of "The Victim of Chancery," etc. [Fred-
erick Jackson]. New York: Josiah Adams, 1847.
Contains 3 illustrations. That facing p. 96 is
signed "Chapin Del. & Sc." and probably the
others are also Chapin's work.

This appears to be the rarest of Jackson's
books. Wright I (1464) fails to locate any
copy. To anyone who has read it, its rarity may
seem providential. Orig. cloth.

THE NEW YORK JOURNAL. Vols. I and II.
New York: 1853-1854. Chapin has 5 illustrations in Vol. I (pp. 8, 73, 104, 209, and 273),
engraved on wood by J. D. Felter (1) and N.
Orr (2), the others not being signed by the engraver. [See Item 1838]

1556. THE HISTORICAL PICTURE GALLERY;
OR, SCENES AND INCIDENTS IN AMERICAN
HISTORY . . . By Jno. R. Chapin. Boston: D.
Bigelow & Co., 1856.

This is the fifth of a series of advertising
publications which appear to have been much
in vogue about the middle of the century. With
their "picture galleries" they were no doubt intended to repose on the parlor table where the
casual visitor might be inveigled into reading
some of the many advertisements contained in
them. In this fifth volume there are over 100 illustrations of historical scenes drawn by Chapin.
A number of wood engravers were used including N. Orr, Whitney & Jocelyn, Lossing-Barritt, Roberts, Baker-Andrew, Whitney, Jocelyn
& Annin, Avery, Lauderbach-Hoffman, W. J.
Baker, John Andrew, Tarbell, J. H. Byram,
Felter, Taylor-Adams, Howland, Swinton, Ris-
don-Cogger, Dodd, and Fay.

Many of the advertisements carry elaborate
wood engravings, on some of which the draftsman's name appears. On pp. 89, 133, and 345
will be found drawings by A. Hill, engraved by
John Andrew. On pp. 185, 321, and 365 appears work of Hyde, also engraved by Andrew.
Kilburn has a drawing on p. 77, engraved by
W. J. Baker, and A. Waud signs the illustration on p. 441 as draftsman.

In the "Index to Advertisements" appear the

names of several wood engravers, viz.: John Andrew, D. B. Gulick, Hoffman & Knickerbocker, Holton & Jardine, J. W. Orr, N. Orr, A. Prentiss, and Taylor & Adams. It is interesting to read the claims of these various engravers. J. W. Orr has a particularly elaborate advertisement, showing specimens of his craft.

Orig. cloth, decorated in gold.

THE WEEKLY NOVELETTE. Boston: 1857-1862. Illustrations by Chapin will be found in Vol. III, p. 34 of the July 1858 extra, and p. 400; and Vol. IV, pp. 200, 201, and 208. The engravers whose names appear are Bricher, Pilliner, and Peirce. [See Item 1545]

THE NOVELETTE. Boston: 186?. Novelette No. 91 contains an illustration by Chapin. [See No. 1 of Item 1546]

1557. ORIGINAL WOOD BLOCK from which was printed Chapin's illustration of the Marais Des Cygnes massacre in Albert D. Richardson's *Beyond the Mississippi* (Item 1136). It was engraved by J. H. Richardson and will be found at p. 117 of the book. This massacre, in which, according to Albert D. Richardson, 11 quite unoffending citizens were shot down for the crime of holding Free State sentiments, took place in Kansas on May 19, 1858 and was commemorated by Whittier in his poem, "Le Marais du Cygne":

How paled the May sunshine
O Marais du Cygne!
On death for the strong life,
On red grass for green!

SPECTACLES FOR YOUNG EYES. New York: 1869. Facing p. 51 is an illustration by Chapin, engraved on wood by Felter. [See Item 1713]

F. A. Chapman
(See Main Catalogue, p. 89)

YUSEF. New York: 1853. Contains at least 3 illustrations by Chapman. [See Item 1541]

1558. THE MAGIC SPECTACLES. By Chauncey Giles. New York: Joseph R. Putnam, 1868. The frontispiece, according to the title-page, is after a drawing by "Chapman." This is probably F. A. Chapman. It is engraved on wood by Howland. Orig. cloth.

THE ILLUSTRATED CHRISTIAN WEEKLY. New York: 1871. The illustration on p. 180 is by Chapman, engraved on wood by Brightly. [See Item 1627]

John G. Chapman
(See Main Catalogue, p. 90)

THE LIFE OF CHRIST, IN THE WORDS OF THE EVANGELISTS. New-York [before December 25, 1838]. Half title after a drawing by Chapman. [See Item 1393]

LIVES OF CELEBRATED WOMEN. Boston: 1844. The half title is after a drawing by Chapman. It is engraved on wood by Adams. [See Item 1395]

Maurice Charles

A wood engraver who was working in New York City in the fifties (see Groce and Wallace, p. 121).

MILLER'S NEW YORK AS IT IS. New York: 1862. At p. 52 is a view of the Episcopal Seminary signed "Charles Del." This may be Maurice Charles. It is engraved on wood by Richardson-Cox. [See Item 1971]

George Edward Clark

A native of Salem, Mass., Clark soon took to a sailor's life and tells of some of his adventures and numerous incidents of his own daring and prowess in the Item listed below. It includes some of his experiences in the United States Navy during the Civil War.

1559. SEVEN YEARS OF A SAILOR'S LIFE. By George Edward Clark, "Yankee Ned," of Lynn, Mass. Boston: Adams & Company [cop. 1867]. Wright II (533). With 9 "elegant" illustrations which the title-page states were engraved from the author's sketches. The name of the wood engraver does not appear. Orig. cloth.

Robert A. Clarke

A painter of animals, Clarke was born in Ireland in 1817 and was settled in New York City by 1843. By 1850 he had moved to Philadelphia where he exhibited at the Pennsylvania Academy. See Groce and Wallace, p. 129.

THE ILLUSTRATED NEWS. Vol. I. New York: 1853. The drawing of the trotting horse "Taconey" on p. 344 is by "Robert Clarke" and the drawing on the following page of a race in which "Taconey" took part is probably his also. As this race took place in Philadelphia, it seems likely that these 2 drawings are by the Philadelphia animal painter, Robert A. Clarke. [See Item 1836]

A. P. Close

(*See Main Catalogue, p. 92*)

1560. WHITE AND RED; A NARRATIVE OF LIFE AMONG THE NORTHWEST INDIANS. By Helen C. Weeks. New York: Hurd and Houghton, 1869. 8 illustrations by Close, the name of the wood engraver not appearing. Orig. cloth. Fig. 16.

BOTH SIDES OF THE STREET. Boston [cop. 1870]. An illustration by Close, engraved on wood by Kilburn, will be found at p. 307. [See Item 1550]

1561. ISAAC PHELPS, THE WIDOW'S SON; OR, THE RUGGED WAY MADE SMOOTH. By M.M.B. Boston: Henry Hoyt [cop. 1870].
The frontispiece and one other full-page illustration are signed by Close as the draftsman. A third illustration is probably his also. The only name of a wood engraver to appear is that of Johnson Dyer. Orig. cloth.

MOTH AND RUST. Boston [cop. 1870]. 1 illustration by Close at p. 161, engraved on wood by Kilburn. [See Item 1551]

TOM BENTLEY. Boston [cop. 1870]. 1 full-page illustration by Close, the name of the engraver not appearing. [See Item 1552]

THE BODLEYS TELLING STORIES. New York: 1878. On p. 74 is an illustration by Close which first appeared on p. 331 of Vol. III of *The Riverside Magazine for Young People*. [See Item 1732]

Cyrus and Darius Cobb

(1834-1903)   (1834-1919)

These twin brothers worked together in Boston from the mid-1850s painting portraits and historical and religious pieces. Darius also painted landscapes. They served together in the same Massachusetts regiment during the Civil War. See Groce and Wallace, p. 133; Appleton, Vol. I, p. 668.

1562. THE VETERAN OF THE GRAND ARMY. A NOVEL. By the Brothers Cobb. In Eight Parts. Boston: Cyrus and Darius Cobb, 1870. In addition to working together in their painting, the Brothers Cobb collaborated in this novel. Even the frontispiece is "Drawn by the Authors." Orig. cloth.

Gershom Cobb

ca. 1780-1824

Cobb was a Boston writing master and bank clerk who occasionally did some engraving. Dunlap (Vol. III, p. 290) says that he engraved "a bookplate on copper and a wood cut in Boston about 1810." He died in Dorchester, Mass., on October 3, 1824. See Groce and Wallace, p. 133.

1563. THE ORDER FOR DAILY MORNING AND EVENING PRAYER, AND THE ADMINISTRATION OF THE HOLY COMMUNION, ACCORDING TO THE USE OF THE PROTESTANT EPISCOPAL CHURCH IN THE UNITED STATES OF AMERICA. WITH THE PSALTER OR PSALMS OF DAVID. Boston: Charles Williams, 1812. On the title-page is an elaborate wood engraving by Cobb, which shows familiarity with the use of the white line. Orig. boards, with bookplate of Charles E. Goodspeed.

ELEGY, IN REMEMBRANCE OF JAMES LAWRENCE, ESQUIRE [Boston, 1813]. At the top of this broadside is a wood engraving by Cobb after a drawing by Nathan Winship Munroe. [See Item 1869]

Frederick M. Coffin

1822-
(*See Main Catalogue, p. 92*)

Born in Nantucket, Coffin came to Auburn, N.Y., in 1845. He displayed an aptitude for drawing and for a time drew figures for a fresco painter in Boston. On his return to Auburn he became a merchant's clerk but continued his drawing and in 1849 began to work for wood engravers and to make portraits in crayon as well. After a year in the Collector's office in Buffalo, he spent the next three years in drawing on wood for publishers of Auburn, Buffalo and New York. In 1854 he went to New York City and devoted himself principally to drawing and designing for the book and magazine publishers of that City and Boston. He served three years in the Civil War. After the war he devoted his time to painting horses, cattle, and pastoral scenes. After the death of his father and his brother, the support of his mother and aunt fell solely on him and he gave up his art studies "and dutifully devoted himself to his relatives—an interesting and forcible illustration of the beauty of his character."

The foregoing facts are taken from a sketch of Coffin appearing in Elliot G. Storke's *History of Cayuga County*, Syracuse, 1879, at p. 68. At the time of the publication of the Main Catalogue the writer had not seen this sketch and was unable to give any facts regarding Coffin's life.

THE CHILD'S PAPER. Vols. I-IV. New York etc.: 1852-1855. An illustration by Coffin, engraved on wood by Bookhout, will be found on p. 47 of Vol. IV. [See Item 1605]

1564. THE AUSTRALIAN CAPTIVE; OR, AN AUTHENTIC NARRATIVE OF FIFTEEN YEARS IN THE LIFE OF WILLIAM JACKMAN . . . Edited by Rev. I. Chamberlayne. Auburn: Derby & Miller . . . 1853. With 4 illustrations by Coffin, engraved on wood by N. Orr. Preceding the title-page are 2 portraits of Jackman also engraved on wood by N. Orr. Orig. cloth.

1565. FERN LEAVES FROM FANNY'S PORTFOLIO. [By Sarah Payson Parton.] Auburn: Derby and Miller . . . 1853.

This is another copy of Item 499. Several clippings relating to Frederick M. Coffin and Fanny Fern are pasted in, and laid in is a signature of "Fanny Fern" written under the lines:

"This earth is very lovely. Oh my God,
    I thank thee that I live."

Orig. cloth.

1566. DANIEL BOONE, AND THE HUNTERS OF KENTUCKY. By W. H. Bogart. Auburn and Buffalo: Miller, Orton & Mulligan, 1854. With 4 full-page illustrations, engraved on wood by N. Orr. One of them (at p. 87) is signed by Coffin and the others resemble his style. Orig. cloth, in a board slipcase.

1567. HILLS, LAKES, AND FOREST STREAMS: OR, A TRAMP IN THE CHATEAUGAY WOODS. By S. H. Hammond. New York: J. C. Derby . . . 1854. With 4 full-page illustrations (including the half title) by Coffin, engraved on wood by N. Orr. Orig. cloth.

THE TURKISH SPIES. Baltimore . . . and Buffalo: 1855. The illustration on p. 161 is signed "Coffin." [See Item 1721]

1568. ELLEN IRVING, THE FEMALE VICTIMIZER, WHO CRUELLY MURDERED SIXTEEN PERSONS IN COOL [sic] BLOOD, FOR REVENGE ON HER FIRST LOVE, WILLIAM SHANNON, WHO HAD BETRAYED HER. ALSO, AN ACCOUNT OF HER ASSOCIATION WITH CHARLES DORIAN, AN ITALIAN MURDERER. Edited by Rev. Robert B. Russel. Published by Arthur R. Orton, Baltimore, Philadelphia, New York, and Buffalo, 1856. The front wrapper states that the book is published by M. A. Milliette (successor to A. R. Orton). It was copyrighted by Orton in 1855. For a discussion of Orton and Milliette see Item 1640.

On the verso of the title-page is a wood engraving of "The Female Victimizer" signed "Coffin Del." and "Pilliner Sc." It is repeated on the front wrapper. The cut on p. 29 also bears the name of Coffin. It must be admitted that neither the style of these drawings nor the style of the 2 signatures are altogether characteristic of Frederick M. Coffin and it is possible that some other Coffin was responsible for the illustrations. On the other hand, none of the other Coffins listed by Groce and Wallace seems a likely candidate for the illustrator of this book. There are 2 other illustrations, both unsigned, on pp. 40 and 48.

The narrative is told by Ellen Irving and at the end is appended a letter from her to the Rev. Robert B. Russel in which she says that a sermon of his had so affected her that she had resolved to sin no more and that she sent him her history in the hope that it might be the means of turning others from the path of guilt. A final note of Russel's states that Ellen had committed suicide by taking laudanum on July 12, 1854. While purporting to be a true tale, the book reads like pure fiction. However, it is not in Wright.

Orig. wrappers, back wrapper missing.

1569. CAPTAIN MOLLY. THE STORY OF A BRAVE WOMAN. By Thrace Talmon [Mrs. Ellen Tryphosa Harrington Putnam]. New York: Derby & Jackson, 1857. 4 full-page illustrations by Coffin, engraved on wood by Bookhout. Orig. cloth.

Wright II (1975) locates only one copy, that at the American Antiquarian Society.

1570. ADVENTURES AND OBSERVATIONS ON THE WEST COAST OF AFRICA, AND ITS ISLANDS . . . By Rev. Chas. W. Thomas, M.A. New York: Derby & Jackson, 1860. With 2 illustrations by Coffin, engraved on wood by Bookhout. There are also 2 wood engravings by N. Orr-Co., the name of the draftsman not appearing. Orig. cloth.

1571. WESTERN BORDER LIFE: OR, WHAT FANNY HUNTER SAW AND HEARD IN KANSAS AND MISSOURI. Philadelphia: John E. Potter and Company [cop. 1863]. The frontispiece is by Coffin, engraved on wood by Bookhout. There are other illustrations by Dallas and Nanteuil. Orig. cloth.

This is a reprint of Wright II (2685) which was published in 1856. The 1st edition apparently was not illustrated.

William Cook

(*See Main Catalogue, p. 94*)

1572. THE OLIVE GROVE. POEMS BY REV. WILLIAM COOK. Salem: 1853. No. 4 of Jenkins' list.

Contains 6 cuts, the meanings of which are explained in a short foreword on the verso of the title-page. They are quite effective, particularly that immediately preceding the preface. There are 1 or 2 small tailpieces and 2 large cuts on the wrappers. Orig. wrappers, a portion of the front wrapper torn away.

1573. THE PLOUGHBOY'S HARROW, NUMBER THREE. By Rev. William Cook, A.B. Salem: January 1860. This is another copy of Item 521. It is complete with the wrappers. Presented by Edward Naumburg, Jr.

1574. THE COLUMBIA. AN ADDRESS BY REV. WILLIAM COOK, A.B. BEFORE THE COLUMBIAN ASSOCIATION. Delivered Salem, August 22, 1863. Salem: January 1864. This is a reprint, the address having originally been issued in November 1863 (see Jenkins' No. 25). Contains 2 large cuts, both touched up with pencil. Orig. wrappers, with a small cut on front wrapper.

1575. MARTYN. SIXTH PART OF THE COR FELIX . . . By Rev. William Cook, A.B. Salem, June 1873. No. 40 of Jenkins' list. Contains 3 full-page cuts touched up with pencil and a cut on the front wrapper of what may be intended as a palm tree. Orig. wrappers.

1576. TALK ABOUT INDIANS. SEVENTH PART OF THE COR FELIX . . . By Rev. William Cook, A.B. . . . Salem, June 1873. No. 41 of Jenkins' list. Contains 3 full-page cuts, rather heavily touched with pencil. The cut on the front wrapper is colored. Orig. wrappers.

1577. WOMAN. EIGHTH PART OF THE COR FELIX . . . By Rev. William Cook, A.B. . . . Salem, May & September, 1874. No. 42 of Jenkins' list.

Contains 3 full-page cuts, colored, as is also the cut on the front wrapper. Orig. wrappers.

John Cranch

1807-1891

According to Charles Cist's *Cincinnati in 1841*, Cranch was a painter of "portraits and fancy pieces." He was a brother of Christopher Pearse Cranch (see Main Catalogue, Item 526). We find him in New York City in the late thirties, but he went to Cincinnati in 1839 where he stayed for several years. He again returned to New York where he worked from 1848 to 1854. From 1857 to at least 1878 he was in Washington, D.C. He died in Urbana, Ohio. His paintings were exhibited in New York, Boston, and Washington. See Groce and Wallace, p. 152.

THE AMERICAN PIONEER. Cincinnati, O.: 1842-1843. The title-page of each of the bound volumes of this periodical was designed by Cranch and engraved on wood by Munson. [See Item 1946]

William Croome

(*See Main Catalogue, p. 96*)

1578. THE CROCKETT ALMANAC 1839. Nashville, Tennessee: Published by Ben Harding [1838]. Contains many illustrations, at least 3 of which are by Croome, engraved on wood by Hartwell.

This is a copy of the same almanac which will be found in Item 1004, but the present copy is uncut, just as originally issued. Sewed.

1579. ILLUSTRATIVE ANECDOTES OF THE ANIMAL KINGDOM: By the Author of Peter Parley's Tales [S. G. Goodrich]. Boston: Bradbury, Soden & Co., 1845. 2 vols. 1st ed. On the half title is a wood engraving by Alexander Anderson after a drawing by Croome. Orig. wrappers.

1580. ROSA OF LINDEN CASTLE: OR, FILIAL AFFECTION. A TALE FOR PARENTS AND CHILDREN. By the Author of "The Basket of Flowers." Translated, Altered and Arranged, by A. J. Lochman. Philadelphia: Perkins & Purves . . . 1845.

In addition to some small head- and tailpieces, the book contains 7 full-page illustrations and the publisher's notice says "It is but due to an accomplished artist, to say, that the larger illustrations found in this volume are from the pencil of Mr. William Croome, of this city." The illustration facing p. 107 is signed "W. Roberts Sc. W. Croome Del." The frontispiece and the illustrations facing pp. 19 and 83 were engraved on wood by Gilbert & Gihon. The name of the engraver of the other 3 does not appear. Orig. cloth.

1581. THE INDIANS AND THE GOLD MINES; OR, THE SOURCE OF TRUE RICHES. Philadelphia: Lindsay & Blakiston [ca. 1850-1852]. With 8 full-page wood engravings after drawings by Croome. No engraver's name appears and Croome may have been his own engraver. Orig. cloth.

1582. ROBERT MORTON, OR THE STEP-MOTHER: A BOOK FOUNDED ON FACT. CONTAINING EDMUND AND IONE, LETTERS FROM THE SOUTH, &C., &C. By Caroline E. Rush. Philadelphia: Published for the Authoress by Crissy & Markley, 1850. Frontispiece drawn by Croome and lithographed by P. S. Duval. Orig. cloth.

1583. SKETCHES OF LIFE AND CHARACTER. By T. S. Arthur. Philadelphia: J. W. Bradley, 1850. Wright I (162).

Contains a portrait of the author and 16 full-page illustrations, engraved on wood. That of "The Pic-Nic" facing p. 191 is signed "W. Croome" and it is tempting to assign the others to him also as the style of many of them resembles his. That facing p. 290, however, is not his, for on the left it is signed "G.C.L." and on the right "T. & L. Sc." It may possibly be early work of George Cochran Lambdin, a Philadelphia painter. Orig. cloth.

1584. THE LIGHTS AND SHADOWS OF REAL LIFE. By T. S. Arthur. Boston: L. P. Crown & Co. Philadelphia: J. W. Bradley [cop. 1851].

This is the same as *Illustrated Temperance Tales* (Item 542), with 8 new stories added at the end (see Wright II, 106). It contains the same illustrations as Item 542, namely 5 signed by Croome, 2 signed by Dallas, and 1 unsigned. The 8 additional tales are unillustrated. Full leather with ornately gilded back and the name "Verona Kennedy" stamped on front cover.

1584a. THE PILGRIM'S PROGRESS FROM THIS WORLD TO THAT WHICH IS TO COME. By John Bunyan. Collated, for the first time, with the early editions . . . With Illustrative Notes by Thomas Scott, D.D. Containing, also, an Essay on the Life and Writings of Bunyan, by Josiah Conder, A.M. Philadelphia, John B. Perry . . . 1852.

The frontispiece and first half title were lithographed and printed in colors by Thomas Sinclair after drawings by Croome. There are also a second half title and 6 full-page wood engravings by C. N. Parmelee, unsigned by the draftsman, but which may possibly be after drawings by Croome also. The artists and craftsmen employed on this edition appear to have been confined to Philadelphians—Sinclair as lithographer, Parmelee as wood engraver, and Croome as designer.

Full cont. morocco with gilt borders on both covers enclosing a gilt design which is taken from the second half title—an interesting Victorian binding.

1585. THE LAST PENNY, AND OTHER STORIES. By T. S. Arthur. Philadelphia: Lippincott, Grambo & Co., 1853. 5 illustrations designed by Croome. That at p. 126 is engraved on wood by Waitt. The name of the engraver of the others does not appear. Orig. cloth.

1586. MAGGY'S BABY, AND OTHER STORIES. By T. S. Arthur. Philadelphia: Lippincott, Grambo & Co., 1853. This is the 1st edition of Item 557, with the same illustrations. There are only 5 illustrations by Croome. In Item 557, the half title or Series title was included as a Croome illustration, but it probably is not his work. Orig. cloth.

1587. (1) LEAVES FROM THE BOOK OF HUMAN LIFE. By T. S. Arthur. Philadelphia: J. W. Bradley, 1854. Contains 30 wood engravings, 13 of which are signed with Croome's name or initials. He was unquestionably the draftsman of all of them. The engravers were B. F. Waitt and J. Green. There is a frontispiece by Sartain after a drawing by Hamilton.

The 1st edition of this book was published by Bradley in Philadelphia in 1853, which was the year of its copyright. The present copy is probably of the 2nd edition. The only edition listed by Wright was published in 1855 (see Wright II, 103).

Orig. cloth, a particularly effective Victorian binding, elaborately gold tooled.

(2) A copy of a later edition published in Philadelphia by John E. Potter and Company, without date, and with the same illustrations. Orig. cloth.

1588. (1) WHO ARE HAPPIEST? AND OTHER STORIES. By T. S. Arthur. Philadelphia: J. B. Lippincott & Co., 1857. This is one of Arthur's Juvenile Library. Contains 5 illustrations by Croome. On 2 of them Waitt's name appears as the engraver. Orig. cloth.

(2) Also a copy of the 1st edition of this book published by Lippincott, Grambo & Co. in Philadelphia in 1852. Unfortunately the illustration "Thin Shoes," which will be found at p. 115 in (1) above, is missing in this copy. Orig. cloth.

1589. THE INDIAN: ON THE BATTLE-FIELD AND IN THE WIGWAM. By John Frost, LL.D. Boston: Wentworth, Hewes & Co., 1858.

In his preface the author says "By the aid of Mr. Croome, and other eminent artists, I have been able to illustrate the volume quite profusely with engravings." Throughout the book there are many wood engravings, quite a number of which may well be after Croome's designs. Orig. cloth.

GLEASON'S WEEKLY LINE-OF-BATTLE SHIP. Boston: 1859. Croome's initials appear on a number of sporting views, viz.: "Smelt Fishing," March 5, "Snipe Shooting," August 20, "Woodcock Shooting," September 10, and "Partridge Shooting," October 8, but it seems likely that he was the draftsman of some 9 others in the Series (see numbers for February 5, April 16, May 21, June 18, July 16, October 29, November 26, December 10, and December 24). The only names of wood engravers to appear are Pierce, Hayes, and C. Minton. Croome may have engraved some of them himself. [See Item 1961]

George H. Cushman
(See Main Catalogue, p. 99)

STORIES FROM FAMOUS BALLADS. Boston: 1859. Frontispiece drawn by Cushman, engraved on steel by S. A. Schoff. [See Item 1509]

Jacob A. Dallas
(See Main Catalogue, p. 100)

1590. M'MAKINS MODEL AMERICAN COURIER. Edited by Andrew M'Makin. Philadelphia: Saturday, December 28, 1850.

On the front page of this issue of this "Family Newspaper-Neutral in Politics and Religion" appears a very large wood engraving by Brightly after a drawing by Dallas. It shows St. Nicholas surrounded by all that is good to eat and drink, and immediately below him a representation of the Nativity, and below this a drawing of a large Christmas party. In an editorial the newspaper calls it "the most appropriate and magnificent holiday picture that has ever been issued" and one which "reflects great honor on Mr. J. A. Dallas, by whom it was designed expressly for the Courier."

THE LIGHTS AND SHADOWS OF REAL LIFE. Boston [cop. 1851]. Contains 2 illustrations signed by Dallas and engraved on wood by Waitt. [See Item 1584]

THE ILLUSTRATED NEWS. Vol. I. New York: 1853. Illustrations by Dallas will be found on pp. 105 and 120. The first is engraved by Leslie. [See Item 1836]

1591. WILD NORTHERN SCENES; OR SPORTING ADVENTURES WITH THE RIFLE AND THE ROD. By S. H. Hammond. New York: Derby & Jackson, 1857. Frontispiece and 3 other full-page illustrations by Dallas, engraved on wood by N. Orr-Co. Orig. cloth.

1592. THE FAIRIES IN AMERICA. By Spencer W. Cone. New York: Pudney & Russell, 1858.

Contains 4 full-page illustrations, including the half title, all in colors and engraved on wood by N. Orr & Co. The publisher's note on p. 4 states, "After the completion of this little volume, the literary world has been grieved at learning the sudden and unexpected demise of Mr. Dallas, the eminently gifted artist, from whose rising talent the public justly expected more matured compositions of national worth. It may perhaps be a matter of consolation to his friends and an admiring public to be informed, that the designs contained in this volume are the very last productions of his pencil, and that he has, in these illustrations, bequeathed, as it were, a memento of his Talent, inspired by a fond desire to render cheerful the countenances of childhood, upon which he was about to cast a final and loving farewell."
Orig. cloth.

MANUAL OF GEOGRAPHY. New York: 1861. The design which almost completely fills the front cover was drawn by Dallas and engraved on wood by Richardson-Cox. [See Item 1642]

WESTERN BORDER LIFE. Philadelphia [cop. 1863]. With 2 illustrations by Dallas (at pp. 166 and 350), engraved on wood by N. Orr. [See Item 1571]

Felix Octavius Carr Darley
(See Main Catalogue, p. 101)

1593. A COLLECTION OF ORIGINAL DRAWINGS IN PENCIL, PEN AND INK AND SEPIA BY F.O.C. DARLEY, commencing with those made at the early age of six years. 1826-1866.

This album, whose title-page in pencil reads as given above, contains over 90 drawings by Darley. Since Darley was born in 1822, the person who wrote the title-page was obviously confused or too wishful regarding the dates of the drawings. All seem to be beyond the capacity of a six year old, even Darley. It does begin with some of his childhood work and contains many excellent drawings of his maturity. Many are signed by him and many dated. Figs. 19 and 23.

A number of the drawings were made for illustrations. Those which so far have been identified are as follows:

p. 7—2 drawings for illustrations which appeared in *Cinderella*, Philadelphia, *ca.* 1847 (Item 592[11]).

p. 25—A drawing for the illustration on p. 37 of *Major Jones's Courtship*, Philadelphia, 1844 (Item 573).

p. 30—A drawing for the cover of *The John-Donkey*, New York and Philadelphia, 1848 (Item 1597).

p. 32—A drawing for the illustration facing p. 208 in *A New Home—Who'll Follow?*, New York, 1850 (Item 607).

p. 33—Drawings for the frontispiece and for the illustration on p. 67 of *The Big Bear of Arkansas*, Philadelphia, 1845 (Item 575).

p. 41—A drawing for the illustration facing p. 130 of *Sketches Abroad with Pen and Pencil*, New York, 1868 (Item 671).

On the whole, it is an interesting collection of Darley's drawings, illustrating many phases of his work.

1594. IN TOWN & ABOUT, OR PENCILLING, & PENNINGS. Designed & Drawn by Felix O. C. Darley. With Illustrative Descriptions by Joseph C. Neal, Author of Charcoal Sketches. Philadelphia: Godey & McMichael [cop. 1843]. No. 1.—Price, 50 cts.

This is the first part of a very scarce publication issued in 6 parts, each part containing 3 lithographs by Thos. Sinclair after drawings by Darley. The 3 drawings in the first part are "The News Boy," "The Boys that run with the Engine," and "Corner Loungers." The drawings on the title-page, also lithographed by Sinclair, are undoubtedly also by Darley.

According to Bolton (3), p. 143, this is the second book illustrated by Darley. The New York Public Library has all 18 plates while Harvard University has 12 of them. The University of Minnesota has one of the parts.

In orig. plain wrappers.

1595. GHOST STORIES; COLLECTED WITH A PARTICULAR VIEW TO COUNTERACT THE VULGAR BELIEF IN GHOSTS AND APPARITIONS. Philadelphia: Carey and Hart, 1846. With 10 illustrations by Darley, engraved on wood by G. I. White (possibly George Irwine White—see Groce and Wallace, p. 680).

This is the 1st edition of the stories contained in *Curious Stories*, Item 669, and has the same illustrations. Cont. boards, calf back.

1596. STREAKS OF SQUATTER LIFE, AND FAR-WEST SCENES. A SERIES OF HUMOROUS SKETCHES DESCRIPTIVE OF INCIDENTS AND CHARACTER IN THE WILD WEST. TO WHICH ARE ADDED OTHER MISCELLANEOUS PIECES. By "Solitaire," (John S. Robb, of St. Louis, Mo.,) Philadelphia: Carey and Hart, 1847.

This is the 1st edition and another copy of Item 594. It contains all 8 of the Darley illustrations, 1 of which (that at p. 69) was missing in Item 594. Modern boards with calf back.

1597. THE JOHN-DONKEY. New York: George Dexter . . . ; Philadelphia, G. B. Zieber & Co. . . . 1848. A bound file of this weekly comic paper containing Vol. I (January 1, 1848—June 24, 1848) complete and 7 numbers (July 1, 1848—August 12, 1848) of Vol. II. The final number was October 21, 1848, so that the last 10 numbers are missing. Harvard has a complete file of both vols., but the present file and one of similar length at the American Antiquarian Society appear to be the most complete files on record, next to that of Harvard.

Each number, in addition to other illustrations, contains a full-page cartoon and Mott, Vol. I, p. 782, expresses the opinion that Darley probably drew most of these. Darley's initial appears on the cartoon on p. 25 of Vol. I and his name on that on p. 41 of the same volume; a number of others might well be his also. They demonstrate that caricature was not his forte. Darley, however, is not the draftsman of all the cartoons for that on p. 377 of Vol. I is signed "P. Kramer, Del." and in some of the others the drawing hardly seems good enough for Darley.

Darley's name or initial also appears on the illustrations on pp. 20 and 94 of Vol. I. The first is an illustration for the serial "The Adventures of Don Key Haughty" and he may possibly have made all the drawings for that serial. The cover design for *John-Donkey* is also by Darley (see Item 1593). It is reproduced by Mott at p. 622.

Most, if not all, of the illustrations, including the cover design, were engraved on wood by C. T. Hinckley of Philadelphia [see p. 147 of the Main Catalogue] whose advertisement appears frequently throughout the periodical. He holds himself out as furnishing designs "by able artists, at reasonable rates."

While much of *John-Donkey's* humor has become dated, there is still a great deal of amusement to be found in its pages. Its editors were George G. Foster and Thomas Dunn English whose feud with E. A. Poe is well known. It is not surprising, therefore, to find many caustic comments on the writings, habits, and even morals of the author of *The Raven*. At p. 364 of Vol. I will be found the "Tale of a Gray Tadpole," an amusing take-off on Poe's "Germanesque" style, while at p. 100 Poe, who has been visited in jail by Don Key Haughty, recites to the latter a poem which he has written called "Rosaline" and, at the end, is made to say, "There! That is a *true* poem. If anybody can find any sense in that, I am much mistaken."

For a full discussion of *The John-Donkey*, see Mott, Vol. I, p. 780. Mott, Vol. I, p. 426, calls it "the best humorous periodical that had yet been attempted, labored though some of its wit appears."

Old boards with leather back and corners.

1598. STRAY SUBJECTS, ARRESTED AND BOUND OVER. BEING THE FUGITIVE OFFSPRING OF THE "OLD 'UN" [Francis A. Durivage] AND THE "YOUNG 'UN," [G. P. Burnham], THAT HAVE BEEN "LYING ROUND LOOSE," AND ARE NOW "TIED UP" FOR FAST KEEPING. Philadelphia: Carey and Hart, 1848.

This is the 1st edition of Item 604 and contains the same illustrations. On the front wrapper appears the imprint "Philadelphia, Getz, Buck & Co." Getz, Buck & Co. began the publication of some of the titles of the *Library of Humorous American Works* in 1851 (see Bolton [3], p. 153), and at that time they probably acquired some of Carey & Hart's old unbound sheets. This may account for the appearance of Getz & Buck wrappers on a Carey and Hart publication of 1848.

1599. WAGGERIES AND VAGARIES. A SERIES OF SKETCHES, HUMOROUS AND DESCRIPTIVE. By W. E. Burton. Philadelphia: Carey & Hart, 1848.

This is the 1st edition of Item 615 with the same illustrations except that the illustration which should face p. 175 is missing in this copy, as are also the wrappers. It is, however, a difficult book to find in any condition. In a cloth case.

1600. ILLUSTRATED POEMS BY MRS. L. H. SIGOURNEY. With Designs by Felix O. C. Darley, Engraved by American Artists. Philadelphia: Carey and Hart, 1849.

Contains 13 steel engravings after designs by Darley. The engravers were R. Hinshelwood, W. H. Dougal, G. H. Cushman, W. Humphrys, W. G. Armstrong, and J. Smillie. There is also a portrait of the authoress engraved by Cheney and Armstrong. This is a sumptuous volume, but the lack of inspiration in the poems is reflected in Darley's designs. Full morocco gold tooled, probably the "Turkey morocco" binding which was sold for $7.00.

1601. MONEYPENNY, OR, THE HEART OF THE WORLD. A ROMANCE OF THE PRESENT DAY. [By Cornelius Mathews.] New York: Dewitt & Davenport, 1849-1850.

Contains a frontispiece designed by Darley and engraved by T. Horton & Co. It has been torn and repaired. On the title-page is a vignette designed by Tudor Horton.

This is probably the 2nd edition (Wright I, 1833) and contains the text of both parts of the book. The title-page is dated 1849. In the copy at the New York Public Library (the only copy of the 2nd edition located by Wright) the wrappers of both parts I and II have been bound in. On the front wrapper of Part I are the words "Second Edition." On the front wrapper of Part II the name of Cornelius Mathews appears and the date 1850. Part I (Wright I, 1832) ended on p. 155 at the conclusion of Chapter XVII. In the New York Public Library's copy of the 2nd edition there are 2 pages numbered 155, one containing only the final lines of Chapter XVII, the other containing not only these lines but the commencement of Chapter XVIII, this marking the beginning of Part II. The 2 parts combined contain 270 pages.

The present copy appears to be similar to that at the New York Public Library except that the duplication of p. 155 has been avoided and only the page containing the beginning of Chapter XVIII has been retained. Also the wrappers have not been bound in and a number of advertisements at the rear of the book have been omitted. In both copies a Table of Contents covering the first 17 chapters follows the title-page while another Table of Contents, covering Chapters XVIII through XXXIII, appears at the end, printed on a leaf the verso of which contains an advertisement of *New York by Gas-Light*, a publication of Dewitt & Davenport in 1850.

All early editions of this novel appear to be scarce. Modern cloth.

1602. THE BATTLE SUMMER: BEING TRANSCRIPTS FROM PERSONAL OBSERVATION IN PARIS, DURING THE YEAR 1848. By Ik. Marvel [Donald G. Mitchell]. New York: Baker and Scribner, 1850. Frontispiece by Darley, engraved on wood by Leslie. The half title is by Wallin. Orig. cloth.

1603. REVERIES OF A BACHELOR: OR A BOOK OF THE HEART. By Ik. Marvel [Donald G. Mitchell]. New York: Baker & Scribner, 1850. 1st ed. in blue gift binding. Laid in is a slip signed by the author.

Frontispiece and half title by Darley, engraved on wood by A. Kinnersley.* In morocco-backed cloth case. With the Arthur Swann bookplate.

1604. THE WORKS OF LAURENCE STERNE, IN ONE VOLUME: WITH A LIFE OF THE AUTHOR, WRITTEN BY HIMSELF. Philadelphia: Lippincott, Grambo & Co., 1850. With 6 full-page illustrations by Darley. Those facing pp. 52, 294, and 321 are signed "Gilbert & Gihon" and this firm of wood engravers probably engraved all 6 of them. Orig. cloth, elaborately decorated in gold.

* These illustrations do not appear in the "illustrated edition" of 1852 [Item 619].

1605. THE CHILD'S PAPER. Published by The American Tract Society in New York, Boston, Philadelphia, Baltimore, Cincinnati, and New Orleans. Bound volume containing the issues of the first 4 volumes of *The Child's Paper*, January 1852–December 1855.

The magazine is full of wood engravings. Indeed, Mott, Vol. II, p. 100, states that the monthly was famous for its excellent wood engraving. Among the engravers whose work will be found in these first 4 volumes are P. Annin, B. F. Childs, E. J. Whitney, A. Kinnersley, Peckham & Bookhout, Ward, E. D. Hayes, Bobbett & Edmonds, Lossing-Barritt, W. Howland, Bogert, Felter, and J. Minton. Linton in his *History of Wood-Engraving in America*, Boston, 1882, at p. 21, reproduces one of Whitney's and one of Annin's engravings, pointing out (p. 24) that they show a "richer and bolder handling than usual."

When it comes to the illustrators, however, only a few names appear and it is probable that many of the cuts were re-engraved from foreign publications. There are 2 illustrations signed by Darley, viz.: p. 25 of Vol. I and p. 37 of Vol. III, both engraved by Childs. The illustration depicting the capture of André on p. 41 of Vol. II looks very much like a Darley but is not signed by him.

J. Oertel has 3 drawings, S. Wallin 2 drawings, and Herrick, Wade, E. Purcell, Coffin, and T.H.M. (probably T. H. Matteson) 1 each. Orig. cloth.

1606. HUMORISTISCH-SATYRISCHER VOLKS-CALENDER FÜR DIE VEREINIGTEN STAATEN AUF DAS JAHR 1853. Philadelphia: King und Baird [1852].

Contains 12 wood engravings on which Darley's name appears as draftsman. 11 of these bear the names of Leslie & Traver, as engravers, and 1 is signed by Childs & Jocelyn. All of these illustrations are to be found in *Life in the South* by C. H. Wiley, Item 618 in the Main Catalogue. In the book the engravings illustrate the story, while in the almanac they are used for various purposes.

This almanac is bound with *Lustiger Illustrirter Almanach des New Yorker Humorist für 1859*, published in New York by Max Cohnheim and Otto Brethauer, which contains a number of unsigned cartoons and other illustrations, and with *Thomas'scher Unterhaltungs-Calender für das Jahr 1857*, published in Philadelphia by F. W. Thomas, which contains a few unsigned illustrations. Cont. boards with leather spine and corners.

1607. CHRONICLES OF PINEVILLE: EMBRACING SKETCHES OF GEORGIA SCENES, IN-CIDENTS, AND CHARACTERS. By the Author of "Major Jones's Courtship" [William Tappan Thompson]. Philadelphia: Getz, Buck & Co., 1853. With the same illustrations which appeared in the 1st edition (Item 577).

The cut on the title-page is repeated on the front wrapper. This may be the 2nd Getz-Buck edition (see Bolton [3], p. 158). Orig. pictorial wrappers.

THE ILLUSTRATED NEWS. Vol. I. New York: 1853. On p. 144 is a full-page illustration by Darley, engraved by Leslie. [See Item 1836]

1608. THE NEW ORLEANS SKETCH BOOK. By "Stahl" [George M. Wharton]. Philadelphia: A. Hart, late Carey & Hart, 1853.

Contains 4 illustrations, unsigned by the draftsman, but which resemble Darley's work and are probably by him. On the front wrapper, which was lithographed by T. Sinclair and contains some amusing figures, appear the words "Library of Humorous American Works, with Illustrations by Darley." Orig. wrappers.

Wright II (2692) locates 2 copies, one at the Huntington Library and the other at the Library of Congress. There is, however, a copy in the Barrett collection at the University of Virginia, and a copy at the American Antiquarian Society. Of these 4 copies only the Barrett copy is in original wrappers.

1609. THE PRETTY PLATE. By John Vincent, Esq. [Jedediah Vincent Huntington]. Fourth thousand. New York: Redfield, 1853. It was first published in 1852.

Contains 5 illustrations which the title-page states are by Darley. The frontispiece, half title, and the illustration facing p. 46 were engraved on wood by Whitney & Annin; those facing pp. 54 and 101 were engraved on wood by Richardson-Cox. Orig. cloth. Presented by Howard Mott.

1610. THE HIVE OF "THE BEE-HUNTER," A REPOSITORY OF SKETCHES, INCLUDING PECULIAR AMERICAN CHARACTER, SCENERY, AND RURAL SPORTS. By T[homas] B[angs] Thorpe, of Louisiana. New-York: D. Appleton and Company . . . 1854.

Contains 9 illustrations engraved on wood by Whitney, Jocelyn & Annin (2), Brightly (2), and R. S. Gilbert (2), the names of the engravers of the others not appearing. 5 of them (pp. 47, 66, 153, 220, and 246) appeared originally in the 1st edition of *The Mysteries of the Backwoods*, Philadelphia, 1846 (Item 585). 4 of these 5 carry Darley's name and, according to the title-page of *The Mysteries of the Backwoods*, all are by Darley. There were 6 illustrations in the latter book but one of them (at p. 128) was not used in *The Hive of the Bee-Hunter*. The remaining 4 illustrations in *The Hive of the Bee-Hunter* may also be by Darley but they are unsigned. Orig. cloth.

According to Wright II (2495) 14 of the sketches in this book had been previously published. The rest, the titles of which Wright gives, are new.

MRS. PARTINGTON'S CARPET-BAG OF FUN. New York: 1854. 2 illustrations by Darley on pp. 79 and 265. [See Item 1840]

1611. WOODCRAFT OR HAWKS ABOUT THE DOVECOTE. A STORY OF THE SOUTH AT THE CLOSE OF THE REVOLUTION. By W. Gilmore Simms, Esq. New and Revised Edition. New York: Redfield, 1854. See Wright II (2231).

The frontispiece and half title, while unsigned by the draftsman, are undoubtedly after Darley and are attributed to him in the advertisements at the rear of the book. They are engraved on wood by Whitney-Jocelyn-Annin.

The first recorded appearance of this novel appears to have been in 1852 under the title of *The Sword and the Distaff; or, "Fair, Fat and Forty"* (see Wright II, 2230), which was not illustrated. Orig. cloth.

ALBUM OF WOOD ENGRAVINGS by John Andrew, etc. [*ca.* 1855-1875]. 5 engravings after Darley. [See Item 1472(2)]

THE TURKISH SPIES. Baltimore . . . and Buffalo: 1855. The illustrations on pp. 172 and 196 carry Darley's name. [See Item 1721]

1612. CONFESSIONS OR THE BLIND HEART. A DOMESTIC STORY. By W. Gilmore Simms, Esq. New and revised edition. New York: Redfield, 1856. Frontispiece and half title engraved on wood by Whitney & Jocelyn, after designs by Darley. The 1st edition of this book was published by Lea and Blanchard in Philadelphia in 1841 (Wright I, 2415), but without illustrations. Orig. cloth.

1613. PETER PLODDY, AND OTHER ODDITIES. By Joseph C. Neal. Philadelphia: T. B. Peterson, 102 Chestnut Street [cop. 1856]. This is another copy of Item 574 (2) but in the original pictorial wrappers. Darley's illustration which is reproduced in the Main Catalogue in Fig. 54 appears on the front wrapper of this edition.

1614. VASCONSELOS. A ROMANCE OF THE NEW WORLD. By W. Gilmore Simms, Esq. New York: Redfield, 1857. The frontispiece and half title are engraved on wood by Whitney-Jocelyn after designs by Darley. The 1st edition of this book was published by Redfield in 1853 (Wright II, 2232), but without illustrations. Orig. cloth.

1615. THE BIG BEAR OF ARKANSAS, AND OTHER SKETCHES, ILLUSTRATIVE OF CHARACTERS AND INCIDENTS IN THE SOUTH AND SOUTH-WEST. Edited by William T. Porter. Philadelphia: T. B. Peterson and Brothers, 306 Chestnut Street [after 1858]. A late Peterson edition with the same illustrations as in Item 575. The blocks, however, have probably been recut. Orig. pictorial wrappers, from the Harry T. Peters collection. In half morocco case with Items 635(2), 645(2), and 1623.

MY SHOOTING BOX: Philadelphia [*ca.* 1859?]. 2 of Peterson's editions of *My Shooting Box*, each of which contains the 2 Darley illustrations found in Item 822. The blocks, however, appear to have been re-engraved. Each is signed by Van Ingen as the engraver and both Darley's name and Herrick's name have disappeared. [See Item 1707]

1616. SAUL SABBERDAY: OR, THE IDIOT SPY. A TALE OF THE MEN AND DEEDS OF '76. By Ned Buntline [Edward Zane Carroll Judson]. New York: Frederic A. Brady [n.d.]. Copyrighted by Cauldwell, Southworth & Whitney in 1860. Wright II (1447) records a similar edition but with the copyright notice dated 1858.

Contains 5 full-page illustrations unsigned by either draftsman or wood engraver. In the advertisements at the end of *The Grossbeak Mansion* (Item 1620) Brady lists *Saul Sabberday* and says that it is illustrated "with several full-page engravings by Darley." If Darley was really the draftsman, he must have been having an off-day, as the drawings have very little merit. Modern cloth.

1617. DARLEY'S COOPER VIGNETTES. New York: W. A. Townsend and Company [*ca.* 1861]. 8 vols.

This is a reissue, on India paper backed on French Plate Paper, of the 64 steel engravings made for the 32-volume set of the novels of J. Fenimore Cooper published by W. A. Townsend and Company in 1859-1861 (see Item 647). 62 of these steel engravings were after drawings by Darley. The prospectus, signed by W. A. Townsend and Company, which appears in the first volume, sings Darley's praises and claims that his Cooper drawings "for dramatic, picturesque and vivid interest, have perhaps no superiors in modern art." It goes on to point out that the bank-note system of this country had developed a style of art superior to anything which European burins afforded, a style marked by delicacy, clearness, precision, and great mechanical beauty of line, but too laborious and costly for the ordinary purposes of the publisher. "The Cooper vignettes, however, have been engraved in this style, being the first attempt, we believe, to introduce the deep cutting and solid lining of a bank-note die into book-work."

The 64 plates were issued in 8 folios at $3.00 each and the proofs were limited to 500 impressions. Each proof was accompanied with descriptive letter-press and at the foot of the letter-press appeared one of the small wood engravings after Darley which had been used in the Townsend edition of Cooper's works.

At the end of the eighth and last volume appears a title-page reading "The Cooper Vignettes. From Drawings by F.O.C. Darley. India Proofs Before Letter. New York: James G. Gregory, (Successor to W. A. Townsend & Co.,) 1862," and on the verso of this title-page appears a copyright notice in Gregory's name, dated 1861. There follows a "Publisher's Preface," unsigned but dated 1861, in which it is stated that, as far back as 1856, the publisher had arranged with Darley for a series of 62 drawings to illustrate Cooper's novels. "The acknowledged superiority which these plates possess over everything of the kind hitherto published in this country . . . induced the publisher to undertake the issue of a series of Artist's Folios, containing impressions on 'India before letter' from each of the plates . . . the publisher believes he does not claim too much when with unaffected pride he presents it to the American public as a monument of national art." Finally there is a complete list of the plates and of the engravers. This title-page, "Publisher's Preface," and list of plates all appear in Gregory's one-volume edition of *The Cooper Vignettes* [Item 656].

It seems probable that Townsend originated the idea of the 8 folios of proofs and that when, in about 1861, Gregory succeeded Townsend he completed the enterprise and then went on to publish the one-volume edition of 1862. It would be interesting to know whether, in order to do so, he printed more than 500 proofs of the plates.

The 8 vols. are in orig. boards with one of Darley's drawings on the front covers.

1618. HILLIARE HENDERSON; OR, THE SECRET REVEALED. AN ANTECEDENT TO "THE DEATH MYSTERY." By Ned Buntline [Edward Zane Carroll Judson]. New York: Frederic A. Brady [cop. by Cauldwell, Southworth & Whitney, 1861].

Contains 7 full-page illustrations which, while signed by neither draftsman nor engraver, are stated on the front wrapper to be by Darley. That on p. 9 is repeated on the front wrapper. On the recto of the back wrapper is an advertisement of *Whitelaw; or, Nattie of the Lake Shore*,

by J. H. Robinson, with illustrations by Darley, one of the illustrations being shown.

According to Albert Johannsen in his *The House of Beadle and Adams*, Oklahoma [1950], Vol. II, pp. 169 and 185, this novel was published in *The New York Mercury* as a serial beginning June 15, 1861, was republished in 1871 as No. 22 of "Frank Starr's Fifteen Cent Illustrated Novels" under the title of *The Planter's Ward; or, A Woman's Love and a Woman's Hate*, and was again reprinted in 1877 as No. 27 of "Cheap Edition of Popular Authors" under the title of *A Fiery Heart; or, A Woman's Love and a Woman's Hate*. Orig. wrappers.

Wright II (1426) locates copies at Columbia University and the Library of Congress, but there is also a copy at the American Antiquarian Society. Wright dates the book [1865], this being the year in which the Library of Congress copy was deposited for copyright.

1619. LARGE BROADSIDE OR POSTER issued by Cauldwell, Southworth & Whitney, the Proprietors of *The New York Mercury*, announcing that the publication of *Catholina or The Niche in the Wall*, a Tale of Louisiana, by Dr. J. H. Robinson, would be commenced in *The New York Mercury* for Saturday, January 5, 1861, and stating that "The magic realms of romance never produced a tale so attractive in every particular." A substantial portion of the poster is taken up by a very large wood engraving by Shugg which is unsigned by the draftsman. The poster states that Felix O. C. Darley's graphic pencil will illustrate its (*The New York Mercury's*) tales and romances and this unusually large illustration may be his work. Or possibly J. H. Howard was the draftsman. [See Items 1753 and 1754]

Catholina was published by Brady. Wright II (2067) locates only 1 copy, that at Yale.

1620. THE GROSSBEAK MANSION. A MYSTERY OF NEW YORK. By Ned Buntline [Edward Zane Carroll Judson]. New York; Frederic A. Brady [n.d.]. Copyrighted by Cauldwell, Southworth & Whitney in 1862. Wright II (1425), who locates only 2 other copies of this book, those at the American Antiquarian Society and the Henry E. Huntington Library.

Contains 7 full-page illustrations, unsigned by either draftsman or wood engraver. In the advertisements at the end, under the heading "Brady's Celebrated 'Mercury' Stories," it is stated that this book is illustrated "with eight full page engravings by Darley." As the wrappers are missing in this copy, it would be natural to suppose that a frontispiece is also missing. However, both the American Antiquarian Society's copy and that at the Huntington Library lack frontispieces, although both are in the original wrappers. 1 of the 7 illustrations is repeated on the front wrapper and this may constitute the eighth illustration. A photostat of the front wrapper from the Huntington copy is laid in. Modern cloth.

1621. MOUNTAIN MAX; OR, NICK WHIFFLES ON THE BORDER. A TALE OF THE BUSHWHACKERS IN MISSOURI. By Dr. J. H. Robinson. New York: Frederic A. Brady [cop. 1862 by Cauldwell, Southworth & Whitney]. With 6 full-page illustrations which the front wrapper states are by Darley and which do resemble his work. That on p. 33 is repeated on the front wrapper.

Wright II (2075) locates only the Library of Congress copy but the writer is informed that there is a copy at Yale also. According to Albert Johannsen in his *The House of Beadle and Adams*, Oklahoma [1950], Vol. I, p. 131, this novel was published by Cauldwell, Southworth & Whitney in 1859 and began to run in *The New York Mercury* in October 1862. It was republished in the Second Series of *American Tales* in 1869.

Orig. wrappers.

1622. (1) STORIES OF THE SEA: BEING NARRATIVES OF ADVENTURE, SELECTED FROM THE "SEA TALES." By James Fenimore Cooper. A Book for Boys. New York: James G. Gregory, 1863. Contains 4 full-page illustrations by Darley, engraved on wood by N-Orr Co.

This was an attempt to condense some of the more stirring incidents of Cooper's *Tales of the Sea*, viz., *The Red Rover*, *The Water-Witch*, *The Pilot*, *Afloat and Ashore*, *Miles Wallingford*, and *The Crater*. A note states: "The sketches, with the exception of the introductory paragraphs, are given in the author's own language, but necessarily condensed."

Orig. blue cloth.

(2) STORIES OF THE WOODS; OR, ADVENTURES OF LEATHER-STOCKING SELECTED FROM THE "LEATHER-STOCKING TALES," By James Fenimore Cooper. A Book for Boys. New York: James G. Gregory, 1863. Contains 4 full-page illustrations by Darley, engraved on wood by N-Orr Co.

This is a companion volume to (1) above and attempts to do for the *Leather-stocking Tales* what (1) does for the *Sea Tales*. The volumes are not identically bound. This is in its original green cloth and, while the design stamped in gold on its spine is the same as that on the spine of (1), the design on the front cover is different.

A presentation copy from C. G. Leland to J. Milton Colton, Christmas 1864.

1623. MYSTERIES OF THE BACKWOODS. INCLUDING CHARACTER, SCENERY AND RURAL SPORTS. By T. B. Thorpe, Esq. . . . Philadelphia: T. B. Peterson & Brothers, 306 Chestnut Street [cop. 1865].

A late Peterson edition with the same illustrations as in Item 585, except that the illustration at p. 128 in Item 585 is lacking. In this case the original blocks appear to have been used and it is possible that this particular block had been lost. There is nothing to indicate that the illustration in question has been removed from this copy. Orig. pictorial wrappers, from the Harry T. Peters collection. In half morocco case with Items 635(2), 645(2), and 1615.

1624. (1) EVANGELINE, A TALE OF ACADIE. By Henry W. Longfellow. Boston: Ticknor and Fields, 1867. Contains 8 full-page illustrations, together with vignettes on the title-page and the last page, by Darley, engraved on wood by A. V. S. Anthony. Orig. cloth. Fig. 22.

(2) Pencil drawing by Darley which appears to be a preliminary sketch for his illustration, appearing at p. 93 of (1) above. Fig. 21.

> Then in his place, at the prow of the boat, rose one of the oarsmen,
> And, as a signal sound, if others like them peradventure
> Sailed on those gloomy and midnight streams, blew a blast on his bugle.

1625. THEATRICAL MANAGEMENT IN THE WEST AND SOUTH FOR THIRTY YEARS. INTERSPERSED WITH ANECDOTICAL SKETCHES: Autobiographically given by Sol. Smith [Solomon Franklin Smith], Retired Actor. New York: Harper & Brothers, 1868.

This appears to be a reissue of *The Theatrical Apprenticeship and Anecdotical Recollections of Sol. Smith*, Philadelphia, 1846 (Item 588[1]), with many changes and much new material. It contains the same 8 illustrations by Darley,* together with 7 additional illustrations, 4 by A. R. Waud, 2 unsigned and 1 signed C.B. (probably C. G. Bush). ¾ cont. calf, with an autograph inscription reading "To Hon. Daniel Dougherty from his Friend & Admirer, S.S. Smith." From the estate of Henry N. Paul.

1626. A WASH DRAWING showing an old man seated on a rocky ledge, with a young man standing behind him, looking over water toward

* In Item 588(1) it is stated that only 1 of these 8 illustrations was engraved by Anderson. As a matter of fact he engraved 2 of them. In the illustration facing p. 18 in Item 588(1) the initials "AA" can hardly be seen but they are clear on the impression of this engraving on p. 15 of Item 1625.

a setting sun. It is signed "F.O.C. Darley fecit." It is a good example of Darley's work and probably was done sometime in the 1860s.

SPECIMEN PAGES AND ILLUSTRATIONS FROM APPLETONS' JOURNAL. [New York: 1870.] With a folding wood engraving of "The Seasons" after a drawing by Darley, engraved by Bogert, which had accompanied the number of the *Journal* for June 26, 1869. [See Item 1731]

1627. THE ILLUSTRATED CHRISTIAN WEEKLY. Vol. I complete, beginning with the number for April 15, 1871, and ending with the number for December 30, 1871, including the Christmas supplement. It was published in New York by the American Tract Society and Lyman Abbott was the editor.

A note in the first number says "Messrs. F.O.C. Darley, H.W. Herrick, R.S. Gifford, William Hart, T.P. Rossiter, D. J. Woodward, F.A. Chapman, Aug. Will, and other eminent artists have already furnished illustrations or have promised so to do." The work of only a few of these appear in Vol. I, but the publication of *The Weekly* continued for several years.

Illustrations by Darley will be found on pp. 24, 41, 65, 177, 209, 253, and 272. The wood engravers whose names appear are Kinnersley, E.D. Hayes, Filmer, and Henry Linton. Orig. boards with leather back.

1628. OLDTOWN FIRESIDE STORIES. By Harriet Beecher Stowe. Boston: James R. Osgood & Company, 1872. Wright II (2395).

Contains 12 full-page illustrations, the list of illustrations stating that the drawings are "by F.O.C. Darley, Augustus Hoppin, and John J. Harley." All are unsigned except the frontispiece which bears Darley's name. Bolton(3), at p. 176, states that the book contains 1 wood engraving after Darley and 11 process blocks after Hoppin and Harley. Orig. cloth.

1629. THE PRAIRIE. A TALE. By J. Fenimore Cooper. New York: D. Appleton and Company, 1872, 8 illustrations by Darley, including the half title which is repeated on the front wrapper. 3 are engraved on wood by W. H. Morse and 1 bears what appears to be the name of Harley. The rest are unsigned. Orig. wrappers.

1630. CHRISTMAS EVE AND CHRISTMAS DAY. TEN CHRISTMAS STORIES. By Edward E. Hale. Boston: Roberts Brothers, 1873. Wright II (1051). With a frontispiece by Darley. Orig. cloth.

1631. THE PILOT: A TALE OF THE SEA. By J. Fenimore Cooper. New York: D. Appleton and Company, 1873.

Contains 8 illustrations by Darley. These are the same illustrations as those in Item 681. The illustration on the half title, which is repeated on the front cover, bears W. H. Morse's initials as the engraver. In the impression of this illustration in Item 681 these initials were not decipherable and hence the engraving was not attributed to Morse. Orig. wrappers.

1632. THE VENERABLE MAYHEWS AND THE ABORIGINAL INDIANS OF MARTHA'S VINEYARD. Condensed from Rev. Experience Mayhew's History Printed in London in 1727, and Brought Down to the Present Century. By William A. Hallock, D.D. New York: American Tract Society [cop. 1874]. With a wood engraved frontispiece after Darley, showing a redskin in Darley's best Indian style.

A note on the copyright page says "The cost of stereotyping and printing this volume . . . was borne by a donation from Moses Allen and William A. Hallock, who, in 1825, were the original Treasurer and Corresponding Secretary of the American Tract Society, and in 1874 were its only surviving founders." Orig. cloth.

PIONEERS IN THE SETTLEMENT OF AMERICA. Boston: 1876-1877. 7 of the wood engravings bear Darley's name as draftsman (see plates opposite pp. 402 and 456 in Vol. I, and opposite pp. 274, 320, 354, 368, and 394 in Vol. II). According to Bolton (2), there are 9 Darleys in all, and, as others than those listed above might well be by him, Bolton is no doubt correct. [See Item 1922]

ADIRONDACK TALES. Boston: 1877. Contains 8 full-page illustrations which are stated to be designed by Darley and Merrill. 4 are signed by Merrill and the rest are unsigned. None resemble Darley's work. [See Item 1857]

POSTER advertising for agents to sell *Sunlight and Shadow* by John B. Gough. Hartford [*ca.* 1881]. 1 illustration by Darley, engraved on wood by John Foster, which will be found at p. 250 of *Sunlight and Shadow*. [See Item 1985]

KALOOLAH. New York: 1887. With 1 illustration by Darley. [See Item 1672]

Alexander Jackson Davis
1803-1892

Davis, who became a well-known architect, early showed a talent for drawing and in the decade of the 1820s made a series of drawings of important buildings in New York City and elsewhere. In 1827 or 1828 he drew directly on the stone his famous view of the State House in Boston. Pendleton was the lithographer and this lithograph is now considered the best representation of the State House when it was first built. In 1829 Davis entered into partnership with the architect, Ithiel Town. The firm of Town & Davis designed many buildings including 4 State Capitols, viz.: Indiana, North Carolina, Illinois, and Ohio. Indeed, Davis at one time claimed to have designed more buildings than any other living American architect. See D.A.B., Vol. V, p. 103; Dunlap, Vol. III, p. 210.

THE CABINET OF INSTRUCTION, LITERATURE, AND AMUSEMENT. New-York: 1829. In No. 15 is a drawing by Davis of Erasmus Hall, engraved on wood by Alexander Anderson. Erasmus Hall was an Academy, situated at Flatbush, Long Island and, as the article in *The Cabinet* states, its Principal, Mr. J. W. Kellogg, was eminently qualified to instruct youth "in all the branches of a useful, classical, and ornamental education." [See Item 1441]

1633. TWO PROOFS OF A WOOD ENGRAVING by A. J. Mason of the Capitol at Washington after a drawing by Davis. The first, and probably earlier one, has printed under it simply the words "Capitol, Washington." The other proof, in addition to these words, has at the left side the words "Engraved by Mason" and on the right the words "from a sketch by Davis, N.Y." The engraving was probably made in the early 1830s, as Mason did not come to this country until December 1829. The sketch might have been made earlier, at a time when Davis was employed in making drawings of important buildings.

WOOD ENGRAVING by Alexander Anderson of the "Mansion of Belmead," after a drawing by Davis. Anderson's receipt of payment for the engraving is dated 1850. [See Item 1462]

Benjamin H. Day, Jr.
(See Main Catalogue, p. 116)

VANITY FAIR. Vols. 1-6. New York: 1859-1862. For possible illustrations by Day in this magazine, see Item 1933.

WIDOW SPRIGGINS, MARY ELMER, AND OTHER SKETCHES. New York: 1867. With 2 full-page illustrations at pp. 217 and 265 signed "B.D." which may be the work of Day. [See Item 1756]

1634. A WOMAN IN ARMOR. By Mary Hartwell [Mrs. Mary (Hartwell) Catherwood]. New York: G. W. Carleton & Co. . . . 1875. With 6 full-page illustrations by Day. Wright II (476).

In addition to *A Woman in Armor*, the book contains 2 short stories, viz., "Old Gargoyle" (pp. [169]-187 and "The Man Who 'Hadn't Time'" (pp. [191]-196). This is Mrs. Catherwood's first novel (see B.A.L. 2934A). Orig. cloth.

GUARDING THE MAILS. Hartford: 1876. The frontispiece is by Day and all the illustrations in Chapter 2 (excepting the first illustration) and in Chapters 20 and 22 are either signed by Day or seem clearly to be his work. [See Item 1998]

Nathaniel Dearborn
(See Main Catalogue, p. 116)

1635. A MONUMENT OF PARENTAL AFFECTION, TO A DEAR AND ONLY SON. [By Joshua Gilpin.] Boston: Lincoln & Edmands, 1812. Fig. 25.

The frontispiece, a wood engraving showing the father mourning over the grave of his son with a weeping willow behind him and the sexton, spade in hand, ready to fill in the grave, is signed "N.D." This is the earliest work of Dearborn which the writer has seen and tends to corroborate Dearborn's claim to have commenced wood engraving about 1811. The original wrappers are lacking.

1636. A BRIEF ACCOUNT OF THE HAPPY DEATH OF MARY ANN CLAP, DAUGHTER OF MR. JESSE AND MRS. BETSY CLAP, WHO DIED JULY 15, 1816, IN THE ELEVENTH YEAR OF HER AGE; EXHIBITING AN EXAMPLE OF MEEKNESS AND SUBMISSION; FURNISHING THE CLEAREST EVIDENCE OF EARLY PIETY; AND IMPORTING THE SWEETEST CONSOLATION TO PIOUS FRIENDS. By Joshua Bates, A.M., Pastor of the First Church in Dedham. Fourth Edition. Boston: Printed by Nathaniel Coverly, Jr., 1816. Welch gives a 3rd and 5th edition printed in Boston (67.3 and 67.5), but no 4th edition.

With a full-page frontispiece, engraved on wood, showing Mary Ann Clap in one of her most pious moments. It is signed "N.D." and is repeated on the front wrapper. The back wrapper is missing. The title-page of this copy is torn. Accompanying it is another copy of the same book with the title-page intact but lacking both wrappers.

1637. THE HISTORY OF SINDBAD THE SAILOR: CONTAINING AN ACCOUNT OF HIS SEVERAL SURPRISING VOYAGES AND MIRACULOUS ESCAPES. Boston: J. P. Clark, 1829.

Contains 7 full-page wood engravings. Those

facing pp. 64, 73, and 88 are signed "N.D." and probably all are the work of Dearborn. Orig. boards, rebacked. Presented by Sinclair H. Hitchings.

1638. HISTORY OF THE DISCOVERY OF AMERICA, OF THE LANDING OF OUR FORE-FATHERS, AT PLYMOUTH, AND OF THEIR MOST REMARKABLE ENGAGEMENTS WITH THE INDI-ANS IN NEW-ENGLAND . . . TO WHICH IS AN-NEXED THE PARTICULARS OF ALMOST EVERY IMPORTANT ENGAGEMENT WITH THE SAVAGES AT THE WESTWARD TO THE PRESENT DAY. IN-CLUDING THE DEFEAT OF GENERALS BRAD-DOCK, HARMER AND ST. CLAIR, BY THE IN-DIANS AT THE WESTWARD; THE CREEK AND SEMINOLE WAR, &C. By Henry Trumbull. Bos-ton: George Clark, 1836.

This is a later edition of Item 446. The fold-ing wood-engraved frontispiece is now signed "N. Dearborn Sc." although it is clearly copied, with a number of details altered, from the earlier cut by Bowen. This is also true of the cut at p. 225, showing "Milly Francis entreating her Father to spare the life of an American Cap-tive," which is now signed "N.D." The cut of King Philip at p. 69 is unsigned but has been recut from Bowen's earlier portrait which is found in Item 446. The new cut is probably by Dearborn.

The earliest edition which the writer has seen in which the folding frontispiece bears Dear-born's name is Clark's edition of 1833, but in that edition the other 2 cuts still carry Bowen's initials. This arrangement is also found in Clark's 1835 edition. Clark's 1836 edition ap-pears to be the first in which Bowen's 3 cuts have all disappeared and been replaced by Dear-born's cuts.

Orig. boards, cloth back. On the front cover appears the cut of King Philip, while on the back cover appears Dearborn's "Milly Francis" cut.

MOTHER GOOSE'S MELODIES. Boston [ca. 1845]. Contains 1 wood engraving by Dearborn (p. 26) which had previously appeared in Item 690. [See Item 1459(1)]

1639. QUOTATIONS OF HUMOR, WIT AND WISDOM. Boston: Printed and Published by Nathaniel Dearborn, 1849.

Contains a number of interesting wood en-gravings, none of which are signed. As the book was copyrighted, printed, and published by Dearborn and was probably compiled by him as well, it is hard to resist the conclusion that he must have had a hand in at least some of the engravings, although none of them can be said to be clearly in his style. Orig. cloth.

M.F.H. DeHaas
(See Main Catalogue, p. 117)

THE BODLEYS TELLING STORIES. New York: 1878. On p. 83 is an illustration by De Haas, engraved on wood by John Andrew, which first appeared on p. 79 of Vol. I of *The River-side Magazine for Young People* (Item 958). [See Item 1732]

George T. Devereux
(See Main Catalogue, p. 118)

THE ILLUSTRATED NEWS. Vol. I. New York: 1853. A drawing by Devereux of Chestnut Street, Philadelphia, appears on p. 377. [See Item 1836]

THE NEW YORK JOURNAL. Vols. I and II. New York: 1853-1854. Devereux has 3 illus-trations in Vol. I (pp. 105, 129, and 169), en-graved on wood by N. Orr (1) and S. H. Wal-lin (2). [See Item 1838]

1640. BOADICEA; THE MORMON WIFE. LIFE-SCENES IN UTAH. Edited by Alfreda Eva Bell. Baltimore, Philadelphia, New York, and Buffalo: Arthur R. Orton [cop. 1855].

The frontispiece is signed "Devereux Sc." and no doubt other wood engravings in this lavishly illustrated book are also his. Whether he was also the designer it would be difficult to say. Orig. wrappers.

Wright II (253) locates only 2 copies of the book, those at the Newberry Library and Yale. Other copies, however, will now be found at the Huntington Library (2 copies), the University of Virginia, and the University of Utah.

On the front wrapper of the present copy under the title and a portrait of a woman, prob-ably intended to represent the Mormon wife, appears the name of M. A. Milliette, "Succes-sor to A. R. Orton." At the back are 3 pages numbered 98, 99, and 100 (the verso of p. 100 being blank) on which are printed advertise-ments of books just published, or about to be published, by Arthur R. Orton, viz., *Ellen Irv-ing, The Russian Sisters,* and *The Three Sisters.* On the back wrapper (its recto is blank) ap-pears an advertisement for 1000 agents "to cir-culate my Publications," signed by M. A. Mil-liette, "Successor to Arthur R. Orton." The ad-dress he gives is 116 Chestnut Street, Philadel-phia, Pa., and 161 Main Street, Buffalo, N.Y.

On one of the copies at Huntington the front wrapper is similar except that the words "pub-lished by Arthur Orton" appear in the place of Milliette's name. This Huntington copy, therefore, would seem to be the earliest issue recorded.

The other copy at Huntington and the copy at Yale seem to be identical with the present copy except that p. 100 is not numbered and contains an advertisement of *The Fireman's Bride*, published by M. A. Milliette, 320 Chestnut Street. This book was actually published by Milliette in 1858 (Wright II, 2050). Milliette's name appears in the Philadelphia directory in 1857, 1858, 1859, and 1860 at 320 Chestnut Street and then disappears. The 116 Chestnut Street address is never given. Arthur R. Orton's name appears only in 1856. The name of A. Elizabeth Orton appears in 1857 and 1858 and "Anne E. Orton—wid. of Arthur R." in 1860. It seems likely that Orton died about 1856 or 1857, that Milliette shortly thereafter succeeded him and, after spending a short time at 116 Chestnut Street, moved to 320 Chestnut Street. The present copy of *Boadicea* would, therefore, seem to be of slightly earlier issue than the second Huntington copy and the Yale copy.

The copy of *Boadicea* at the University of Utah lacks the wrappers, but contains advertisements of the same 3 Orton Publications as appear in the present copy. In addition the Utah copy has a p. 102 containing an advertisement of *The Turkish Spies*, a book published by Orton in 1855 (Item 1721). On the back of this page is an advertisement of *The Camden Boat Tragedy* "published by M. A. Milliette," a book which is not given in Wright. Milliette's address nowhere appears. It is difficult, therefore, to say whether this copy comes before or after the second Huntington and Yale copies.

The copies of *Boadicea* at the Newberry Library and Virginia lack wrappers and advertisements.

THE WEEKLY NOVELETTE. Boston: 1857-1862. Illustrations signed "Devereux Del" will be found in Vol. II, pp. 160 and 361; Vol. III, pp. 296, 297, and 304; Vol. IV, p. 176; and Vol. VIII, pp. 304 and 384. The engravers whose names appear are W. J. Baker and F. Hedge. [See Item 1545]

GLEASON'S WEEKLY LINE-OF-BATTLE SHIP. Boston: 1859. With 3 illustrations by Devereux in the numbers for April 2, April 16, and December 17, the last of which was engraved on wood by Major. [See Item 1961]

THE NOVELETTE. Boston: 186?. Novelette No. 90 contains an illustration by Devereux. [See No. 7 of Item 1546]

Carl Emil Doepler
(See Main Catalogue, p. 119)

THE ILLUSTRATED NEWS. Vol. I. New York: 1853. Drawings by Doepler of the Capitol and the White House at Washington appear on pp. 32 and 172. [See Item 1836]

A PICTORIAL HISTORY OF THE UNITED STATES. New York: [cop. 1854]. Frontispiece by Doepler, engraved on wood by Lossing-Barritt. [See Item 1801]

1641. THE SAINT AND THE SINNER. A TALE, NOT STRANGER THAN TRUE. New York: E. N. Grossman, 1854. With a frontispiece by Doepler, engraved on wood by Lossing-Barritt. An interesting poem of Victorian vintage. Orig. decorated boards.

ALBUM OF WOOD ENGRAVINGS by John Andrew, etc. [*ca.* 1855-1865]. Several engravings after Doepler. These illustrations appeared in Abbot's *Rollo on the Rhine*. [See Item 1472(1)]

1642. MANUAL OF GEOGRAPHY; COMBINED WITH HISTORY AND ASTRONOMY ... By James Monteith. Revised edition. New York: A. S. Barnes & Burr, 1861.

Contains numerous wood engravings. 11 of these bear Doepler's name or initials as draftsman (pp. 8, 20, 40, 44, 54, 55, 61, 71, 77, 84, and 88). They are engraved by Graff (2), Richardson-Cox (4), and J. W. Orr (3), the name of the engraver not appearing on the other 2. There are also illustrations by Herrick, W. Roberts, J. Wells, and Wilson. Many of the illustrations are unsigned by the illustrator. The design on the front cover is by Dallas.

In addition to the engravers named above, the work of C. Edmonds, Felter, and Jocelyn & Purcell will be found. Orig. boards.

MILLER'S NEW YORK AS IT IS. New York: 1862. View of the Custom House by Doepler (p. 32), engraved on wood by J. W. Orr. [See Item 1971]

J. Downes
(See Main Catalogue, p. 120)

TALES OF TRAVELS WEST OF THE MISSISSIPPI. Boston: 1830. 6 of the wood engravings bear Downes' initials (pp. 16, 44, 46, 64, 86, and 126). [See Item 1538]

1643. THE AMERICAN COMIC ALMANAC [for] 1835 WITH WHIMS, SCRAPS AND ODDITIES. Boston: Sold by Allen & Co. .... Published by Charles Ellms, Agent [1834]. Fig. 26.

Contains numerous wood engravings. Those on pp. 7, 8, 12, 17, and 30 are signed with Downes' name or initials. The cut on p. 8 is a graphic representation of Cape Cod and Gay Head. Sewed.

THE PEOPLE'S MAGAZINE. Vol. I. Boston: 1834. With 1 wood engraving signed "J.D." [See Item 1785]

1644. THE TEMPERANCE FAMILY ALMANAC FOR THE YEAR OF OUR LORD 1835 . . . Boston: Russell, Odiorne & Metcalf, School Booksellers. Ford & Damrell, (Temperance Press.) [1834]. The large wood engraving on the title-page is signed "Downes" and that on p. 16 appears to be signed with a "D." There are 4 other cuts but nothing to indicate that Downes was either engraver or draftsman. Sewed.

1645. THE COMIC TOKEN, FOR 1836, A COMPANION TO THE COMIC ALMANAC. Boston: Sold by Lemuel Gulliver, 82 State Street, Published by Charles Ellms, Agent [1835]. Contains numerous comic wood engravings. That on p. 5 is signed "Downes" and others are no doubt his work also. Disbound.

1646. THE TRANSCRIPT. Concord, N.H., Wednesday, April 1, 1835. Vol. I, No. 12. The first leaf of this number. The recto is almost completely filled with a large and hideous caricature of "Captain Pollywog." It is a crude wood engraving, and is signed "Downes." There is no record of any engraver named Downes working in Concord at that time and it seems likely that J. Downes is responsible for it.

The Transcript was a Democratic sheet which came out for a few numbers during the election campaign of 1835 (see *History of Concord, New Hampshire*, prepared under the supervision of the City History Commission, Concord, 1903, Vol. II, pp. 1037-38). No. 12 states that "With this number we suspend for the present the publication of the Transcript." However, it was resurrected later in the year for the New Hampshire Historical Society has a copy of an issue of Vol. II, dated July 15, 1835. Captain Pollywog was Dudley S. Palmer, the editor of *The Courier*, or "The Courier of Iniquity," as *The Transcript* calls it. He served as New Hampshire's Secretary of State in 1830, having deserted the Jacksonian party to win election as a Federalist. Hence the almost incredible vituperation which *The Transcript* pours upon his head. "Without a thought or a sentiment that ever soared above that of a groveling swine, he never is at home unless retailing scandal in the *street*. . . . A virtuous man on meeting him experiences the same sensation he feels at the sight of some

venomous reptile that derives its sustenance from the noxious vapor of a filthy and loathsome dungeon." Downes' wood engraving is about on a level with *The Transcript* language.

Peter Paul Duggan
(See Main Catalogue, p. 120)

1647. A JOURNEY IN THE SEABOARD SLAVE STATES, WITH REMARKS ON THEIR ECONOMY. By Frederick Law Olmsted. New York: Dix & Edwards . . . 1856.

Contains 10 wood engravings after drawings which appear to be all by the same hand. That on p. 415 is signed "Duggan" and those on pp. 358, 387, 423, and 629 are signed "P.D." The engravers were Richardson-Cox and Bobbett-Hooper. Orig. cloth.

1647a. ABOUT NEW YORK: AN ACCOUNT OF WHAT A BOY SAW IN HIS VISIT TO THE CITY. By Philip Wallys. New York: Dix, Edwards & Co., 1857.

Contains 21 illustrations, all engraved on wood by Richardson-Cox, except that on p. 60 which bears the name of W. Orr and except those on pp. 31, 34, and 92 which bear no engraver's name. All of them, with the exception of those on pp. 60, 62, and 70, carry the initials "P.D." and are probably the work of Duggan. They are interesting New York scenes and lend much attraction to the book. The three lacking Duggan's initials are not by him. Orig. cloth.

Harrison Eastman
(See Main Catalogue, p. 121)

1647b. SACRAMENTO TRANSCRIPT. [Fitch, Upham & Co.]: Sacramento City, California, May 28, 1850. Volume 1, Number 25.

The masthead is composed of a circular drawing showing a steamboat on a placid river and around it the words "Sacramento City. Chartered by the People. Oct. 13th, 1849." A circle of stars follows and underneath are the words "Harrison Eastman Del. et Sc. San Francisco." On one side of this circular device is the word "Sacramento" and on the other the word "Transcript" in decorative letters. It is not a drawing of any distinction, but it establishes the fact that Eastman was working in San Francisco somewhat earlier than 1853, the date suggested by Groce and Wallace.

This masthead appeared in the first issue of the *Sacramento Transcript* on April 1, 1850. On p. 2 of this issue will be found the following comment:

"The readers of the *Sacramento Transcript* will, no doubt, wonder where we were enabled to procure for our paper the elegant and tasteful head with which we this day appear. Our State has but recently sprung into existence, and we would naturally suppose that nothing of the kind could be procured here. If, however, it is a new State, it is also a land of wonders.—Not only is genius and science in our midst, but art, too, in its highest perfection, finds its home among us. As will be seen by the vignette, the work was performed by Harrison Eastman, Esq., of San Francisco. The vignette is the seal of Sacramento city, and was designed by Mr. Eastman."

On p. 4 of the issue for May 28, 1850, will be found the advertisement of E. L. Barber, "Wood Engraving Done to Order." Edmund Lorenzo Barber was born in New Haven and appears to have begun his wood engraving there (see Groce and Wallace, p. 28 and Item 375). He established his engraving business in Sacramento in March 1850, and about 1854 he joined forces with George H. Baker as engravers and publishers (see the introduction to *Sacramento Illustrated*, a reprint of the original edition issued by Barber & Baker in 1855, Sacramento Book Collectors Club, Sacramento, 1950). In their first announcement of *Sacramento Illustrated*, Barber & Baker state that they "have now the largest Engraving Establishment on the Pacific Coast."

Hutchings' Illustrated California Magazine. San Francisco: 1857-1861. Contains a number of drawings by Eastman (pp. 55, 397, 466, 488, 529, and 544 of Vol. I; p. 1 and probably the remaining illustrations in the first article in Vol. IV; and pp. 158 and possibly 321 of Vol. V). Many of the other illustrations are signed simply "Eastman" without any indication whether he was draftsman or engraver or both and it is quite possible that, in these cases, he both designed and engraved the illustration (see pp. 49, 57, 145, 197, 200, and 201 of Vol. I; and pp. 530 and 532 of Vol. IV). [See Item 1874]

Scenes of Wonder and Curiosity in California. San Francisco [cop. 1860]. Work by Eastman will be found on pp. 185, 195, and 197. [See Item 1875]

1647c. Broadside. Overland Mail Route to Oregon. Through in Six Days to Portland!! [Wood engraving as described below.] Connecting With The Daily Stages To all the Interior Mining Towns in Northern California

and Southern Oregon . . . Passengers Avoid Rush of Ocean Travel . . . Fare Through, Fifty Dollars. Ticket Office at Sacramento, near the Steamboat Landing. H. W. Corbett & Co., Proprietors Oregon Stage Line. July 20, 1866. W. D. Carter, Printer, Front St., Portland, Oregon.

The broadside is printed in red and blue lettering on enamel stock. Near the top, running the entire width of the broadside, is a wood engraving showing one of the stage coaches, drawn by six horses and going at a breakneck pace. There are five passengers inside with three more on the roof with the driver. On the side of the coach are the words "California Stage Comp'y." The engraving is signed on the left side "H. Eastman" and on the right "W. Keith," but there is nothing to indicate which was the designer and which the engraver. Perhaps the two acted in both capacities, for each was a draftsman as well as an engraver.

A portion of the right side of the broadside has been water stained, affecting the enamel in places but not affecting to any extent the wood engraving or the legibility of the broadside. Framed under glass.

Brevet Lieutenant Colonel Eaton, U.S.A., and F. A. Percy of El Paso

1648. El Gringo; or, New Mexico and her People. By W.W.H. Davis, Late United States Attorney. New York: Harper & Brothers, 1857.

Contains 13 full-page wood engravings of which the author's preface says, "The beautiful drawings that adorn the work were executed by Brevet Lieutenant Colonel Eaton, U.S.A., on duty in that territory [Territory of New Mexico], and F. A. Percy, Esq., of El Paso, Texas, to whom I am much indebted . . ." The drawings are excellent but they may have been touched up somewhat by a professional illustrator, for 2 of them (pp. 140 and 344) are signed "Thwaites." Orig. cloth, with the book mark of Thomas W. Streeter.

Alexander Edouart
1818-1892

Alexander Edouart was the son of Auguste Edouart, the silhouettist. Born in London and educated in Edinburgh, he studied art in Italy and became a portrait and landscape painter.

He was in New York City in 1848-1850 where he exhibited at the National Academy and the American Art-Union. He went to California in 1852 where he spent practically the entire balance of his life. He painted some California landscapes but in San Francisco was best known for his photography. See Groce and Wallace, p. 206.

HUTCHINGS' ILLUSTRATED CALIFORNIA MAGAZINE. San Francisco: 1857-1861. In Vol. V there are a number of illustrations signed "A.E." and it seems likely that these are the work of Alexander Edouart (see pp. 145, 148, 149, 151, 193, 197, 199, 206, 241, 251, and 293). No engravers' names appear, but that on p. 241 is signed "M.N." [See Item 1874]

H. Egbert, Jr.
(See Main Catalogue, p. 122)

1649. THE COMPLETE LETTER WRITER; CONTAINING A GREAT VARIETY OF LETTERS ON THE FOLLOWING SUBJECTS: RELATION-SHIP, BUSINESS, LOVE, COURTSHIP AND MAR-RIAGE, FRIENDSHIP . . . ETC., ETC. Selected from Judicious and Eminent Writers. New York: Leavitt, Trow & Co., 1848.

Contains 11 full-page wood engravings. None of them gives any indication of the draftsman or engraver except that facing p. 5, which is signed "H. E. Del." The others may well be by the same hand. If not works of great art, they are at least amusing. Orig. cloth.

John W. Ehninger
(See Main Catalogue, p. 122)

HARPER'S BAZAAR. Vols. I-III. New York: 1867-1870. A Christmas drawing by Ehninger appears at p. 9 of Vol. III. [See Item 1729]

Leo (or Lee) Elliot
(See Main Catalogue, p. 122)

1650. PUZZLEDOM. AN ORIGINAL COLLEC-TION OF CHARADES, CONUNDRUMS, PUZZLES, AND GAMES. Philadelphia: Willis P. Hazard, 1854.

Contains numerous illustrations, all probably by the same draftsman. Many of them are signed "Elliot" and 2 of them (pp. 53 and 99) are signed "L. Elliot." Gihon's name appears as the engraver on p. 73. Otherwise no engraver's name is to be found. Orig. cloth.

Sol Eytinge, Jr.
(See Main Catalogue, p. 123)

COLTON AND FITCH'S INTRODUCTORY SCHOOL GEOGRAPHY. New York: 1856. On p. 17 is an illustration by Eytinge. [See Item 1986]

1651. ST. TWEL'MO; OR, THE CUNEIFORM CYCLOPEDIST OF CHATTANOOGA. By C. H. Webb. New-York: C. H. Webb, 1867. Wright II (2668). This is the 1st ed. It contains 10 illustrations by Eytinge. In 1876 it was republished (see Item 724) with the same illustrations. Orig. cloth.

1652. THE READINGS OF MR. CHARLES DICKENS, AS CONDENSED BY HIMSELF. DOM-BEY AND SON AND MRS. GAMP. Illustrated Copyright Edition. Boston and New York: Tick-nor and Fields, 1868. This is the wording of the front wrapper. Each of the two pieces, viz., "The Story of Little Dombey" and "Mrs. Gamp" has its own title-page and each has a frontis-piece by Eytinge.
On the first page of "The Story of Little Dom-bey" appears the signature of Annie S. Higgin-son, probably the sister of Thomas Wentworth Higginson. She may have carried the book with her to Dickens' readings for on the title-page of "Mrs. Gamp" is written 'Dicken's [sic] last Read-ing in Boston at Tremont Temple-night of April 8th, 1868. He read "Mrs. Gamp" & "Dr. Mari-gold," ' and there are scorings and annotations in the text, which might have been made while Dickens was reading. Orig. wrappers.

1652a. A CHRISTMAS CAROL IN PROSE. BE-ING A GHOST STORY OF CHRISTMAS. By Charles Dickens. Boston: Fields, Osgood, & Co., 1869. With 25 illustrations by Eytinge, engraved on wood by A.V.S. Anthony. Orig. cloth.

1653. TREASURE TROVE. [By Leonard Case.] Boston: James R. Osgood and Company, 1873. With 25 illustrations by Eytinge, en-graved on wood by Anthony. Orig. cloth.

1654. SEVENOAKS. A STORY OF TO-DAY. By J. G. Holland. New York: Scribner, Armstrong & Co., 1875. 12 illustrations by Eytinge, 5 en-graved on wood by J. P. Davis and 4 by J.G.S. (J. G. Smithwick), the remaining 3 being un-signed. Orig. cloth.

Harman Faber
1832-1913

Harman Faber came to this country from Ger-many in 1854 when he was about 22 years old.

During our Civil War he worked as an illustrator for the Surgeon General's medical record of the war. He was also a portrait painter. See Groce and Wallace, p. 218.

1655. SAL-O-QUAH; OR, BOY-LIFE AMONG THE CHEROKEES. By Rev. F. R. Goulding. Philadelphia: Claxton, Remsen & Haffelfinger . . . 1870. 4 full-page illustrations, all but one signed by H. Faber as the draftsman and J. Green as the wood engraver. This is one of "The Woodruff Series." Orig. cloth.

1656. SECRETS OF THE CONVENT AND CONFESSIONAL: AN EXHIBITION OF THE INFLUENCE AND WORKINGS OF PAPACY UPON SOCIETY AND REPUBLICAN INSTITUTIONS. By Mrs. Julia M'Nair Wright. National Publishing Company: Cincinnati, O.; Memphis, Tenn.; and Atlanta, Ga. Jones Brothers and Company: Philadelphia, Penn., and Chicago, Ill., 1873.

Contains 16 full-page illustrations, of which 8 (front. and pp. 62, 125, 224, 289, 318, 355, and 498) bear Faber's name or initials. 2 others (pp. 337 and 495) appear to be his work also. H. Sebald was the wood engraver.

It would be impossible to attribute any of the other 6 illustrations to Faber. 1 (p. 72) is signed "W. H. Thomas," 1 (p. 351) is signed by Felter, the engraver, and 1 (p. 439) is signed "H.W."

This is not the 1st edition which had appeared in the previous year. Wright II (2815) locates only the Library of Congress copy of the 1st edition. Orig. cloth.

Gaston Fay

(See Main Catalogue, p. 125)

SPECIMEN PAGES AND ILLUSTRATIONS FROM APPLETONS' JOURNAL. [New York: 1870.] With 2 folding wood engravings after indifferent drawings by Fay, one of them engraved by Langridge. [See Item 1731]

1657. BEYOND THE SNOW; BEING A HISTORY OF TRIM'S ADVENTURES IN NORDLICHTSCHEIN. By P[eter] Fishe Reed. Chicago: Lakeside Press, 1873.

Contains half title and 12 full-page illustrations showing considerable imagination. They are engraved on wood by Baker-Co., but are unsigned by the draftsman except that the one on p. 267 has the monogram "G.F." or "F.G." All of them are obviously by the same draftsman.

The author of the book was a landscape and figure painter of some prominence who in 1873 was living in Chicago (see Groce and Wallace,

p. 529; Lakeside Monthly, Vol. X, No. 55, p. 78), and it would be natural to assign the illustrations to him were it not for the fact that the before-mentioned monogram does not fit. The monogram does bear considerable resemblance to that sometimes used by Gaston Fay and accordingly the illustrations have been attributed to him, although it must be admitted that they are more imaginative than is customary with him. Orig. cloth.

Wright II (2004) locates only 2 other copies of the book.

THE BODLEYS TELLING STORIES. New York: 1878. On pp. 52 and 99 are illustrations by Fay which had first appeared in *The Riverside Magazine for Young People* [Item 958] at pp. 192 and 526 of Vol. I. [See Item 1732]

Harry Fenn

(See Main Catalogue, p. 125)

ALBUM OF WOOD ENGRAVINGS by John Andrew, etc. [*ca.* 1855-1875]. 3 engravings after Fenn. [See Item 1472 (2)]

1658. ARMSMEAR: THE HOME, THE ARM, AND THE ARMORY OF SAMUEL COLT. A MEMORIAL. New York: 1866.

This book was privately printed as a tribute to Samuel Colt, the inventor of the Colt revolver, who had died in 1862. It contains a description of Armsmear, Colt's estate in Connecticut. It is a lavish volume with numerous wood engravings, a great many of which bear Fenn's name. Others undoubtedly are also his. The engraver was N. Orr. The vignette title-page, a steel engraving by S. V. Hunt, is also after a drawing by Fenn. Almost all of these drawings are excellent and typical of Fenn's work.

This copy is inscribed by Mrs. Samuel Colt under date of January 11, 1867. Full morocco with Colt coat of arms in gold.

QUEER LITTLE PEOPLE. Boston: 1867. There is an illustration by Fenn on p. 86. [See Item 1938]

SPECIMEN PAGES AND ILLUSTRATIONS FROM APPLETONS' JOURNAL. [New York: 1870.] With 2 folding wood engravings after Fenn, viz.: "View of Castle Garden, and New York Bay" and "Fairmount, Philadelphia," both engraved by John Filmer, which had accompanied the numbers of the *Journal* for May 15, 1869, and September 25, 1869. Also on the first page of the issue of the *Journal* for October 23, 1869, there is an attractive drawing by Fenn, engraved on wood by F. W. Quartley. [See Item 1731]

THE ILLUSTRATED CHRISTIAN WEEKLY. New York: 1871. 4 illustrations by Fenn (pp. 36, 73, 140, and 172), engraved on wood by Bookhout (1) and Brightly (2), the name of the engraver of the other not appearing. [See Item 1627]

1659. GOOD OLD TIMES; OR, GRANDFATHER'S STRUGGLES FOR A HOMESTEAD. By Rev. Elijah Kellogg. Boston: Lee and Shepard . . . 1878.

Contains 12 illustrations. That facing p. 33 is signed by Fenn and engraved on wood by W. H. Morse. That facing p. 106 bears Fenn's initials and is engraved on wood by Redding(?). The illustrator's name does not appear on the others, but probably Fenn was responsible for a good many of them. Orig. cloth.

W. Fiske

(See Main Catalogue, p. 128)

VANITY FAIR. Vols. 1-6. New York: 1859-1862. Beginning with a few illustrations in Vol. 2 (pp. 180 and 193) and Vol. 3 (pp. 156, 196, 209, 290, and 295), the later volumes contain a great deal of his work. [See Item 1933]

Flag

PICTURE OF SLAVERY IN THE UNITED STATES OF AMERICA. Middletown: 1834. 1 illustration signed "Flag, del." [See Item 1870]

Mary Hallock Foote

(See Main Catalogue, p. 129)

1660. KATHERINE EARLE. By Adeline Trafton [Mrs. Adeline (Trafton) Knox]. Boston: Lee and Shepard . . . 1874. Wright II (1497). 5 full-page illustrations, 4 of which bear Miss Hallock's monogram. The only wood engravers whose names appear are Langridge and J. P. Davis. Orig. cloth.

1661. LUCY MARIA. By Mrs. Abby Morton Diaz. Boston: James R. Osgood and Company, 1874. Wright II (749). With 8 full-page and 1 small illustration by Miss Hallock. The only engraver's name which can be made out is that of Langridge on the illustration facing p. 100. Orig. cloth.

1662. THE SCARLET LETTER. By Nathaniel Hawthorne. Boston: Houghton, Mifflin and Company [cop. 1878 by Rose Hawthorne Lathrop].

Contains 29 illustrations by Mrs. Foote, 12 of them full-page, engraved on wood by Anthony. They exhibit Mrs. Foote's careful and competent draftsmanship. This is not the first appearance of these illustrations, which will be found in an edition published by James R. Osgood & Co. in 1877 (see Nina E. Browne, A Bibliography of Nathaniel Hawthorne, Boston, 1905, p. 63). Orig. decorated cloth.

McGUFFEY'S SECOND ECLECTIC READER. Cincinnati and New York: [cop. 1879]. With 5 illustrations by Mrs. Foote (pp. 22, 95, 149, 153, and 156), engraved on wood by Jueng-Mill. [See Item 1907a(2)]

Edwin Forbes

(See Main Catalogue, p. 130)

PEBBLES AND PEARLS FOR THE YOUNG FOLKS. Hartford: 1868. An illustration by Forbes will be found at p. 87. Another illustration by him is listed as appearing at p. 271 but is missing in this copy. [See Item 1939]

SPECIMEN PAGES AND ILLUSTRATIONS FROM APPLETONS' JOURNAL. [New York: 1870.] With a folding wood engraving after Forbes, "Among the Prairie Chickens," engraved by John Filmer, which had accompanied the number of the Journal for December 11, 1869. [See Item 1731]

Elisha Forbes

A wood engraver working in New Orleans in 1830 and later in New York City. See Groce and Wallace, p. 234.

HISTORY OF SCHOHARIE COUNTY. Albany: 1845. The wood engraving on p. 123 was designed and engraved by E. Forbes and that on p. 644 was designed by him. As Edwin Forbes was too young at this time to have done this work, it seems likely that Elisha was the draftsman. Elisha may also have been the illustrator of Item 756 as here again Edwin would seem to have been too young. [See Item 1795]

THE ILLUSTRATED AMERICAN BIOGRAPHY. New York: 1854. Contains 3 illustrations for advertisements by Forbes (pp. 153, 254, and 257), all engraved on wood by J. W. Orr. [See Item 1964]

Frederick E. Fox

A wood engraver whose name appears in Boston directories of 1852-1860 and after. He was probably some relation of Charles Fox, the publisher. See Groce and Wallace, p. 237.

1663. The Discontented Robins, and Other Stories, for the Young. By Miss Mary Anna Fox. Boston: Charles Fox, 1849. Contains 5 illustrations, of which 2 (front. and p. 59) were drawn and engraved on wood by Fox. That at p. 51 is signed "Fox sc." and the remaining 2 are unsigned. It is probable that Fox drew and engraved them all. Orig. cloth.

Ephraim P. Frazer
1829-

A wood engraver of Cincinnati and a member of the firm of Frazer & Dennis, active in the fifties. His partner was Julian N. Dennis. See Groce and Wallace, p. 241.

1664. Gospel Fruits; or, Bible Christi- anity Illustrated; A Premium Essay. By Maria Goodell Frost. Cincinnati: Am. Reform Tract and Book Society, 1856.

Contains frontispiece and 3 other full-page wood engravings, all of which are probably by the same hands. The frontispiece is signed "Frazer Del." and "Grosvenor Sc." In addition there are some smaller illustrations and that on p. 148 was also drawn by Frazer and engraved by Grosvenor.

The American Reform Tract and Book So- ciety was authorized by a donor to offer a premium of $100 for "the best manuscript for a religious Anti-Slavery Sunday School book, showing that American chattel slave-holding is a sin against God, and a crime against man, and that it ought to be immediately repented of and abolished." 48 manuscripts were received and the committee appointed to examine them awarded the premium to Mrs. Maria Goodell Frost of Janesville, Wisconsin, for her *Gospel Fruits*. Orig. cloth.

Alfred Fredericks
(*See Main Catalogue, p. 130*)

Album of wood engravings by John An- drew, etc. [*ca.* 1855-1875]. 1 engraving after Fredericks. [See Item 1472(2)]

1665. Unsworth's Burnt Cork Lyrics . . . Edited and Compiled by J. H. Collins. With Photographic Illustrations by Fredericks. New York: Robert M. De Witt [cop. 1859]. Con- tains several wood engravings by N-Orr Co. The use of the word "photographic" on the title- page is somewhat mysterious. Possibly Freder- icks drew them on the block from photographs.

James Unsworth appears to have been a Min- strel or, as the Preface puts it, "a star of the first magnitude amid the Ethiopian constella- tion."
Orig. wrappers.

1666. Nina's Atonement, and Other Stories. By Christian Reid [Mrs. Frances Chris- tine (Fisher) Tiernan]. New York: D. Apple- ton and Company, 1873. Wright II (2510). Contains 4 full-page illustrations signed with Fredericks' initials and 2 others which are al- most certainly his. The wood engravers are J. Karst (2), J. Filmer (3), and H. Linton (1). There are 2 illustrations by Sheppard. Orig. cloth.

1667. A Daughter of Bohemia. A Novel. By Christian Reid [Mrs. Frances Christine (Fisher) Tiernan]. New York: D. Appleton and Company, 1874. Wright II (2505). 16 full-page illustrations by Fredericks. The only wood engravers whose names or initials appear are J. Filmer and A. Bobbett. Orig. cloth.

1668. Rape of the Gamp. A Novel. By C[harles] Welsh Mason. New York: Harper & Brothers, 1875. Wright II (1677).

With full-page frontispiece and 16 smaller wood engravings after drawings by Fredericks. 5 (front. and pp. 10, 71, 78, and 118) are signed "J.T.H." and that on p. 100 is signed "Howland." All of these were, no doubt, en- graved by J. T. Howland. A. Bobbett was the engraver of 8 of the illustrations (pp. 24, 37, 52, 87, 91, 110, 122, and 147). The name of the engraver does not appear on the other 3 illustrations. Orig. cloth.

1669. We and our Neighbors: or, The Records of an Unfashionable Street. (Sequel to "My Wife and I.") A Novel. By Harriet Beecher Stowe. Wright II (2402). New York: J. B. Ford & Company [cop. 1875]. 8 full-page illustrations by Fredericks, of which 5 are signed by the wood engraver, viz.: A. Bobbett (4) and E. C., possibly Clement (1). Orig. cloth.

1670. The Boy's Mabinogion being the Earliest Welsh Tales of King Arthur in the famous Red Book of Hergest. Ed- ited for Boys with an Introduction by Sidney Lanier. New York: Charles Scribner's Sons, 1881. With 12 excellent full-page illustrations by Fredericks, engraved on wood by Karst. Orig. cloth.

1671. Beatrix Randolph. A Story. By Julian Hawthorne. Boston: James R. Osgood and Company, 1884. With 4 full-page illustrations by Fredericks. Orig. cloth.

1672. KALOOLAH. THE ADVENTURES OF JONATHAN ROMER. By W. S. Mayo, M.D. The Framazugda Edition. Illustrated by Fredericks. New York and London: G. P. Putnam's Sons, 1887. Fredericks has 38 illustrations (including 1 repeated), most of them small linecuts. 12 of them, however, are full-page and reproduced in half-tone. The cut used on p. 167 as a tailpiece was drawn by Darley. Orig. decorated cloth.

Paul Frenzeny

Frenzeny was a Frenchman who probably came to this country in the late sixties after serving in the French Army and spending some years in Mexico. His first illustrations here appeared in *Harper's Weekly* in 1868. In 1873 that publication commissioned Frenzeny and Jules Tavernier, another Frenchman, to make a series of Western sketches which, signed by the two artists, appeared from time to time in *Harper's Weekly* during the seventies. They throw valuable light on the West of that time. After reaching California on that trip, Frenzeny remained there for some years. He probably returned to New York about 1879. In the eighties many of his sketches appeared in *Harper's Weekly*, some illustrating New York scenes and others illustrating California. The last we hear of him is in 1889 when he illustrated Harrington O'Reilly's *Fifty Years on the Trail*. See Robert Taft, *Artists and Illustrators of the Old West*, New York, 1953, p. 95, *et seq*.

HARPER'S BAZAAR. Vols. I-III. New York: 1867-1870. A full-page drawing by Frenzeny will be found at p. 845 of Vol. III. It shows "The Two Homes," on one side the victorious Prussian, flushed with triumph, on the other the unhappy Frenchman, wounded and heartbroken. [See Item 1729]

Lucy Gibbons
(*See Main Catalogue, p. 132*)

THE BODLEYS TELLING STORIES. New York: 1878. According to a note in the book, some of the illustrations in Chapter VI are by Lucy Gibbons (now Lucy Gibbons Morse). Some of them had appeared in *The Riverside Magazine for Young People* (see Vol. III, p. 552). [See Item 1732]

R. Swain Gifford
(*See Main Catalogue, p. 132*)

THE ILLUSTRATED CHRISTIAN WEEKLY. New York: 1871. On p. 276 is a wood engrav- ing by R. A. Muller, after a drawing by R. S. Gifford. [See Item 1627]

Sanford Robinson Gifford
(*See Main Catalogue, p. 133*)

1673. OUT OF TOWN. A RURAL EPISODE. By Barry Gray [Robert Barry Coffin]. New York: Hurd and Houghton, 1866. Wright II (593). The frontispiece is engraved on wood by J. P. Davis-Speer after a design by S. R. Gifford. There are also engravings after designs by J. F. Weir, J. G. Brown, Gignoux, and Beard. Orig. cloth.

Regis F. Gignoux
(*See Main Catalogue, p. 133*)

OUT OF TOWN. New York: 1866. At p. 166 is a wood engraving by J. P. Davis-Speer after a design by Gignoux. [See Item 1673]

George Gilbert
(*See Main Catalogue, p. 133*)

1674. ALBUM containing over 1000 wood engravings. Its spine is labeled "Proof cuts" and at the bottom appear the initials A.S.S.U. It appears to be a collection of cuts used in books published by the American Sunday School Union of Philadelphia. Judging from the dates which occasionally occur, the period covered is from the early 1820s to about 1831. All have been carefully numbered.

Over 70 of the cuts are signed with Gilbert's name or initial and undoubtedly many others are his work also. One cut (No. 968) is signed "Mason" and another (No. 826) is signed "M," probably the work of William Mason, whose pupil Gilbert may have been. There are a number signed with the letter "G" and immediately before it a letter, printed backwards, which might be either a C or a G. As this would be a very unusual signature for Gilbert, it is suggested that these cuts may have been engraved by Christian Gobrecht (see Nos. 895, 905, 913, 958, 963, 995, 1002, 1003, 1006, 1008, 1015, 1016, 1021, and 1050).

There is one cut (No. 571) signed with Anderson's "A" and another (No. 325) signed with J. W. Barber's initials. It would be interesting to know how these cuts got into the hands of this Philadelphia institution.

There are several cuts by Richard G. Harrison, of Philadelphia, best known as a banknote engraver (see Nos. 970, 971, 985, 1024, and 1025).

There are also a number of steel engravings by James B. Longacre. Line engravings by P. E. Hamm, J. H. Nesmith, C. G. Childs, Charles Tappan & Co., and Joseph Drayton are also included.

It might be noted that cut No. 243 by Gilbert appears again near cut No. 511 but part of it has been eliminated. This cut was copied, with some changes, by the American Tract Society and appears, without signature, in that Society's *Falsehood Chastised*, published in New York from its 144 Nassau Street address between 1827 and 1833. A copy of this tract accompanies the Album.

Cut No. 521 was used as a frontispiece in *The Youth's Instructor*, by the Rev. B. H. Draper, published by the American Sunday School Union in Philadelphia in 1830, a copy of which accompanies the Album.

Most of the cuts in the Album were intended for use in juveniles and many have that delightful naïveté which we associate with children's books of that period. Here and there is a touch of the refined sentiments of our ancestors. Thus at the foot of cut No. 608, portraying Adam and Eve in the Garden of Eden, has been penciled "not to be used unless clothed." On the whole it is an interesting lot of cuts which throw some light on early engraving in Philadelphia, a subject which has never been given the study it deserves.

Orig. boards with leather back.

1675. THE LIFE OF GEORGE WASHINGTON [By Anna C. Reed], Second Edition. Philadelphia: American Sunday-School Union, 1829. Contains 6 wood engravings, 4 of which are signed "Gilbert" or "G." The frontispiece is a steel engraving by Chas. Tappan & Co. after Thomas Sully's painting of Washington crossing the Delaware. Orig. boards with leather back.

1676. THE SHEPHERD OF SALISBURY PLAIN. By Hannah More. New Edition with 2 new wood engravings. Revised by the Committee of Publication. Philadelphia: American Sunday School Union, 1830. The 2 new engravings bear the initials "G.G."

At the end of the book are some facts about the Shepherd, concluding with the statement that a tombstone is now being erected to his memory at the expense of the Rev^d. R. C. Caswall, Vicar of West Lavington. This has been altered in this copy to show that the tombstone was really being erected at the expense of Mr. Caswall's sons. This copy was presented to the Rev^d. R. C. Caswall by his "affectionate son, H. C." in Boston on July 22, 1833.

Orig. boards, leather back. Presented by Alexander D. Wainwright.

1677. MY MOTHER. A POEM. [By Jane Taylor. Philadelphia: *ca.* 1835-1840.] A small juvenile with a number of wood engravings. That on the back wrapper is signed by George Gilbert and some of the others may be his also. Orig. wrappers.

1678. AMERICANISCHER STADT UND LAND CALENDER AUF DAS 1844STE JAHR CHRISTI . . . Philadelphia: Conrad Zentler [1843]. Contains full-page wood engraving signed "Gilbert" showing Father Time and Death, the latter snuffing a candle. Sewed.

1679. AMERICANISCHER STADT UND LAND CALENDER AUF DAS 1849STE JAHR CHRISTI . . . Philadelphia: Conrad Zentler [1848]. Contains full-page wood engraving signed "G. Gilbert," entitled "Die Auswanderer," showing a prairie fire with an emigrant family in the foreground and a wagon train in the distance. Sewed.

W. and J. Gilman
(*See Main Catalogue, p. 134*)

1680. THE HISTORY OF A PIN. AS RELATED BY ITSELF. INTERSPERSED WITH A VARIETY OF ANECDOTES: POINTING OUT TO THE YOUTH OF BOTH SEXES, THE SUPERIORITY OF A GENEROUS MIND OVER ONE THAT IS CONTRACTED. Printed and Sold by Whittingham and John Gilman, Middlestreet . . . Newburyport, February 1808. 36 leaves. Welch 481.2. Fig. 27.

The frontispiece is a cut showing a very elegant young lady, copying a drawing. It appears to be signed "I.G.," which would indicate that John Gilman was the engraver. There is an engraved ornament on the title-page and a small cut at the top of p. [5] which may be the work of John also. Orig. wrappers.

1681. THE PARENT'S GIFT: OR, COMPANION FOR YOUNG MASTERS AND MISSES. Newburyport: W. & J. Gilman. It is undated but on the verso of the final leaf an early owner has written his name and the date "February—1808."

There are relief cuts on the front and back wrappers and a number of such cuts throughout the text. It is difficult to say whether these are on wood or typemetal. W. Gilman's name appears on the cut on p. 12 and that on p. 20 is signed "Gilman." It would appear that Whittingham Gilman as well as John Gilman occasionally did a little engraving. Orig. wrappers.

1682. DR. WATTS' DIVINE SONGS, FOR THE USE OF CHILDREN. Newburyport: W. & J. Gilman [*ca.* 1815].

On the verso of the front wrapper is a wood

engraving entitled "Of Such is the Kingdom of God," showing Christ surrounded by little children. It is signed "Gilman." On the title-page and in the text are 23 additional wood engravings, of which 2 (pp. 3 and 28) bear the Gilman name. One of the text cuts is repeated on the front wrapper. Orig. wrappers.

1683. PRETTY POEMS FOR CHILDREN. Newburyport: W. & J. Gilman [ca. 1820]. The front wrapper refers to it as a "new edition." Contains numerous wood engravings. Those on p. 4 and the back wrapper are signed "Gilman," while the cut on p. 9 appears to be signed "W. & J. Gilman." The cut on the back wrapper is particularly elaborate. Orig. wrappers.

1684. THE BROTHER'S GIFT. Newburyport: W. & J. Gilman [n.d. but not later than 1825, as a former owner has signed her name and under it the year "1825" on the title-page]. Contains 10 wood engravings, that on p. 8 signed "Gilman." No wrappers are present but there is nothing to indicate that the book was issued in wrappers.

Stephen Henry Gimber

Gimber was an engraver and a portrait and miniature painter. He came from England, settling in New York City in 1829 and moving to Philadelphia in 1842. Fielding (p. 139) says that he "was a good portrait engraver in stipple and mezzotint." See Groce and Wallace, p. 260.

THE PANORAMA OF PROFESSIONS AND TRADES. Philadelphia: 1836. The preface states that Gimber was one of the illustrators, but none of the illustrations are signed by him. [See Item 1866]

John H. Goater

(See Main Catalogue, p. 134)

THE ILLUSTRATED NEWS. Vol. I. New York: 1853. Work by Goater will be found on pp. 101, 189, and 213. [See Item 1836]

THE ILLUSTRATED AMERICAN BIOGRAPHY. New York: 1854. On p. 101 is a drawing by Goater of the magnificent domed emporium of Lord & Taylor at the corner of Grand and Chrystie Streets, New York City. It is engraved on wood by W. Roberts. [See Item 1964]

MRS. PARTINGTON'S CARPET-BAG OF FUN. New York: 1854. While the title-page states that Goater is one of the illustrators, none of the illustrations are signed by him. [See Item 1840]

1685. A NEW FLOWER FOR CHILDREN. By L. Maria Child. For Children from Eight to Twelve Years Old. New York: C. S. Francis & Co., 1856. B.A.L. 3182.
Contains frontispiece signed "J.H.G." engraved on wood by Avery. There are a number of small wood engravings throughout the text. McLenan has a cut on p. 154 and possibly another on p. 157. That on p. 305 bears the initials "T.W." (Thomas Worth?). Orig. blue cloth with gilt decorations, edges plain.

VANITY FAIR. Vols. 1-6. New York: 1859-1862. Illustrations by Goater will be found in Nos. 43-47, 50-51, and 53 of Vol. 2, Nos. 54-62, 65-66, 75, and 77 of Vol. 3, and Nos. 86, 95, 98, 99, and 101 of Vol. 4. [See Item 1933]

1686. A POLITICAL CARTOON ENTITLED "DOMESTIC TROUBLES," BEING STRONG'S DIME CARICATURES—NO. 1. It was copyrighted 1861. It is engraved on wood by T. W. Strong after a drawing by Goater whose initials appear in the lower lefthand corner.
It shows a mother hen labeled "Union," surrounded by her loyal chicks, with an empty feeding pan labeled "U.S. Treasury" beside her. At a little distance is a group of ducklings over which hovers the hawk of "Anarchy." The mother hen is saying "Those Secession Ducks give me a great deal of trouble. They emptied the dish before they went, and there's no telling what will happen to 'em now they've left my wing. If that hungry hawk pounces on them, they will have no one but themselves to blame!"

MILLER'S NEW YORK AS IT IS. New York: 1862. Views of the Astor House (p. 59) and Clarendon Hotel (p. 76) by Goater, engraved on wood by Richardson-Cox. [See Item 1971]

Christian Gobrecht

1785-1844

Gobrecht was born in Hanover, Pa., and, after serving an apprenticeship to a clockmaker in Manheim, Pa., established himself in Baltimore. There he learned engraving and die sinking. In 1810 he engraved a creditable portrait of Washington for a biographical dictionary published in Baltimore. It was no doubt during this period that he made the cuts for Item 1687 listed below. In 1811 he went to Philadelphia and engaged in sinking dies for medals and in making portrait plates for the publishers of that city. In 1836 he was appointed assistant engraver at the U.S. mint in Philadelphia and in 1840 he became chief engraver to the mint. His dies are esteemed for their excellent work.

See Stauffer, Vol. I, p. 103; D.A.B., Vol. VII, p. 336; Groce and Wallace, p. 263.

1687. A Present for a Little Girl. Baltimore. Printed by Warner & Hanna, and sold by them and J. Vance & Co., 1806.

Contains 23 different cuts. The full-page frontispiece, "The Cottage of Content," which is repeated at p. 20, is signed "C.G.," while the smaller cuts on pp. 10 and 22 are signed "G." The full-page cut on p. 47 appears to be signed "Gobrecht sculp," although this is difficult to decipher. Probably all the cuts are by Gobrecht. There is much white line but it is difficult to say whether the cuts were done on wood or typemetal.

Roger Pattrell Bristol in his *Maryland Imprints 1801-1810*, Charlottesville, 1953, No. 486, locates only one copy of this juvenile, at the American Antiquarian Society.

Orig. marbled back wrapper present, but front wrapper missing. Sewed in old paper covers.

1688. A Key to French Conversation and French Idiom . . . By M. L'Abbé Bossut, Professor of Languages. And also, An Introduction to Natural History of Birds and Beasts. Baltimore: Warner & Hanna, 1812.

In the sections devoted to the "Natural History of Beasts" and the "Natural History of Birds" there are numerous wood engravings. Those on pp. 86, 99, and 163 (the latter a full-page engraving of the peacock) are signed "Gobrecht" and those on pp. 93, 116, and 124 are signed "G." Probably Gobrecht was responsible for all of them. Orig. boards, rebacked.

Album containing over 1000 wood engravings probably used in books published by the American Sunday School Union in Philadelphia during the 1820s. Several engravings bear initials which might be those of Gobrecht. [See Item 1674]

1688a. Thirty-nine small volumes containing tracts of the American Sunday School Union, published in Philadelphia at the office of the Union, No. 146 Chestnut Street. None are dated but they probably were issued from about 1830 to 1840. More than half of the volumes contain 2 tracts. Except in a few instances the tracts are not numbered, but a number appears on the spine of each volume. These numbers run 1 to 50, the missing vols. being nos. 5, 11, 17, 26, 28, 35, 38, 40, 41, 47, and 48, or 11 in all. Fig. 29.

Including a few repeats, there are over 180 wood engravings throughout the 39 vols., many of them full-page. Unfortunately most bear no signature of any kind but they are interesting examples of Philadelphia wood engraving in the first half of the century. The writer does not know the sources from which the designs may have come, but a number are vigorous and effective and others have the charm of so much of the work of that period.

A number of the engravings bear the letter "G" and immediately preceding it an inverted initial which might be either a "C" or a "G." In describing Item 1674, the writer suggested that this monogram might be that of Christian Gobrecht, since it would be a very unusual way for George Gilbert to sign an engraving. Among the numerous engravings in these tracts there are 15 which carry this monogram, viz.: p. 12 of the first tract and front. of the second tract in vol. 3; pp. 4 and 11 of the first tract and 1 and 3 of the second tract in vol. 14; p. 3 of the first tract in vol. 15; p. 3 of the first tract in vol. 18; p. 14 of the first tract in vol. 19; p. 14 of the first tract in vol. 20; p. 14 of the first tract in vol. 21; pp. 7 and 12 of the first tract in vol. 22; front. of vol. 37; and front. of vol. 45. The writer confesses that these cuts stir some doubts in his mind whether the monogram in question should be ascribed to Gobrecht. In some of them the inverted initial looks very much like a "G." and in the frontispiece in vol. 45 some letters appear to follow the monogram which the writer has been unable to decipher, but which could hardly spell out either the name "Gobrecht" or the name "Gilbert." Nevertheless the present item has been here listed under Gobrecht in the hope that some future adventurer in the field of American wood engraving may solve the problem.

On p. 2 of the second tract in vol. 10, the cut is signed with the letter "G," the initial looking much like the "G." in the monograms.

All 39 vols. in orig. boards with leather backs.

Thomas Butler Gunn
(See Main Catalogue, p. 135)

The New York Journal. Vols. I and II. New York: 1853-1854. On p. 64 of Vol. I is an illustration by Gunn, engraved on wood by N. Orr. [See Item 1838]

The Know Nothing Almanac [for] 1855. New York [1854]. 3 of the illustrations carry Gunn's name or initials. [See Item 1839]

John H. Hall
(See Main Catalogue, p. 135)

1689. (1) The Popular Story of Blue Beard. Cooperstown: H. and E. Phinney, 1824.

With numerous wood engravings, the frontispiece and those on pp. 9 and 15 being signed with Hall's initials or initial. All are probably his. The cut on p. 15 is repeated on the front wrapper. Orig. wrappers.

(2) A copy of another edition, with the same cuts, published by H. & E. Phinney in 1839. Orig. wrappers.

1690. THE HOLY BIBLE, CONTAINING THE OLD AND NEW TESTAMENTS: Translated out of the Original Tongues, and with the Former Translations Diligently Compared and Revised . . . Cooperstown (N.Y.): H. & E. Phinney, 1826.

The frontispiece is a wood engraving of the Creation signed by Hall. The source of the design does not appear but it is well composed and Hall, young as he must have been, has done justice to it. Possibly it was engraved while Hall was still studying with Anderson and the latter may have helped him with it. There is another wood engraving in the book (opp. p. 657) which, while unsigned, is probably by Hall. It shows the appearance of Christ to Mary Magdalene.

There are 8 line engravings throughout the text. Some of these are signed by W. M. Craig as the draftsman and I. Chorley as the engraver. They were made for "Teal's Edition" of the Bible and the impressions here are very weak.

Between the Old and the New Testament some pages are inserted for family records and one of the entries records the death in Cooperstown, on August 23, 1841, of Mary Phinney, "consort of the late Elihu Phinney." This copy, therefore, may have been in the family of the printer.

Cont. calf.

1691. BIOGRAPHICAL SKETCH OF THE LIFE OF ANDREW JACKSON, MAJOR-GENERAL OF THE ARMIES OF THE UNITED STATES, THE HERO OF NEW-ORLEANS. [By Robert Walsh.] Hudson, N.Y.: William E. Norman, 1828. Fig. 28.

The frontispiece is a wood engraved portrait of Jackson, signed "Hall." This is early work of Hall's and it is an interesting bit of engraving. Opposite p. 36 there is a rather crude cut of the "Battle of New-Orleans," but it is unsigned. For the authorship of the book, see Howes W68. Orig. boards, with leather back.

THE CABINET OF INSTRUCTION, LITERATURE, AND AMUSEMENT. New-York: 1829. No. 14 contains an interesting wood engraving by Hall of Mr. David Gordon's new patent Steam Carriage. This carriage was operated by propellers which, by the revolution of a crank, were successively forced out against the ground in a backward direction and then drawn up again, precisely in the manner of the hind legs of a horse. [See Item 1441]

1692. THE CRIES OF LONDON. Cooperstown: H. & E. Phinney, 1834. 26 wood engravings, 9 of which (pp. 8, 11, 14, 20, 23, 26, 27, 29, and 31) carry Hall's name or initials. Orig. wrappers with wood engravings.

THE PEOPLE'S MAGAZINE. Vol. I. Boston: 1834. With 3 wood engravings which appear to bear Hall's initials. [See Item 1785]

NATURAL HISTORY OF QUADRUPEDS. Cooperstown: 1841. 5 wood engravings by Hall (pp. 5, 19, 21, 23, and 27). [See Item 1455]

HISTORY OF SCHOHARIE COUNTY. Albany: 1845. The wood engraving on p. 114 is signed "Hall Sc." [See Item 1795]

BIRDS OF THE WOODLAND AND THE SHORE. Boston: 1855. Wood engravings with initials resembling those of Hall will be found on pp. 47 and 75. [See Item 1534]

W. Hall

THE AMERICAN PIONEER. Cincinnati, O.: 1842-1843. The frontispiece for the May 1842 number (Vol. I, p. 162) is a wood engraving by Grosvenor after a drawing by W. Hall. It shows the court house and jail at Marietta, Ohio. [See Item 1946]

J. Halpin
(See Main Catalogue, p. 138)

1693. THE LIFE OF THE CHEVALIER BAYARD . . . By W. Gilmore Simms. New York: Harper & Brothers, 1847. With full-page frontispiece and 13 smaller wood engravings in the text. Those on pp. 1, 56, 90, 162, 239, 262, and 384 are signed by Halpin as the draftsman and no doubt all are his. Avery was the engraver. Cont. calf.

James Hamilton
(See Main Catalogue, p. 138)

LEAVES FROM THE BOOK OF HUMAN LIFE. Philadelphia: 1854. The frontispiece by Sartain is after a drawing by Hamilton. [See Item 1587]

1694. ARCTIC EXPLORATIONS: THE SECOND GRINNELL EXPEDITION IN SEARCH OF SIR JOHN FRANKLIN, 1853, '54, '55. By Elisha

Kent Kane, M.D., U.S.N. Philadelphia: Childs & Peterson . . . 1856. 2 vols. This is the 1st ed. of Item 796.

Hamilton's illustrations, after sketches done by Kane, added a good deal to the popularity of this book. William Elder in his *Biography of Elisha Kent Kane*, Philadelphia, 1858, at p. 219, quotes a review from Blackwood's Edinburgh Magazine to the effect that, "The engravings of Dr. Kane's book are eminently happy as the productions of a man who is a real poet in art, Mr. Hamilton, whose good taste scatters beautiful vignettes like gems through the two volumes . . ."

Orig. cloth.

Augustus Choate Hamlin

According to Groce and Wallace, p. 288, Dr. A. C. Hamlin was a landscape painter of Bangor, Maine, who exhibited at the National Academy in 1859. As the prefatory note to the book listed below is dated "Bangor, September, 1866," it seems probable that this Dr. A. C. Hamlin of Bangor was its author. He appears to have been a medical inspector in the U.S. Army during the Civil War.

1695. MARTYRIA; OR, ANDERSONVILLE PRISON. By Augustus C. Hamlin, Late Medical Inspector U.S. Army, Royal Antiquarian, etc. Boston: Lee and Shepard, 1866.

The book contains some 18 views of different parts of Andersonville, of which 4 are from photographs. A note to the List of Illustrations (p. 255) says, "The Illustrations were drawn by the author from sketches upon the spot, and from photographs which were taken by the rebels during the occupation of the prison. The figures are by Charles A. Barry, Esq., and the engraving by Henry Marsh, Esq."

Orig. cloth.

Marie Louise Hankins

Marie Louise Hankins was the editress of the pictorial "Family Newspaper" and authoress of "Human Life"; "The Old Woman's Revenge"; "Bigamy"; "The Bankrupt's Wife"; etc., etc., etc. Her "Family Newspaper," according to her own advertisement, was the "*First* and only *Successful* Paper *Ever* published by a *Lady*. It always aims to help the deserving, when they try to help themselves, and it has no sympathy with 'strong-minded' women." Nevertheless, the editress appears to have been a very "strong-minded" woman herself.

1696. WOMEN OF NEW YORK. Written and Illustrated by Marie Louise Hankins. New York: Marie Louise Hankins & Co., 1861.

In addition to some small vignettes and 4 full-page drawings, printed on green paper, which are in the nature of frontispieces, the authoress contributes no less than 32 extraordinary portraits of New York women, such as "Angelina Plump, the lap-dog's mother," "Rhoda Alwyn, the perjured bride," and "Priscilla Wiggins, the man-hater." It is a book to be treasured and is very properly dedicated to "all industrious and worthy females, who have spirit and pride enough to honestly earn their own living, instead of idly subsisting upon the charity and bounty of relatives and friends. . . ."

Orig. cloth.

James Kimball Harley

1828-1889

A Canadian by birth, Harley settled in Baltimore. He studied for some three years in Antwerp, but returned to Baltimore in 1849, where he became a fashionable portrait painter. He committed suicide in 1889. See Groce and Wallace, p. 292.

1697. MARY LEE, OR THE YANKEE IN IRELAND. By Paul Peppergrass, Esq. [John Boyce]. Baltimore: Kelly, Hedian & Piet . . . 1860. Wright II (329).

The frontispiece is signed "Harley" and the half title is signed "J. Harley," both being engraved on wood by Keating. Since the book is a Baltimore publication, it seems likely that these illustrations are the work of James Kimball Harley. Orig. cloth.

Richard G. Harrison

Harrison was born in Philadelphia between 1790 and 1796, and was engraving as early as 1814. Philadelphia directories list him as an engraver from 1825 to 1844 and as a banknote engraver from 1845 to 1861. He was best known as a bank-note engraver but in his younger days occasionally did some wood engraving, as appears from the Item listed below. He seems to have produced 5 sons, all of them engravers. See Groce and Wallace, p. 295.

ALBUM containing over 1000 wood engravings probably used in books published by the American Sunday School Union in Philadelphia during the 1820s. Several engravings bear Harrison's initials. [See Item 1674]

William M. Hart

(See Main Catalogue, p. 139)

THE ILLUSTRATED CHRISTIAN WEEKLY. New York: 1871. 1 illustration by Hart on p. 60, engraved on wood by Brightly. [See Item 1627]

Alonzo Hartwell

(See Main Catalogue, p. 139)

HISTORY OF BOSTON . . . Boston: 1825. Hartwell may have engraved the cut which faces p. 266. If so, it is the earliest work of his which the writer has seen. [See Item 1526]

1698. THE FAITHFUL LITTLE GIRL. A STORY FOR CHILDREN. Boston: Munroe and Francis . . . [cop. 1827]. On the back of the frontispiece is written "Martha P. Pickering's Book 1828." The frontispiece is engraved by Hartwell as is also the wood engraving on the front wrapper. On the back wrapper is a view of the book store of Munroe & Francis. Orig. wrappers.

1699. BIOGRAPHICAL SKETCHES OF GREAT AND GOOD MEN DESIGNED FOR THE AMUSEMENT AND INSTRUCTION OF YOUNG PERSONS. [By Mrs. Lydia Maria (Francis) Child.] Boston: Putnam & Hunt . . . 1828. 10 wood engravings, of which 6 are signed with Hartwell's name or initials. Probably all are his. Orig. boards with leather back. Presented by Seven Gables Book Shop.

TALES OF TRAVELS WEST OF THE MISSISSIPPI. Boston: 1830. The final cut on p. 162 is signed "Hartwell." [See Item 1538]

A PRESENT FROM PETER PARLEY TO ALL HIS LITTLE FRIENDS. Philadelphia: 1831. The final engraving is signed "Hartwell." [See Item 1539]

1700. PS AND QS . . . Second Edition. Hingham: C. & E. B. Gill, 1831. Wright I (2084). The 1st edition was published in 1828. Both editions are scarce. On the title-page is a wood engraving by Hartwell. The name of the draftsman does not appear but the style is very like that of D. C. Johnston. Orig. boards.

YOUTH'S KEEPSAKE. Boston: 1831. Wood engravings by Hartwell will be found on pp. 51, 83, and 216. [See Item 1528]

1701. VOLNEY'S RUINS; OR, MEDITATION ON THE REVOLUTIONS OF EMPIRES. Translated under the immediate inspection of the author from the sixth Paris edition. TO WHICH IS ADDED, THE LAW OF NATURE, AND A SHORT BIOGRAPHICAL NOTICE, by Count Daru: ALSO, THE CONTROVERSY BETWEEN DR. PRIESTLY AND VOLNEY. Boston: Charles Gaylord, 1835.

With wood engravings by Hartwell on the front and back covers. The wood engraving on the back cover also appears as the book's frontispiece. Orig. boards with cloth back. Presented by Sinclair H. Hitchings.

THE CROCKETT ALMANAC 1839. Nashville: Ben Harding [1838]. At least 3 wood engravings by Hartwell. [See Item 1578]

PEOPLE'S ALMANAC [for] 1842. Boston [1841]. 4 wood engravings by Hartwell after drawings by Manning. [See Item 1818]

TALES OF THE OCEAN. Boston: 1842. Contains a large number of wood engravings by Hartwell. [See Item 1819]

MOTHER GOOSE'S MELODIES. Boston [ca. 1845]. Contains at least 2 wood engravings by Hartwell (pp. 66 and 82). Both appeared in Item 690, but the Main Catalogue fails to mention the last of these 2. It will be found at p. 82 of Item 690. [See Item 1459(1)]

1702. RECOLLECTIONS OF THE UNITED STATES ARMY. A SERIES OF THRILLING TALES AND SKETCHES. By an American Soldier. Written during a Period in "The Service," since 1830. Second Edition. Boston: James Munroe and Company, 1845. Wright I (2106).

Contains 8 full-page wood engravings, of which 4 are signed with Hartwell's initial (pp. 26, 54, 63, and 88). George Loring Brown engraved the cut on p. 130. The other 3 are unsigned. The vignette on the title-page is also unsigned. Orig. cloth.

POEMS. By Oliver Wendell Holmes. Boston: 1849. 2 wood engravings probably by Hartwell. [See Item 1502]

ALLEN CRANE. Troy, N.Y.: [ca. 1851]. One of the wood engravings of the frontispiece bears Hartwell's initial as does what appears to be a view of Boston at the head of *Daniel's History.* [See Item 1463]

PLYMOUTH AND THE PILGRIMS. Boston: 1851. Contains 1 cut signed "Hartwell." [See Item 1720]

HISTORY OF BOSTON, FROM 1630 TO 1856. Boston: 1856. Contains 3 engravings by Hartwell. [See Item 1763]

William John Hennessy

(See Main Catalogue, p. 142)

1702a. LADY GERALDINE'S COURTSHIP. By Elizabeth Barrett Browning. New York: Charles Scribner and Company, 1860. This is a deluxe copy of Item 820. It is printed on China paper, a comparatively early use of such paper in this country, of slightly larger sheet size, with marbled end papers and in an unusual morocco binding with a simple gold stamped design. Like Item 820, it was printed by H. O. Houghton and Company, at Riverside, Cambridge.

Mr. O. J. Rothrock, Curator of the Graphic Arts Division of the Princeton University Library, writes about the book as follows: "the China paper and softer toned illustrations do not harmonize very well with the page design, which ought to have been changed. Item 820 is more consistently designed . . . and in that sense is more artful. But I find the Victorian paradox of the de luxe version's failure at art, in striving for art, lends it a certain charm and, in view of the later leadership of H. O. Houghton and Riverside in reviving good design . . . it acquires historical importance."

Orig. morocco.

1702b. THE LAST DAYS OF THE 69TH [New York] IN VIRGINIA. A NARRATIVE IN THREE PARTS. By Thomas Francis Meagher, Captain, Company K ("Irish Zouaves"). New York: Published at the Office of the "Irish American" [cop. 1861]. With a handsome portrait of the author drawn by Hennessy and engraved on wood by Avery.

This 15-page pamphlet contains an account of the actions of the 69th Regiment just before and during the first battle of Bull Run, which was fought on July 21, 1861. Bruce Catton quotes from this pamphlet in his *The Coming Fury*, Garden City, 1961, at pp. 446-47. Orig. wrappers.

SPECIMEN PAGES AND ILLUSTRATIONS FROM APPLETONS' JOURNAL. [New York: 1870.] On the first page of the issue of the *Journal* for December 18, 1869, is a characteristic drawing by Hennessy of "The Poet of our Woods," showing W. J. Bryant sitting in the midst of a woodland scene. The name of the engraver does not appear. [See Item 1731]

1703. EDWIN BOOTH IN TWELVE DRAMATIC CHARACTERS. Boston: James R. Osgood & Company, 1872. With a biographical sketch of Edwin Booth by William Winter. Contains a pictorial title-page and 12 wood engravings by W. J. Linton after drawings by W. J. Hennessy. The latter's drawings of Booth in his 12 roles

are stated to be "from life." They constitute some of Hennessy's best work. Orig. cloth.

John Henry

Henry was an engraver who worked in Philadelphia in 1793 and in Baltimore in 1818. In 1828 we find him in Lancaster, Pa. See Groce and Wallace, p. 309.

1704. AGRICULTURAL ALMANAC, FOR THE YEAR OF OUR LORD 1831 . . . Lancaster, John Bear [1830]. On the front wrapper is a large wood engraving of agricultural significance signed "Henry Sc." Orig. wrappers.

Henry William Herbert (Frank Forester)

(See Main Catalogue, p. 144)

1705. THE COMPLETE MANUAL FOR YOUNG SPORTSMEN . . . By Frank Forester [Henry William Herbert]. New York: Stringer & Townsend, 1856. 1st ed.

Contains full-page frontispiece and 54 small illustrations in the text which are stated to have been "originally designed or adapted [from Craven's *Recreations in Shooting*] and drawn on wood by the author." One of the small cuts (p. 128) is repeated on p. 221. Herbert's initials appear on the cuts on pp. 17 and 222. Most of the illustrations in the first portion of the book are signed by N. Orr—Co. as the engravers. In the portion of the book entitled "Game Fish, and the Best Modes of Fishing Them. For Young Sportsmen" only the cut on p. 363 is signed by N. Orr—Co., but a number are signed by B & E [Bobbett & Edmonds]. The half title is drawn by C. A. Barry. Orig. cloth.

1706. THE DEERSTALKERS: A SPORTING TALE OF THE SOUTH-WESTERN COUNTIES By Frank Forester [Henry William Herbert]. Philadelphia: T. B. Peterson & Brothers, 306 Chestnut Street [ca. 1859?].

Contains 3 illustrations by Herbert, viz.: the frontispiece, "The Bucks and Doe," which is signed by Brightly as the engraver; the half title which is not signed; and, facing p. 88, "The Buck Deer," also unsigned. This latter illustration forms the frontispiece of the 1st edition of 1849, where it is signed "F. Forrester [*sic*] Del." The half title also appears in the 1st edition, where it is signed "F.F.Sc." "The Bucks and Doe," however, was added later and is first found in the 2nd edition of 1852, published by Getz, Buck & Co. In this Peterson edition Forester's name has disappeared from "The Buck

Deer" and his initials from the half title, and there are some slight differences in the cuts which indicate that the illustrations were re-engraved.

This copy corresponds with Van Winkle & Randall's Peterson edition "b," except that the words on the title-page, "Philadelphia: T. B. Peterson & Brothers, 306 Chestnut Street," are in 2 lines instead of 3.* It appears, therefore, to be an unrecorded variant, but where it should be placed in point of time it is difficult to say.

Orig. pictorial wrappers. On the front wrapper appears "The Buck Deer" with some alterations. In cloth case, with the E. R. Gee book-label.

1707. (1) My Shooting Box. By Frank Forester [Henry William Herbert]. With original illustrations by Darley. Philadelphia: T. B. Peterson & Brothers, 306 Chestnut Street [*ca.* 1859?].

This is a later edition of Item 822. It contains the 2 full-page illustrations by Herbert which are found in Item 822, but there are slight differences which indicate that they have been re-engraved and Herbert's name and the names of the engravers have disappeared. The 2 Darley illustrations have also been re-engraved and are signed by Van Ingen, Herrick's name as engraver having disappeared, as has also Darley's name.

This copy corresponds with Van Winkle & Randall's Peterson edition "b," except that the words on the title-page, "Philadelphia: T. B. Peterson & Brothers, 306 Chestnut Street," are in 2 lines instead of 3.** It appears, therefore, to be an unrecorded variant.

Orig. pictorial wrappers. On the front wrapper appears one of the Darley illustrations with some alterations. In cloth case.

(2) Another Peterson edition of *My Shooting Box.* This is Van Winkle & Randall's edition "c" and contains the same illustrations as in (1) above, although differently arranged. It gives the copyright date as 1846, instead of 1848 as in edition "b." The front wrapper is substantially identical with that of (1) above, except that the price of .75 is printed at the bottom. Van Winkle & Randall date it "after 1860."

Orig. pictorial wrappers, in cloth case, with the Harry T. Peters bookplate.

1708. The Quorndon Hounds: or, A Virginian at Melton Mowbray. By Frank Forester [Henry William Herbert]. Philadelphia: T. B. Peterson & Brothers, 306 Chestnut Street [*ca.* 1859?].

* See William M. Van Winkle, *Henry William Herbert . . . A Bibliography of his Writings,* Portland, 1936, pp. 29 and 30.

This is a later edition of Item 828 and contains the same 4 illustrations by Herbert. It corresponds with Van Winkle & Randall's Peterson edition "b," except that the words on the title-page, "Philadelphia: T. B. Peterson & Brothers, 306 Chestnut Street," are in 2 lines instead of 3 and the copyright date is given as 1856, not 1850.*** It appears, therefore, to be an unrecorded variant.

Orig. pictorial wrappers. The illustration on the front wrapper is unsigned and does not appear in the book. In cloth case.

Henry W. Herrick
(*See Main Catalogue, p. 145*)

1709. Not Afraid of a Good Reason. New York: The American Tract Society, 150 Nassau Street [*ca.* 1850]. On p. 11 is a wood engraving by Bookhout after a drawing by Herrick. Orig. wrappers.

The Child's Paper. Vols. I-IV. New York etc.: 1852-1855. An illustration by Herrick will be found on p. 30 of Vol. III. [See Item 1605]

The Rescued Boy. New York: [*ca.* 1860]. With at least 1 illustration by Herrick. [See Item 1987]

Manual of Geography. New York: 1861. On p. 38 is an illustration signed "H.W.H." which is probably by Herrick. It is engraved on wood by Richardson-Cox. [See Item 1642]

1710. Little Threads; or, Tangle Thread, Silver Thread, and Golden Thread. By the author of "Susy's Six Birthdays," "Susy's Six Teachers," "Susy's Little Servants," etc. New-York: Anson D. F. Randolph, 1863. 2 illustrations by Herrick, engraved on wood by N. Orr—Co. Orig. cloth.

1711. John Gay; or, Work for Boys. By Jacob Abbott. New York: Hurd and Houghton, 1864. This is one of a 4-volume set and is called "Work for Spring." Contains 3 full-page illustrations by Herrick, engraved on wood by Richardson. Orig. cloth.

1712. Happy Evenings. New York: Board of Publication of the Reformed Protestant Dutch Church, 1867. With a wood-engraved frontispiece after a drawing by Herrick, the name of the engraver not appearing. There are a number of small unsigned wood engravings throughout the text. Orig. cloth.

** See William M. Van Winkle, pp. 16 and 17.
*** See William M. Van Winkle, pp. 45-46.

PEBBLES AND PEARLS FOR THE YOUNG FOLKS. Hartford: 1868. Contains 2 illustrations by Herrick. [See Item 1939]

1712a. GEMS OF THE BOG; A TALE OF THE IRISH PEASANTRY. By Mrs. Jane D[unbar] Chaplin. Boston: American Tract Society [cop. 1869]. 3 illustrations by Herrick, engraved on wood by Peirce. Orig. cloth.

1713. SPECTACLES FOR YOUNG EYES. New York. By S. W. Lander. New York: Sheldon and Company, 1869.

Contains 12 illustrations, including the half title. Most are anonymous. That facing p. 9 is drawn by Herrick and engraved on wood by M. T. Boyd. Chapin, Perkins and Bellew each have one illustration. The anonymous illustrations, which depict New York characters, such as street-sweepers, the rag-picker, the apple-woman, etc., appear to have been made for the book but the others may have been taken from other publications. This is 1 of 8 volumes, the others covering Boston, St. Petersburg, Peking, Moscow, Zurich, Berlin, and Rome. Orig. cloth.

1714. UNDINE AND OTHER TALES. By Friedrich, Baron de la Motte Fouque. New York: Hurd and Houghton, 1869. One of the "Riverside Classics." With 7 full-page illustrations by Herrick. The only wood engraver's name to appear is that of Peirce at p. 304. Orig. cloth.

1715. WILLIAM GAY; OR, PLAY FOR BOYS. By Jacob Abbott. In Four Volumes. Play for Autumn. New York: Hurd & Houghton, 1869. Contains 3 full-page illustrations by Herrick, probably engraved on wood by Peirce whose name appears on the frontispiece. Orig. cloth.

1716. THE CABIN ON THE PRAIRIE. By Rev. C. H. Pearson. Boston: Lee and Shepard, 1870. With 3 illustrations by Herrick, engraved on wood by Kilburn. This is one of "The Frontier Series" and the Series title is signed "Kilburn." Orig. cloth.

THE SUN-SHINE SERIES. Boston: 1870. Herrick has an illustration in Vol. I of this Series (Honeysuckle Cottage) and another in Vol. V (Timmy Top-Boots). Both are engraved on wood by Peirce. [See Item 1780]

1717. FIRST LESSONS IN NUMBERS, IN THE NATURAL ORDER: FIRST, VISIBLE OBJECTS; SECOND, CONCRETE NUMBERS; THIRD, ABSTRACT NUMBERS. By John H. French, LL. D. New York: Harper & Brothers, 1874. This is number 1 in French's Mathematical Series which first appeared about 1866.

Contains numerous wood engravings. Herrick designed the illustration on the front cover which is repeated on the half title, and his name or initials appear on several others. Probably he was responsible for them all. They must have made the study of numbers a little less dreary than it otherwise would have been. In orig. pictorial boards.

1718. BREAD AND ORANGES. By the Author of "The Wide Wide World" [Susan Bogert Warner]. New York: Robert Carter and Brothers, 1875. 3 full-page illustrations, 2 of which are signed by Herrick and engraved on wood by R. S. Bross. The third is unsigned. Orig. cloth.

THE BODLEYS TELLING STORIES. New York: 1878. Facing p. 102 is an illustration by Herrick, engraved on wood by Fay-Cox. Another illustration by Herrick faces p. 178. The first had appeared in *The Riverside Magazine for Young People* [Item 958] at p. 120 of Vol. I and the other in the same magazine at p. 529 of Vol. III. [See Item 1732]

William F. Herrick

William F. Herrick may have been the brother of Henry W. Herrick. We find him working as a wood engraver in Manchester, N.H., in 1846-1847. Shortly after 1848 he moved to San Francisco and in the 1850s became city editor and later manager of the *Alta California*. Later in life he became an insurance man. As an artist he was principally known for his wood engravings but on occasions he would turn draftsman as well. See Groce and Wallace, p. 311.

HUTCHINGS' ILLUSTRATED CALIFORNIA MAGAZINE. San Francisco: 1857-1861. On p. 1 of Vol. I is a little landscape signed "Herrick Del-Sc." This appears to be his only design for the magazine unless he made the drawings for some of the illustrations which are signed merely "Herrick" (see pp. 194, 195, 439, 441, 443, and 444 of Vol. I). The magazine also contains, especially in its early numbers, a few of Herrick's wood engravings after the designs of others. [See Item 1874]

1719. TRAVELS ON THE WESTERN SLOPE OF THE MEXICAN CORDILLERA, IN THE FORM OF FIFTY-ONE LETTERS . . . By Cincinnatus [Marvin T. Wheat]. San Francisco: Whitton, Towne & Co., 1857. Contains frontispiece or half title and 5 other full-page illustrations, all signed by Herrick. He was certainly the engraver of these and perhaps also the draftsman. Orig. cloth.

A. Hill

(See Main Catalogue, p. 147)

THE HISTORICAL PICTURE GALLERY. Boston: 1856. Among the advertisements are 3 illustrations by Hill. [See Item 1556]

THE WEEKLY NOVELETTE. Boston: 1857-1862. One of the illustrations in *The Bravo's Secret* by Sylvanus Cobb, Jr., one of the illustrations in *The Yankee Champion*, also by Cobb, are signed by Hill and probably all the illustrations in these 2 novelettes are his. Peirce and Tarbell appear to have been the engravers. Miscellaneous illustrations by Hill will be found in Vol. III, pp. 9, 40, and p. 50 of the May 1858 extra; Vol. IV, p. 121; Vol. V, pp. 57 and 345; Vol. VII, pp. 73, 80, 88, 104, 136, 233, 304, and 361; Vol. VIII, pp. 32, 169, 249, and 416; and Vol. IX, pp. 192 and 392. The engravers for these illustrations whose names appear are Peirce, John Andrew, F. E. Fox, Damoreau, and Tarbell. [See Item 1545]

GLEASON'S WEEKLY LINE-OF-BATTLE SHIP. Boston: 1859. Contains 6 illustrations by Hill in the Nos. for March 5, March 26, August 6 (a portrait of Hammatt Billings accompanying an article about him), September 3, October 8 (a view of the Great Eastern), and October 22. The only wood engravers whose names appear are Peirce and Hayes. [See Item 1961]

THE NOVELETTE. Boston: 186?. Novelettes Nos. 9, 99, and 106 contain illustrations by Hill. [See Nos. 5, 30 and 22 of Item 1546]

THE MORMON WIFE. Hartford: 1873. The view of Salt Lake City at p. 89 is signed "A.H." and may be the work of Hill. [See Item 1808]

John Henry Hill

(See Main Catalogue, p. 147)

ALBUM OF WOOD ENGRAVINGS by John Andrew, etc. [*ca.* 1860-1870]. 2 engravings after Hill (Nos. 76 and 77). These illustrations appeared in Item 646. [See Item 1472(3)]

Richard L. Hinsdale

(See Main Catalogue, p. 148)

1720. PLYMOUTH AND THE PILGRIMS; OR, INCIDENTS OF ADVENTURE IN THE HISTORY OF THE FIRST SETTLERS. By Joseph Banvard. Boston: Gould and Lincoln, 1851. Contains a number of wood engravings. The half title is signed "R. L. Hinsdale Del," the name of the engraver not appearing. That at p. 252 might

possibly be Hinsdale's work also. It is signed by Hartwell, the engraver. The small cut on p. 140 is signed "N. Brown," who might have been both engraver and draftsman. Orig. cloth.

THE ILLUSTRATED NEWS. Vol. I. New York: 1853. On p. 172 is an illustration by Hinsdale. [See Item 1836]

DeWitt C. Hitchcock

(See Main Catalogue, p. 148)

THE ILLUSTRATED NEWS. Vol. I. New York: 1853. Hitchcock drew and engraved the masthead (a view of New York Harbor) which was used in the first 10 numbers. Other work of his appears on pp. 5, 13 (engraved by W. Roberts), 69, and 212. [See Item 1836]

COLTON AND FITCH'S INTRODUCTORY SCHOOL GEOGRAPHY. New York: 1856. On p. 62 is an illustration by Hitchcock, engraved on wood by Whitney & Jocelyn. [See Item 1986]

MILLER'S NEW YORK AS IT IS. New York: 1862. View of the City Hall by Hitchcock (p. 30), engraved on wood by Richardson-Cox. [See Item 1971]

WILD SCENES IN SOUTH AMERICA. New York, 1862. An illustration by Hitchcock, engraved on wood by Whitney, Jocelyn and Annin will be found on p. 395. [See Item 1885]

SPARKLES FROM SARATOGA. New York: 1873. 3 illustrations by Hitchcock. They are views in Saratoga. [See Item 1817]

Abram J. Hoffman

A lithographer and engraver of Albany who was active in that city from about 1854 to 1860. See Groce and Wallace, p. 321.

THE ILLUSTRATED AMERICAN BIOGRAPHY. New York: 1854. On p. 330 is a view of Congress Hall in Albany, drawn by Hoffman and engraved on wood by Pease of Albany. [See Item 1964]

Thomas Hogan

(See Main Catalogue, p. 149)

ALBUM OF WOOD ENGRAVINGS by John Andrew, etc. [*ca.* 1855-1875]. 1 engraving after Hogan. [See Item 1472(2)]

SPECIMEN PAGES AND ILLUSTRATIONS FROM APPLETONS' JOURNAL. [New York: 1870.] With 2 folding wood engravings after Hogan, viz.: "The Grand Drive at Central Park," engraved by John Filmer, which had accompanied the first number of the *Journal*, and "Opening Day at Jerome Park," also engraved by Filmer, which had accompanied the number for October 30, 1869. [See Item 1731]

THE ILLUSTRATED CHRISTIAN WEEKLY. New York: 1871. 4 illustrations by Hogan on pp. 136, 180, 189, and 297. The only engravers whose names can be identified are Meeder-Chubb and Bross. [See Item 1627]

Henry Holton
Joseph P. Jardine

Henry Holton and Joseph P. Jardine were wood engravers of New York City who formed a partnership and were active in the fifties. At least one of them held himself out as a draftsman as well, and made some peculiarly atrocious drawings, examples of which will be found in the Item listed below. See Groce and Wallace, pp. 323-24 and 346.

1721. THE TURKISH SPIES ALI ABUBEKER KALED, AND ZENOBIA MARRITA MUSTAPHA: OR THE MOHAMMEDAN PROPHET OF 1854. A TRUE HISTORY OF THE RUSSO-TURKISH WAR. By Lieutenant Murray [Maturin Murray Ballou]. Baltimore, Philadelphia, New York, and Buffalo: A. R. Orton, 1855. Wright II (208).

Contains a half title in chromo-lithograph by one of the Comptons of Buffalo and numerous wood engravings. That on p. 60 is signed "Holton & Jardine Del. & Engr.," that on p. 25 is signed "Jardine & Holton," while those on pp. 43, 54, 80, and 95 are signed "Holton & Jardine." It seems probable that all these illustrations were both designed and engraved by this firm.

The illustrations are poorly printed and in some cases the blocks appear to be worn. Many of them had probably appeared in other publications. 2 bear Darley's name and 1 is signed "Coffin." Orig. cloth.

Winslow Homer

(See Main Catalogue, p. 149)

1722. A COLLECTION OF 260 WOOD ENGRAVINGS after drawings by Homer, removed from *Harper's Weekly* and other magazines (1857-1888). It includes all of those listed by Allen E. Foster in his checklists in the *Bulletin of the New York Public Library*, October 1936,

and July 1940, with the exception of the following Foster Nos.: 152-56, 202-05, 209-11, 216, 223, 224, 246, 8-S, 9-S, 23-S, 26-S, and 32-S.

Foster No. 152 will be found in Item 1546 (No. 2) in this Supplement; Foster Nos. 202-05 and 209-11 will be found in Item 1729 in this Supplement; Foster No. 223 will be found in Item 735 in the Main Catalogue; Foster No. 224 in Item 958 in the Main Catalogue and in Item 1732 in this Supplement; and Foster 26-S in Item 1545 (Vol. VII, p. 272) in this Supplement. Therefore, of Foster's 281 nos. all but 10 are in the Collection.

THE WEEKLY NOVELETTE. Boston: 1857-1862. Illustrations by Homer will be found in Vol. V, pp. 169 and 393; Vol. VI, pp. 185 and 384; Vol. VII, p. 272; Vol. VIII, pp. 73, 392, and 393; and Vol. IX, pp. 120 and 393. The engravers whose names appear are Tarbell, Hayes, Peirce, and Damoreau. All these illustrations first appeared in *Ballou's Pictorial Drawing Room Companion*. In the order given above, they have the following Foster numbers:* 174, 24-S, 159, 25-S, 26-S, 156, 160, 161, 162, and 139. [See Item 1545]

1722a. THE JUMPING JACK'S JOURNEY; OR, THE PERILOUS ADVENTURES OF A JUMPING JACK, A TIN SOLDIER, AND A NUT-CRACKER. Translated from the German by Miss Landor. Boston: Whittemore, Niles, and Hall, 1858.

Contains a few wood engravings of no particular interest. At the end, however, are advertisements of the 12 Juveniles which, in 1858, made up the series of *Mrs. Follen's Twilight Stories* (see Item 1508), each advertisement containing the title-page and (except in the case of the final book of the series, *Little Songs*) the frontispiece.

The title-pages of the first 6 books are each dated 1857 and the frontispieces are by Billings. The title-pages of the final 6 books are each dated 1858 (except that of *Little Songs*, which is dated 1856). The frontispieces of Numbers 7, 8, and 9 bear Homer's initials (see Items 1723, 1724, and 1725). The frontispieces of Numbers 10 and 11 (*Conscience* and *Piccolissima*) are not signed, although the name of D. T. Smith, as engraver, appears on the *Conscience* frontispiece. However, the drawings of these 2 frontispieces bear a sufficient resemblance to those in Numbers 7, 8, and 9 to make it seem more than likely that Homer continued to illustrate the series in Numbers 10 and 11. Orig. cloth.

1723. MAY MORNING AND NEW YEAR'S EVE. By Mrs. Follen [Eliza Lee (Cabot) Follen].

the New York Public Library, October 1936, and July 1940.

* See checklist of Homer's magazine illustrations prepared by Allen Evarts Foster in the *Bulletin of*

Boston: Whittemore, Niles, and Hall, 1858.

With a frontispiece showing a group of boys and girls in a barn. The drawing is quite immature and yet the figure of the lad, who has just had a barrel collapse under his weight, is not unlike some of Homer's later drawings. At the bottom appears the characteristic monogram, "W.H." The illustration is not signed by the wood engraver. There are a number of smaller illustrations, all unsigned, in the text, but none resemble Homer's work.

This is No. 9 of *Mrs. Follen's Twilight Stories*. Homer also drew the frontispiece, in this edition of 1858, for Nos. 7 and 8 [see Items 1724 and 1725]. As these 3 books were all copyrighted in 1857, it is probable that Homer's drawings for them antedated those in *Eventful History of Three Little Mice* [Item 848a] which had previously been thought to be his earliest book illustrations.

The first 6 books of *Mrs. Follen's Twilight Stories* are also in the Collection, but in the edition of 1856, and all illustrated by Billings. For descriptions of these and for further data regarding the volumes added to the series in 1858, see Item 1508.

Orig. cloth.

1724. TRAVELLER'S STORIES. By Mrs. Follen [Eliza Lee (Cabot) Follen]. Boston: Whittemore, Niles, and Hall, 1858. The frontispiece, which apparently illustrates a visit to the Asylum for the Deaf and Dumb in Manchester, England, is signed "W.H." and at least the central figure of the 3 figures shown has a touch of the later Homer. The name of the wood engraver does not appear. There are a number of small wood engravings in the text, but there is nothing to connect Homer with these.

This is No. 7 of *Mrs. Follen's Twilight Stories* (see Item 1723). Orig. cloth.

1725. WHAT THE ANIMALS DO AND SAY. By Mrs. Follen [Eliza Lee (Cabot) Follen]. Boston: Whittemore, Niles, and Hall, 1858. The frontispiece, illustrating an incident on pp. 37-38, is signed with Homer's characteristic monogram. The name of the wood engraver does not appear. There are a number of small wood engravings in the text, but there is nothing to connect Homer with these. Fig. 32.

This is No. 8 of *Mrs. Follen's Twilight Stories* (see Item 1723). Orig. cloth.

1726. BESSIE GRANT'S TREASURE. By Aunt Dora. Boston: Walker, Wise, & Co., 1860. It is copyrighted 1859.

At p. 70 appears the illustration "Bessie Comforting Mrs. Julia" (repeated in the advertisements at the end under the title "Little Bessie consoling Mrs. Julia"), which bears the initials "W.H." and which is referred to in *Alice's Dream* (Item 850) in the Main Catalogue. The frontispiece of "Bessie Showing her Treasure to Winny" (repeated in the advertisements under the title "Winny and Bessie") is also referred to in Item 850. It is not signed. It is, however, quite characteristic of Homer's style and the writer believes it reasonably certain that both illustrations constitute early work of Homer. There is another illustration at p. 26 which is clearly not by Homer. Orig. cloth.

THE NOVELETTE. Boston: 186?. Novelettes Nos. 12 and 88 contain portraits drawn by Homer and Novelette No. 104 contains Homer's "Class Day at Harvard." [See Nos. 12, 24, and 2 of Item 1546]

1727. LEILA AMONG THE MOUNTAINS. Boston: Henry Hoyt [cop. 1861]. Fig. 31.

Contains numerous illustrations. That on p. 30 is signed "Homer," and engraved on wood by Chandler-Duran. Even without this signature, it would be hard to doubt that he was the draftsman. The illustration is not particularly appropriate to the text and it seems likely that it was used in some earlier Boston publication and was probably made before Homer left Boston in 1859.

Hyde has 2 illustrations and H. Muller 1. Orig. cloth.

1728. THE PERCY FAMILY. THE ALPS AND THE RHINE. By Daniel C. Eddy. Boston: Andrew F. Graves . . . 1861. Contains half title showing the "Percy Family," drawn by Homer and engraved on wood by Chandler-Duran, which appeared in the 4 volumes listed in Item 849. This appears to be the fifth and final volume of *The Percy Family in Europe* and, with Item 849, completes the series. Orig. cloth.

1729. HARPER'S BAZAAR. A REPOSITORY OF FASHION, PLEASURE, AND INSTRUCTION. Vols. I-III. New York: Harper & Brothers, 1867-1870. The first 3 volumes of *Harper's Bazaar*, running from November 2, 1867 to December 31, 1870.

Harper's Bazaar was a periodical for women, edited by Mary L. Booth, the historian of New York City (see Item 707). It was lavishly illustrated and became a great success. It is still being published.

Wood engravings which seem certainly to be after drawings by Homer, most of them bearing his initials, will be found on pp. 328-29 (a double-page cut), 588, and 717, of Vol. I, pp. 488 and 620 of Vol. II, and pp. 1 and 473 of

Vol. III. In addition Foster* believes that the cuts on p. 9 of Vol. II and p. 569 of Vol. III may possibly be by Homer, and this writer would not quarrel with such an attribution. Foster also attributes the cut on p. 952 of Vol. I to Homer. This cut is signed "W.H.D.," the "D" being slightly smaller than the "W.H." Foster interpreted this to mean that "W.H." was the draftsman. However, to this writer the work does not appear characteristic of Homer. There was a W. H. Davenport who at one time worked for the Harpers (see Weitenkampf, p. 212), and it is possible that this cut is after a drawing by him, although no other drawings of his appear in the first 3 volumes of *Harper's Bazaar*.

Work by many other illustrators of the period will be found in these volumes, such as Nast, Sheppard, Reinhart, Ehninger, Bellew, Frenzeny, and others. Cloth with leather backs and corners.

1730. A.L.S. from W. J. Linton to Messrs. Roberts of Boston, docketed June 30, 1868, regarding Homer's illustrations for Barnes' *Rural Poems* [Item 855]. Linton writes "I have received from Mr. W. Homer six drawings to be engraved for you, for Barnes' Poems of Rural Life.

"I shall be glad to have your instructions as to price & time and to know if these are all which will appear in the work. With such a house as yours I feel I need not say anything about good printing."

Homer's 6 illustrations for Barnes' *Rural Poems*, published by Roberts Brothers in 1869, constitute some of his most delightful illustrative work. They were actually engraved by W. J. Pierce. It would be interesting to know why Linton lost this commission. He had only come to New York in 1866, and he himself says that his first important engraving work was done for a book published by Scribner in 1869 [see Item 818]. Perhaps the price set by Roberts Brothers was too low to satisfy Linton.

1731. Specimen Pages and Illustrations from Appletons' Journal. [New York: D. Appleton & Co., 1870.]

This is a salesman's dummy or sample book used to secure subscriptions to *Appletons' Journal*. A leaflet giving the 1870 program and the "Splendid Attractions" of the *Journal* is tipped in at the beginning. Then follow 10 steel engravings which had already appeared in the *Journal*, reproducing paintings by American artists. The artists represented are J. F. Kensett (2), A. F. Bellows, Wm. S. Haseltine, J. M.

Hart, F.O.C. Darley, H. Fenn, J. W. Casilear, J. A. Suydam, and A. B. Durand, the engravers being S. V. Hunt (6), R. Hinshelwood (3), and H. B. Hall, Jr. Then follow a number of large, folding wood engravings, which had appeared in the *Journal*. Of these wood engravings, 2 are after drawings by Homer, viz.: "The Beach at Long Branch," engraved by John Karst, which had accompanied the number for August 21, 1869 (Foster 132), and "The Fishing Party," engraved by John Filmer, which had accompanied the number for October 2, 1869 (Foster 133). Samples of the work of other artists are given, e.g., Thomas Hogan (2), A. R. Waud (3), Harry Fenn (2), F.O.C. Darley (1), Gaston Fay (2), Edwin Forbes (1), A. C. Warren (1), and D. E. Wyand (2).

After the sample wood engravings there follow the numbers of *Appletons' Journal* for September 25, 1869, October 23, 1869, November 6, 1869, December 18, 1869, January 15, 1870, and January 22, 1870, and finally a number of blanks on which to enter the names of subscribers.

The first number of *Appletons' Journal* was issued April 3, 1869, and it ran first as a weekly and afterwards as a monthly until 1881 (see Mott, Vol. III, p. 417). It was originally planned to issue with each number a large folding "cartoon" on wood or a steel plate or an illustrated supplement. Samples of each variety are shown in this sample book.

Orig. cloth, decorated in gold.

1732. The Bodleys Telling Stories. By the Author of "Doings of the Bodley Family in Town and Country," "Stories from my Attic," "Dream Children," and "Seven Little People and their Friends" [H. E. Scudder]. New York: Hurd and Houghton . . . 1878.

Contains, facing p. 16, Homer's illustration of "The Moonlight Coast" which first appeared, under the title of "The Midnight Coast," at p. 14 of Vol. I of *The Riverside Magazine for Young People* (Item 958). It also contains work of Bensell, Lucy Gibbons, Gaston Fay, A. P. Close, De Haas, Herrick, Cary, Perkins, and LaFarge, most, if not all, of which had previously appeared in the same magazine. Orig. pictorial boards.

1733. Bookplate of H[ubbard] W[inslow] Bryant of Portland, Maine, dated 1893. It shows a mermaid, flanked by dolphins, with many books falling about her through the water. It is signed "W.H."

Bryant, who was born in Boston in 1837,

---

* See checklist of Homer's magazine illustrations prepared by Allen Evarts Foster in the *Bulletin of*

the New York Public Library, October 1936, and July 1940.

came to Portland in 1861 and carried on the business of an antiquarian bookseller there until his death in 1917. According to information given by a friend of Bryant to one of the book dealers of Portland, Homer often called on Bryant when the former came to Portland from Prout's Neck, and Bryant "pestered" Homer to do the bookplate, Homer protesting that Bryant would probably not be satisfied with it.

For references to the bookplate, see Charles Dexter Allen, *American Book-Plates*, New York, 1894, at p. 353, and *Catalogue of a Loan Exhibition of Book-Plates and Super-Libros held by the Club of Odd Volumes at the Museum of Fine Arts, April 25th to June 5th, 1898*, Boston, 1898, No. 1305 at p. 97. In this catalogue it is described as a photo-mechanical reproduction of a drawing by Homer.

Augustus Hoppin
(*See Main Catalogue, p. 152*)

1734. MY TWO SISTERS: A SKETCH FROM MEMORY. By Emily Judson. Boston: Ticknor, Reed, and Fields, 1854. The half title is by Hoppin, the name of the wood engraver not appearing. Orig. cloth.

1735. TRICKS AND TRAPS OF NEW YORK CITY. PART I. Boston: Charles H. Brainard, 1857. At the top of the title-page are the words "Brainard's Dime-Books." The front wrapper has a woodcut design, with "No. 1" at the right-hand top corner and at the left-hand top corner "10 cents." Then follows "Holcomb & Davis, Designers and Engravers on wood, No. 208 Broadway, New York." Underneath this appear the words "Tricks and Traps of New York. New York: Published by Dinsmore & Co. No. 9 Spruce Street. Mailed free to any part of the United States on receipt of price."

There is a frontispiece, drawn by Hoppin and engraved on wood by Holcomb-Davis, on the back of which is an advertisement of "Brainard's Dime-Books, Illustrated by Hoppin." This advertisement lists the various parts planned in the *Tricks and Traps* Series, 7 parts in all. No mention is here made of Herbert's *Tricks and Traps of Horse Dealers* [Item 1737], and apparently none of the parts here listed (including the present Part I) appeared in *The Spider and the Fly* [Item 899]. It might be noted, however, that the first 3 parts listed correspond with the first 3 listed in *Tricks and Traps of Horse Dealers*, so that there must have been some connection between the two Series.

Following the frontispiece are 4 preliminary pages and then follow pp. [5]-60 of the text. The verso of the final leaf and the recto of the

back wrapper are devoted to advertisements of a sewing machine, while the verso of the back wrapper carries an advertisement for Lovejoy's Hotel at the corner of Park Row and Beekman Street, New York. The verso of the front wrapper carries an advertisement of Dinsmore's publications.

In addition to the frontispiece there are 7 full-page illustrations by Hoppin, engraved on wood by Holcomb-Davis. None of the illustrations appeared in *The Spider and the Fly*. Orig. wrappers, in cloth case together with Item 1737.

1736. A DRAWING by Hoppin, showing a young girl seated at a table which holds a vase of flowers. Her face is in profile and she is leaning on her elbow. While it is not to be found among Hoppin's illustrations in *The Autocrat of the Breakfast Table* (Item 875), the drawing is in much the same style as these illustrations. It is signed "A.H." and dated April 21st, '58, so that it was made at a time when Hoppin must have been working on the book, which was published in November 1858. It is 6 7/16 inches wide by 7 13/16 inches high. Fig. 33.

Thomas Franklin Currier in his article "The Autocrat of the Breakfast Table: A Bibliographical Study," which appeared in Vol. 38 of *The Papers of the Bibliographical Society of America*, at p. 284, discusses Hoppin's illustrations and prints two letters from him to Oliver Wendell Holmes which indicate that Hoppin made at least two attempts at suitable illustrations for *The Autocrat*. In one of these, dated July 27, 1858, Hoppin writes "The 'Autocrat papers' are hardly *illustratable*. There are so many *shades* of ideas, so much that is merely suggested, that it is next to an impossibility to bring them into existence by the pencil. I therefore quite despair of doing any-thing successful in relation to them. I told Mr. Wyman however that I should try again, for the simple *pleasure* of another trial, & I relied upon him to acquaint me frankly with your views of them, & if they did not embody to your perfect satisfaction what you intended to convey, I should insist upon their non-appearance."

It is reasonably clear from this letter that Hoppin's first set of drawings had met with some criticism from Holmes and that Hoppin intended to make a second try at it. It seems plausible to suggest, therefore, that the present drawing, dated only some three months before Hoppin's letter of July 27, 1858, is one of the first set and, if so, that it probably represents his first attempt to depict the school mistress. It makes her appear somewhat young and girlish. In the illustration used in the book Hoppin has given her a more serious deportment and has added a touch of learning by the introduction of the books on the table from which she seems just to have raised her eyes. The drawing is of a less sophisticated girl. Whether or not it was intended for the book, it has Hoppin's gaiety and spontaneity and is typical of his work*

1737. THE TRICKS AND TRAPS OF HORSE DEALERS. By Frank Forester [Henry William Herbert]. Part I. New York: Dinsmore and Company, 1858. This copy, having both the title-page and the wrappers, appears to agree with both Printing A and Printing B of B.A.L. 8163. It seems likely that there was only one printing. In the list of the 7 parts of the *Tricks and Traps* Series on the verso of the title-page, the first 3 parts agree with those listed in Item 1735, but the final 4 differ. These 4 are:

4. TRICKS AND TRAPS OF SEDUCERS—PHILOSOPHY OF SEDUCTION. (In Preparation.)
5. TRICKS AND TRAPS OF HORSE DEALERS—By "Frank Forrester [sic]," of which the present is a copy.
6. TRICKS AND TRAPS OF HORSE DEALERS. By "Frank Forrester [sic]." (In Preparation.) Presumably never published, as Herbert killed himself in 1858 and Part 5 (to quote from its Introduction) "was the last literary work he employed himself upon."
7. TRICKS AND TRAPS OF COURTSHIP AND MARRIAGE. (In Preparation.)

This Part 5 (or Part I of *The Tricks and Traps of Horse Dealers*) contains a portrait of Herbert and 5 full-page illustrations by Hoppin, engraved on wood by Holcomb-Davis.** This Part, together with these illustrations, was reprinted in *The Spider and the Fly* [Item 899].
This first appearance of Herbert's last work is rare. B.A.L. fails to locate a perfect copy. Orig. wrappers, in cloth case together with Item 1735.

1738. POSY VINTON'S PICNIC AND OTHER STORIES. By Mary H. Seymour. New York: E. P. Dutton and Company . . . 1869. The frontis-

piece is after a drawing by Hoppin. Orig. cloth.

1739. CROSSING THE ATLANTIC. Illustrated by Augustus Hoppin. Boston: James R. Osgood & Co., 1872. 1st ed. 24 characteristic illustrations by Hoppin. Orig. boards.
Also a copy of the edition of 1880 with the same illustrations, published in Boston by Houghton, Osgood & Co. Orig. boards.

OLDTOWN FIRESIDE STORIES. Boston: 1872. 11 process blocks after Hoppin and John J. Harley. All of them are in much the same style but unfortunately none are signed. The writer has no information regarding John J. Harley or the date he began illustrating. [See Item 1628]

1740. MARJORIE'S QUEST. By Jeanie T. Gould, author of "A Chaplet of Leaves." Boston: James R. Osgood and Company, 1873. With 8 rather indifferent illustrations by Hoppin. Orig. cloth.

Courtland Hoppin
(*See Main Catalogue, p. 156*)

THE KNOW NOTHING ALMANAC [for] 1855. New York: [1854]. 4 illustrations are signed "Hoppin." They bear little resemblance to the work of Augustus Hoppin and accordingly have been attributed to Courtland Hoppin. [See Item 1839]

1741. PERCY'S YEAR OF RHYMES. New York: Hurd and Houghton, 1867. Contains 6 full-page illustrations, all but one signed "C.H." They are engraved on wood by Fay-Cox. It seems probable that these illustrations are by Courtland Hoppin. Compare, for example, their "C.H." signatures with that on p. 550 of Vol. II of *The Riverside Magazine* [Item 958]. Orig. cloth.

John S. Horton

According to Groce and Wallace (p. 327), John S. Horton was an engraver who worked in Baltimore from 1837 to 1845 and in New York City from 1846 to 1853, where he was asso-

---

* It might be noted that, if, as seems likely, there was a second set of drawings, Holmes did not like these either and tried to have the illustrations eliminated from the copies he was giving his friends (see Thomas Franklin Currier, *A Bibliography of Oliver Wendell Holmes*, New York, 1953, p. 74). In the light of Hoppin's letter, it is difficult to understand why the illustrations were used if Holmes disapproved of them.
** B.A.L. 8163, in describing the Library of Congress copy of this book, mentions "1 folded plate

inserted." This illustration, inserted between pp. 10 and 11, is a view of New York's Astor House, not drawn by Hoppin and engraved on wood by Richardson-Cox. It does not appear to belong to *The Tricks and Traps of Horse Dealers*. The latter, in this Library of Congress copy, is bound with other titles in the *Tricks and Traps* Series, including *Tricks and Traps of New York City*, Parts 1 and 2 and the engraving of the Astor House may well have belonged to one of these where it would have been more appropriate.

ciated with Tudor Horton. He may be the same as the Horton listed by Fielding at p. 176, who probably came from Providence and who in 1830-1835 appears to have engraved portraits and views for Philadelphia and Baltimore publishers.

1742. THE INTRODUCTION TO THE ACADEMICAL READER; COMPRISING A GREAT VARIETY OF PLEASING AND INSTRUCTIVE PIECES, FROM VARIOUS AUTHORS, IN PROSE AND VERSE, INTENDED TO INDUCE AND PROMOTE THE LOVE OF LEARNING, VIRTUE AND PIETY, IN THE MINDS OF JUVENILE CLASSES OF READERS. By John J. Harrod. Baltimore: John J. Harrod, 1830. Fig. 30.

Contains a wood engraved frontispiece and 7 wood engravings of animals in the text. All of these smaller engravings, excepting that of the whale on p. 147, are signed "Horton" or "H." As this is a Baltimore publication, it seems likely that these engravings are the work of John S. Horton of Baltimore. He may also have been the draftsman but on this question the book sheds no light. Orig. boards with leather back. Presented by Alexander D. Wainwright.

1743. PERSIAN FABLES: FOR OLD AND YOUNG. By the Rev. H. G. Keene, M.A. First American, from the last London Edition. Baltimore: John S. Horton, 1836.

Contains 39 wood engravings, 1 repeated. Those on pp. 85 and 90 are signed "Horton" and those on pp. 9 and 87 appear to be signed with the letter "H." John S. Horton was the publisher and probably engraved all the illustrations which were no doubt copied from "the last London Edition." It is an attractive little book. Orig. boards, covered with contemporary cloth.

1744. RUSTIC EXCURSIONS FOR TARRY-AT-HOME TRAVELLERS. A SERIES OF INTERESTING TALES, HAVING A STRICTLY MORAL TENDENCY, AND DESIGNED FOR THE INSTRUCTION OF CHILDREN. By Mrs. Sherwood [Mrs. Mary Martha (Butt) Sherwood]. Baltimore: John S. Horton, 1836.

Contains 8 copperplate engravings unsigned by either engraver or draftsman and 12 wood engraved tailpieces. Of the latter, that on p. 42 is signed "Horton" and that on p. 17 "H." Probably John S. Horton was responsible for them all, but whether as engraver or draftsman or both does not appear. Orig. boards with calf back and corners.

1745. GAMBLING UNMASKED! OR THE PERSONAL EXPERIENCE OF THE REFORMED GAMBLER, J. H. GREEN; DESIGNED AS A WARNING TO THE YOUNG MEN OF THIS COUNTRY; WRITTEN BY HIMSELF. Baltimore: Printed and Published at the Publication Rooms, 1844.

This is another edition of Item 908, listed under "Tudor Horton" in the Main Catalogue. It has the same 9 illustrations, most of which are signed "Horton." Both editions contain copyright notices stating that the book was copyrighted in 1844 by J. H. Green in the Clerk's Office of the District Court of Maryland. In the Main Catalogue it was suggested that Item 908, published in New York in 1844, was the 1st edition but, in view of the place of copyright, it would seem likely that the Baltimore edition preceded the New York edition. This would make it appear that the illustrator was John S. Horton rather than Tudor Horton.

The book seems very rare. In a search made by the Assistant Director of the Peabody Institute in Baltimore, no copy of either the Baltimore or the New York 1844 edition could be found in Baltimore. Orig. wrappers.

Tudor Horton
(See Main Catalogue, p. 156)

1746. THE HISTORY OF THE BOTTLE, AS ORIGINALLY PUBLISHED IN THE NEW-YORK ORGAN. New York: Oliver & Brother, 1848. Wright II (1207). Contains 8 full-page wood engravings each signed "T. Horton & Co.," except one which is signed simply "Horton." As stated on the title-page, they are from engravings designed by Cruikshank. Marbled wrappers, not cont.

1747. THE LOST CHILDREN, A TEMPERANCE TALE, by T. S. Arthur. As Originally Published in The New-York Organ. With Engravings by Tudor Horton. New-York: Oliver & Brother, 1848. Wright II (100). Contains 9 wood engravings, 4 signed "T. Horton & Co. Del. et Sc.," 1 signed "T. Horton Del," 1 signed "T. Horton," 2 signed "T. H." and 1 unsigned. Marbled wrappers, not cont.

MONEYPENNY. New York: 1849-1850. The vignette on the title-page was designed by Horton, who also engraved the frontispiece. [See Item 1601]

1748. THE AMERICAN ILLUMINATED PRIMER; DESIGNED FOR THE USE OF SCHOOLS AND FAMILIES. New York: William H. Murphy [n.d., ca. 1850]. Contains numerous wood engravings. That of "Gathering Fruit" (repeated on front wrapper) is signed "Horton" and that of "The Telescope" is signed "T. Horton & Co." Probably the others came from the same source. Orig. wrappers.

PEBBLES AND PEARLS FOR THE YOUNG FOLKS. Hartford: 1868. The list of illustrations states that the title-page was drawn by Tudor Horton. This probably refers to the half title which is a rather depressing chromo-lithograph. [See Item 1939]

1749. SIX NIGHTS WITH THE WASHINGTONIANS; AND OTHER TEMPERANCE TALES. By T. S. Arthur. Philadelphia: T. B. Peterson & Brothers [cop. 1871]. 6 of the stories in this book were issued in parts in 1842 but apparently without illustrations (see Wright I, 154). Another edition with 5 new stories, again without illustrations, appeared in 1860 under the title of *The Tavern-Keeper's Victims; or, Six Nights with the Washingtonians* (see Wright II, 130). Additional stories appear in this Peterson edition.

There are 7 full-page illustrations signed "T. Horton & Co." and 1 signed "Horton," all illustrating the story of "The Bottle and the Pledge," and there are 2 full-page illustrations signed "H" illustrating "The Reclaimed" and "The Man with the Poker" respectively. They have considerable interest and it seems likely that they are after drawings by Tudor Horton, engraved on wood by his firm. The only other story to be illustrated is that of "The Widow's Son." Here the wood engraver is N. Orr but the name of the draftsman does not appear. The story of "The Widow's Son" was published in the original 1842 edition and the stories of "The Reclaimed" and "The Man with the Poker" appeared in the 1860 edition. "The Bottle and the Pledge" is not to be found in either of the earlier editions.

Cont. morocco.

1750. MY OPINIONS AND BETSEY BOBBET'S. DESIGNED AS A BEACON LIGHT, TO GUIDE WOMEN TO LIFE LIBERTY AND THE PURSUIT OF HAPPINESS, BUT WHICH MAY BE READ BY MEMBERS OF THE STERNER SECT, WITHOUT INJURY TO THEMSELVES OR THE BOOK. By Josiah Allen's Wife [Marietta Holley]. Hartford, Conn.: American Publishing Company . . . 1873. Wright II (1230).

Contains 3 full-page illustrations (pp. 278, 284, and 369) by Horton. 2 smaller illustrations (pp. 335 and 350) are signed "Horton." The full-page illustration at p. 235 is signed "R.H." Could this be Richard Horton of Providence (see Groce and Wallace, p. 327)?

There are also illustrations by James C. Beard and True Williams. Orig. marbled boards with morocco back and corners.

1751. AN INTERESTING TEMPERANCE STORY, THE REFORMED DRUNKARD; Written for Arba Lankton, by Mrs. O. M., of New York. Hartford, Conn.: Arba Lankton, 1874.

Contains a number of wood engravings. The large cut on the back wrapper is signed "T. Horton Del." and some of the others are possibly his also. None of them seem to have much to do with the story and they were probably borrowed from some earlier temperance book. The only engravers whose names appear are D. T. Smith, Bogert, and Andrew-Filmer. Orig. wrappers.

Justin H. Howard
(*See Main Catalogue, p. 156*)

1752. MADELON HAWLEY, OR, THE JESUIT AND HIS VICTIM. A REVELATION OF ROMANISM. By William Earle Binder. New-York: H. Dayton, 1857. Wright II (300). 4 full-page illustrations by Howard, of which at least 2 were engraved on wood by Waggoner. Orig. cloth.

VANITY FAIR. Vols. 1-6. New York: 1859-1862. Drawings by Howard appear in Nos. 114, 116-22, 124, 126-29, and 131 of Vol. 5, and Nos. 132-33, 135-39, 141-44, 146, 148-49, 153, and 155 of Vol. 6. [See Item 1933]

1753. AN EXTREMELY LARGE BROADSIDE advertising the publication for April 7, 1860, in *The New York Mercury*, "the largest two dollar weekly in the world," of the opening chapters of "A New and Soul-Stirring Romance of the Revolution . . . The Swordmaker of the Santee" (see Item 652).

At the top of the broadside is a large wood engraving by Shugg after a drawing by Howard.

The broadside is signed "Cauldwell, Southworth & Whitney, Proprietors" and unblushingly affirms that "The New York Mercury is the Largest, Handsomest, and most Beautifully Illustrated Story Paper in the World! It is All Original, and employs more Literary Talent than all the other New York Weeklies combined! Dr. J. H. Robinson [the author of *The Swordmaker of the Santee*] writes Only for the Mercury."

1754. ANOTHER LARGE BROADSIDE advertising that publication of *Scotto, the Scout; or, The Union Rangers, A Tale of the Great Rebellion*, by Dr. J. H. Robinson, commences in the *New York Mercury* for November 23, 1861. "This thrilling and enchanting tale," says the advertisement, "of glorious exploits, splendid feats of valor, and romantic adventures of our Union Rangers, will prove to be the most brilliant result our National Literature has ever achieved." It is signed in the same name as Item 1753 and contains the statement that each issue of the *New York Mercury* "is illustrated by Darley, the great American Artist."

Almost half of the broadside is taken up with a wood engraving by Shugg after a drawing by Howard, showing a cavalry charge, captioned "Fire when you see the whites of their eyes, Boys." [See also Item 1619]

1755. ARTEMUS WARD IN LONDON, AND OTHER PAPERS. [By Charles Farrar Browne.] New York: G. W. Carleton & Co. . . . 1867. Wright II (394). 6 illustrations by Howard. Orig. cloth.

1756. WIDOW SPRIGGINS, MARY ELMER, AND OTHER SKETCHES. By Mrs. F. M. Whitcher [Mrs. Frances Miriam (Berry) Whitcher]. Edited, with a Memoir, by Mrs. M. L. Ward Whitcher. With Comic Illustrations. New York: Geo. W. Carleton & Co. . . . 1867. Wright II (2698).

The full-page illustration at p. 49 is signed by Howard and those at pp. 97 and 169 appear to be his also. Penfield was the wood engraver. The frontispiece is by Bellew. There are also 2 illustrations signed "B.D." (Benjamin Day?) which illustrate the final sketch "Going to see the President" and which are not nearly so "comic" as those by Howard and Bellew. Orig. cloth.

1757. THE WICKEDEST WOMAN IN NEW YORK. By C[harles] H[enry] Webb. New York: G. W. Carleton . . . 1868. Wright II (269). 8 half-page and a number of smaller illustrations which the title-page states are by Howard. Cloth.

Henry Howe
(See Main Catalogue, p. 157)

HISTORICAL COLLECTIONS OF NEW JERSEY. New York: 1844. The illustration at p. 508 is after a drawing by Howe and others may be his also. [See Item 1485]

Joseph B. Howell

A painter, native of Pennsylvania, who was active in Philadelphia, 1855-1865. His paintings were exhibited at the Pennsylvania Academy. See Groce and Wallace, p. 330.

1757a. CROCKETT ALMANAC [for] 1856. Philadelphia, New York, Boston, Baltimore: Fisher & Brother [1855].

Contains 13 wood engravings, 1 repeated on the title-page. That on the sixth page is signed "Howell" and "H. Sebald sc." and several others have Howell's name. It seems likely that this is the Philadelphia painter, Joseph

B. Howell, and that he designed all the cuts and Hugo Sebald engraved them. However, it is possible that Sebald, who was both an engraver and designer, made the drawings for some of the cuts on which Howell's name does not appear. Sewed.

John Augustus Hows
(See Main Catalogue, p. 158)

ALBUM OF WOOD ENGRAVINGS by John Andrew, etc. [ca. 1855-1875]. 1 engraving after Hows. [See Item 1472(2)]

1758. A FOREST HYMN. By William Cullen Bryant. With Illustrations by John A. Hows. New York: W. A. Townsend & Co. [cop. 1860].

Contains numerous illustrations by Hows, all engraved on wood by N. Orr & Co., except 4 (pp. 13, 16, 20, and 32), which were engraved by Bobbett & Hooper, and 4 others (pp. 17, 21, 22, and 24), which were engraved by Thos. Cox. According to B.A.L. (No. 1668) there were several printings of this book, the sequence not being satisfactorily determined. This is the printing with the words "C.A.Alvord, Printer, New York" on the verso of the title-page. Full morocco, gold-tooled, probably the publisher's binding.

Raphael Hoyle
1804-1838

Born in England, Hoyle came to America with his family when he was about 19 years old. He became a landscape painter and was made a member of the National Academy in 1831. It seems probable that he was the Hoyle who was one of the illustrators of the Item listed below. See Groce and Wallace, p. 331.

THE PANORAMA OF PROFESSIONS AND TRADES. Philadelphia: 1836. The preface states that Hoyle was one of the illustrators, but none of the illustrations are signed by him. [See Item 1866]

R. W. Hulme

PICTORIAL FOR THE MILLION. Philadelphia: 1851. Contains a wood engraving after a drawing by Hulme. [See Item 1500]

Lizzie B. Humphrey
(See Main Catalogue, p. 159)

1759. AN AMERICAN GIRL ABROAD. By Adeline Trafton [Mrs. Adeline (Trafton)

Knox]. Boston: Lee and Shepard . . . 1872. Wright II (1496). 6 full-page illustrations by Miss Humphrey, engraved on wood by John Andrew-Son. Orig. cloth.

1760. LITTLE CANARY'S COUSIN EUGENE. By Mrs. M. A. Osgood. Boston: Lee and Shepard . . . 1873. With frontispiece and 2 other full-page illustrations, all engraved on wood by John Andrew-Son. The monogram on the frontispiece appears to be that of Miss Humphrey and the drawings resemble her other work. This is one of *The Little Canary Series.* Orig. decorated cloth.

1761. TAKE A PEEP. By Paul Cobden. Boston: Lee and Shepard . . . 1874. This is one of "The Beckoning Series." The half title or Series title was drawn by Miss Humphrey and it seems probable that she also made the drawings for the 3 full-page illustrations in the book. John Andrew-Son were the wood engravers. Orig. cloth.

THE GREAT BONANZA. Boston: 1876: According to the Table of Contents, Miss Humphrey illustrated the following articles: "Gold Mining" (6 ills.), "Silver Mining" (7 ills.), "A London Fireman's 'Night of it'" (5 ills.), "Sardines" (7 ills.), and "Ashes of Roses" (6 ills.). This last article is illustrated with sketches by Miss Humphrey "amid the ruins of the Boston Fire." She may also have illustrated the article "A Story of the Olden Time," as her initials appear on the full-page illustration on p. 223. The only wood engraver's name to appear is John Andrew-Son. [See Item 1856]

1762. ODE. INTIMATIONS OF IMMORTALITY FROM RECOLLECTIONS OF EARLY CHILDHOOD. By William Wordsworth. Boston: D. Lothrop and Company [cop. 1884]. Contains 2 illustrations by Miss Humphrey. The engraving was done by George L. Cowee and John Schoelch. There are also illustrations by several other artists, such as Childe Hassam and William T. Smedley, whose work does not fall within the period covered by this Collection. Orig. cloth. Presented by Alexander D. Wainwright.

J. N. Hyde

(See Main Catalogue, p. 160)

ALBUM OF WOOD ENGRAVINGS by John Andrew, etc. [ca. 1855-1865]. 2 engravings after Hyde. [See Item 1472(1) and (3)]

THE HISTORICAL PICTURE GALLERY. Boston: 1856. Among the advertisements are 3 illustrations by Hyde. [See Item 1556]

1763. HISTORY OF BOSTON, FROM 1630 TO 1856. Boston: F. C. Moore & Company, 1856.
Contains numerous wood engravings, many of them forming part of the advertisements which are strewn thickly throughout the book. Hyde made the drawing for the advertisement on p. [55] of John Andrew, "Designer and Engraver on Wood," in which Andrew assures the public that he "continues to execute all orders entrusted to him, in the best style, with promptness, and a due regard to moderation in charges, from A Single Illustration to a whole Book or Illustrated Newspaper." What appears to be Hyde's name also appears on a drawing (engraved by Andrew) of Glades' House, Shirley Point, on p. [86].

J. H. Manning's name appears on the drawing at p. [3] of a charming nude, sitting in a medicated vapor bath, of which he was probably the draftsman. Manning was a member of the firm of designers, Manning & Brown (see Groce and Wallace, p. 421), and the name of this firm appears on one or two of the illustrated advertisements (see pp. [89] and [106]). The work of Taylor & Adams, a Boston firm of wood engravers and designers, will also be found (see pp. [43], [47], [70], and [122]). The advertisement of Daniel T. Smith, "Designer and Engraver on Wood," at p. [94] is of interest, being very possibly designed and engraved by him. Smith was connected with the firms of Baker & Smith, Smith & Pierson, Smith & Hill and Smith & Damoreau (see Groce and Wallace, p. 587). Alonzo Hartwell has an engraving of the Massachusetts General Hospital on p. 180 and smaller engravings on pp. 160 and 166. Other engravers whose work will be found are F. Hedge, F. C. Worcester, W. J. Baker, and N. Brown. Orig. cloth.

LEILA AMONG THE MOUNTAINS. Boston [cop. 1861]. Illustrations by Hyde will be found at pp. 80 and 94, the latter engraved on wood by Cloues. [See Item 1727]

1764. FLORENCE ERWIN'S THREE HOMES. A TALE OF NORTH AND SOUTH. Boston: Crosby and Nichols, 1862. Wright II (924). With 3 illustrations by Hyde, engraved on wood by John Andrew. Orig. cloth.

1765. NINETIETH BIRTH-DAY GATHERING, OF REV. CHARLES CLEVELAND. JUNE 21, 1862. Boston: T. R. Marvin & Son, 1862.
At p. 40 is an illustration by Hyde, engraved on wood by John Andrew. The drawing is after a photograph of the Rev. Mr. Cleveland "giving a loaf of bread to a poor girl," and accompanies some verses relating to this touching event by Mrs. L. H. Sigourney. Other poems

commemorating Mr. Cleveland's 90th birthday are printed in the volume, including one by Adeline D. T. Whitney. This copy was presented by Charles Cleveland to Wm. H. Mackintosh on June 28, 1869, so that he lived to be 97. Orig. cloth.

1766. ZELMA. By Josephine Franklin. Boston: Brown and Taggard, 1862. This is No. VI of the "Martin and Nelly Stories." Contains 4 illustrations by Hyde, engraved on wood by John Andrew. Orig. cloth.

1767. TIM'S SISTER: OR, A WORD IN SEASON. By Mrs. Madeline Leslie [Harriette Newell (Woods) Baker]. Boston: Henry Hoyt [cop. 1863].
Contains frontispiece by Hyde and 4 full-page illustrations, one of which is signed "Hyde." Probably all are his. They are engraved on wood by Peirce (1) and Chandler-Duran (1), the names of the engravers of the others not appearing. This is one of "The Leslie Series of Juvenile Religious Works" and the Series title is drawn by Hyde and engraved on wood by Peirce. Orig. cloth.

1768. UP THE LADDER: OR, STRIVING AND THRIVING. By Mrs. Madeline Leslie [Harriette Newell (Woods) Baker]. Boston: Graves and Young . . . 1863. With 4 full-page illustrations (including the half title) by Hyde, engraved on wood by John Andrew. Orig. cloth.

1769. FRANCES MORTON; OR, THE LIGHT OF WEST MORELANDS. By the author of "Mark Barnett," "Weldon Woods," etc. Boston: Henry Hoyt [cop. 1864]. 3 illustrations by Hyde, engraved on wood by Peirce (2) and Smith-Peirce Co. (1). Orig. cloth.

1770. LIGHT AND SHADE. By Mrs. Madeline Leslie [Harriette Newell (Woods) Baker]. Boston: Henry Hoyt, 1864. With 3 illustrations by Hyde, engraved on wood by Peirce (2) and Felter (1). This is another of "The Leslie Series of Juvenile Religious Works." Orig. cloth.

1771. THE MILL AGENT. By the author of "Opposite the Jail" [Mrs. Mary (Andrews) Denison]. Boston: Graves and Young . . . 1864. Wright II (728). Half title and 3 full-page illustrations by Hyde, engraved on wood by Peirce. Orig. cloth.

1772. ON PICKET DUTY, AND OTHER TALES. By L. M. Alcott [Louisa May Alcott]. Boston: James Redpath [cop. 1864]. Wright II (33). On the front wrapper is a wood engraving by John Andrew after a drawing by Hyde. Orig. green wrappers.

1773. DAVID WOODBURN, THE MOUNTAIN MISSIONARY. By Curris Brandon. Boston: Henry Hoyt [cop. 1865]. Contains 6 illustrations. Of these 4 bear Hyde's name or initials and are engraved on wood by Peirce. The other 2 are unsigned except that what looks like the name of the engraving firm of Chandler-Duran appears on one of them. Modern cloth.
The setting of the story is the Wisconsin frontier. The book appears to be scarce. Wright II (360) locates only one copy.

1774. I WILL BE A SOLDIER. A BOOK FOR BOYS. By Mrs. L. C. Tuthill. Boston: Crosby and Nichols . . . 1865. Half title and 3 full-page illustrations by Hyde, engraved on wood by John Andrew. Orig. cloth.

1775. LITTLE CONQUERORS; OR, THE CHILDREN'S COMFORT-BAGS. By Caroline E. Kelley. Boston: Henry Hoyt [cop. 1865]. Frontispiece and 2 other full-page illustrations by Hyde. Peirce was probably the wood-engraver. The small, and somewhat pleasanter, cuts throughout the book are probably by Hyde also, that on p. 48 being signed "H." Orig. cloth.

1776. THE OLD DISTILLERY; OR, HOPE ARCHER. By A.J.G. [Jane Greenough Avery]. Boston: Henry Hoyt, 1865. Wright II (161). With 4 full-page illustrations, that at p. 97 being drawn by Hyde and engraved on wood by Peirce. That at p. 193, engraved by Smith-Damoreau, is probably after Hyde also. One is after Whitney. Orig. cloth.

1777. THE BROKEN PITCHER; OR, THE WAYS OF PROVIDENCE. By the author of "Luke Darrell, The Chicago Newsboy"; "Mabel Ross, The Sewing-Girl," etc. Chicago: Tomlinson Brothers, 1866. 4 illustrations by Hyde, engraved on wood by Rudd. A Chicago publication before the great fire. Orig. cloth.

1778. ONE-ARMED HUGH, THE LITTLE CORN MERCHANT, OR RALPH AND TIB. By Mrs. A. S. Moffat. Boston: Graves & Young, 1866. The half title and the illustrations facing pp. 199 and 389 are by Hyde, engraved on wood by Peirce (2) and John Andrew (1). The illustration facing p. 300 is probably by Hyde also. It is engraved on wood by Andrew. There is one illustration by E. J. Whitney. Orig. cloth.

QUEER LITTLE PEOPLE. Boston: 1867. An illustration by Hyde, engraved on wood by Kilburn, will be found on p. 179. [See Item 1938]

1779. THE FAMILY DOCTOR, OR, MRS. BARRY AND HER BOURBON. [By Mrs. Mary (Spring) Walker.] Boston: Henry Hoyt [cop.

1868]. With 4 full-page illustrations, engraved on wood by Matthews-Robinson (3) and Morse (1). That engraved by Morse (opp. p. 241) is signed by Hyde who probably made all 4 drawings. Orig. cloth. Fig. 34.

This is a rare temperance novel. Wright II (2610) locates only one copy, that at the American Antiquarian Society. There is, however, another copy at the Huntington Library.

MOTH AND RUST. Boston [cop. 1870]. 1 illustration by Hyde at p. 89, which may have been engraved by Kilburn. [See Item 1551]

1780. THE SUN-SHINE SERIES:
Vol. I. HONEYSUCKLE COTTAGE. By H.N.W.B. Boston: Andrew F. Graves, 1870. 2 full-page illustrations, one by Hyde, the wood-engraver's name not appearing, and the other by Herrick, engraved by Peirce.
Vol. II. THE LITTLE FLORENTINE. By H.N.W.B. Boston: Andrew F. Graves, 1870. The frontispiece, engraved on wood by Felter, is unsigned by the illustrator. There is another full-page illustration engraved by Rudd after a drawing by W. Waud.
Vol. III. THE LOAD OF CHIPS. By H.N.W.B. Boston: Andrew F. Graves, 1870. 2 full-page illustrations, the frontispiece unsigned, the other by Hyde, engraved on wood by S. Cloues.
Vol. IV. TONY AND HIS HARP. By H.N.W.B. Boston: Andrew F. Graves, 1870. 2 wood engravings by Peirce, unsigned by the draftsman.
Vol. V. TIMMY TOP-BOOTS. By H.N.W.B. Boston: Andrew F. Graves, 1870. 2 wood engravings, one by Peirce, and the other by Felter, the frontispiece unsigned by the draftsman, the other drawn by Herrick.
Vol. VI. SOPHIA AND THE GIPSIES. By H.N.W.B. Boston: Andrew F. Graves, 1870. Frontispiece by Hyde, engraved on wood by Kilburn & Mallory. Another engraving by Rudd is unsigned by the draftsman.

These 6 volumes are the complete *Sun-Shine Series*. The authoress is Harriette Newell (Woods) Baker. The Series title, which appears in each volume, is by Billings, engraved on wood by Matthews. All 6 vols. are in orig. cloth.

1781. GUTENBERG AND THE ART OF PRINTING. By Emily C. Pearson. Boston: Noyes, Holmes and Company, 1871. Wright II (1857).

The frontispiece is by Hyde, engraved on wood by Rudd. There are a number of anonymous illustrations and also a number by D. Fisher showing some of the processes involved in the making of a book. Many of these Fisher illustrations are engraved on wood by W. H. Morse. Orig. cloth.

SPARKLES FROM SARATOGA. New York: 1873. 1 illustration by Hyde, a portrait of "The Widow Dash." [See Item 1817]

1782. CHAUNCEY JUDD; OR, THE STOLEN BOY. A STORY OF THE REVOLUTION. By Israel P. Warren. New York: Warren and Wyman [cop. 1874]. Wright II (2653). With frontispiece and 4 other full-page illustrations in the text. That facing p. 59 is signed "J. Hyde Del." The frontispiece bears a signature which looks like "F. Barnes." The others are unsigned. Orig. cloth.

William Samuel Lyon Jewett
1834-1876

A portrait painter and illustrator, Jewett's work appears to have been confined principally to newspapers and periodicals. He covered the trial of John Brown for *Leslie's Illustrated Newspaper* and was expelled from Charlestown (Va., now W. Va.), where the trial took place, under suspicion of being a correspondent for the *New York Tribune*. Several drawings of his appeared in Vols. II and III of *Harper's Bazaar* (listed below). These are signed W.S.L. Jewett. According to Groce and Wallace, he sometimes signed himself "W.J." and it seems likely that the illustrations so signed for James DeMille's novels *Cord and Creese* and *The Cryptogram*, both of which were first published in *Harper's Bazaar*, are his work also. See Groce and Wallace, p. 351.

HARPER'S BAZAAR. Vols. I-III. New York: 1867-1870. Jewett was responsible for the full-page drawing of a "Ladies' Riding-School" on p. 429 of Vol. II. Some other drawings of his, after sketches by others, will be found on pp. 184-85, 313, and 568 of Vol. III. If, as seems likely, the illustrations signed "W.J." are his work, then he was one of the illustrators of James DeMille's *Cord and Creese*, which began in the first number, and also one of the illustrators of Fitz Hugh Ludlow's *The Household Angel*, which began in the number for May 30, 1868, and he illustrated the first 12 chapters of James DeMille's *The Cryptogram*, which began in the number for April 16, 1870, C. S. Reinhart illustrating the balance of the serial.

The Cryptogram was published in book form in 1871 and, in describing this book [Item 1179], the writer suggested that Thomas Worth was responsible for the earlier illustrations. However, it is probable that the monogram on these illustrations stands not for "T.W." but rather for "W.J." and that Jewett is responsible for them. [See Item 1729]

1783. THE MOONSTONE. A NOVEL. By Wilkie Collins. New York: Harper & Brothers, 1868. Fig. 37.

Contains 66 wood engraved illustrations. The initials "W.S.L.J." appear on the illustration on p. 103 and the initials "W.J." on those on pp. 11, 16, 26, 28, 82, 109, 121, 140, 167, 186, 187, and 214. It is probable that these are the work of Jewett. A number carry the initials "C.B." or "C.G.B." or plain "B" and these are probably by Charles G. Bush. Indeed it seems likely that all the illustrations were by either one or the other of these artists. This is the first American edition. Orig. cloth with the bookplate of Barton Wood Currie.

CORD AND CREESE. New York: 1869. The frontispiece and several other illustrations are signed "W.J." Others are certainly by the same hand. They are probably the work of Jewett. [See Item 1894]

David Claypoole Johnston
(See Main Catalogue, p. 162)

1784. THE CAT-FIGHT; A MOCK HEROIC POEM. Supported with Copious Extracts from Ancient and Modern Classic Authors. Meant as Illustrative, though some (not so Immediately Relative) Pressed in by Medium of their Intrinsic Merit; Making Something like what has been Termed a Narrow Rivulet of Text, and Wide Extended Meadow of Notes. By Doctor Ebenezer Mack, Author of "Anatomy in Rhyme," etc. Illustrated with five Engravings, Designed and Executed by D. C. Johnston, of Philadelphia, Author, from Recollection, of "Mathews at Home, In La Diligence, Polly Packet," etc. New York: Sold at 350 Water-Street, 1824.

The 5 comic illustrations bear Johnston's name or initials as both draftsman and engraver. Cont. boards with leather back and corners.

PS AND QS . . . Hingham: 1831. The illustration on the title-page may be after a Johnston drawing. [See Item 1700]

1785. THE PEOPLE'S MAGAZINE. Volume First. Boston: Lilly, Wait, Colman, and Holden, 1834. This volume contains Nos. 1-26 of the magazine, running from March 23, 1833, through March 8, 1834. It was published every other Saturday and did not run beyond March 1836.

On p. 105 is a drawing which is described as being by "Johnson." It is so much in the style of D. C. Johnston that it seems safe to attribute it to him, an attribution which is strengthened by the fact that Johnston in 1833 had contributed the illustrations to *The Life and Writings of Major Jack Downing* (Item 941), also published by Lilly, Wait, Colman, & Holden. The illustration in *The People's Magazine* is engraved on wood by "H. & C." and shows 4 statues, illustrating Burns' "Tale of Tam O'Shanter," then on exhibition in Boston at Harding's Gallery. James Thom of Scotland was the sculptor.

The magazine has many illustrations but only a few are signed. The initials of George Loring Brown appear on 1 (p. 28), those of Abel Bowen on 1 (p. 107), those of J. Downes on 1 (p. 54), and what appear to be those of John H. Hall on 3 (pp. 167, 172, and 198), while Mr. Martins, a Boston artist, contributes a drawing of the town of Lowell. Orig. boards, calf back.

1786. YANKEE NOTIONS. A MEDLEY. By Timo. Titterwell, Esq. [Samuel Kettell]. Second Edition. With illustrations by D. C. Johnston. Boston: Otis, Broaders and Company, 1838. Wright I (1573). Contains 6 Cruikshankian etchings by Johnston. This edition marks the first appearance of these illustrations. Modern cloth.

1787. THREE POLITICAL CARTOONS by D. C. Johnston as follows:

(1) A small campaign piece, engraved by Johnston, used in the Martin Van Buren—William H. Harrison election campaign of 1840. It shows a happy man holding a drinking glass on which are the initials "M.V.B." and the caption reads "A Beautiful Goblet of White-House Champagne." By means of a pull-tab the smile vanishes, the glass becomes a mug with the initials "W.H.H." and the caption changes to "An Ugly Mug of Log-Cabin Hard Cider." This was formerly in the possession of a granddaughter of Johnston.

(2) A small campaign piece, engraved by Johnston, used in the Lewis Cass—Zachary Taylor election campaign of 1848. It shows a man with a broad smile on his face with the caption "Hurra for Cass." By means of a pull-tab the smile gives way to a very mournful expression and the caption changes to "What! Old Zack Elected." Boston: Redding & Co. [*ca.* 1848]. This was formerly in the possession of a granddaughter of Johnston.

(3) Small folded sheet on which is an engraved portrait of Jeff. Davis with the words "Jeff. Davis after the surrender of." Below that is a small window on which appear the words

"Fort Sumter April 13, 1861." By means of a pull-tab, the words in the window change to "Vicksburg July 4, 1863," so that the entire legend now reads "Jeff. Davis after the surrender of Vicksburg July 4, 1863." At the same time the smile on Jeff. Davis' face changes to a very unhappy frown. It was designed and published by D. C. Johnston, probably about 1863.

1788. QUADRUPLE BOSTON NOTION. Extra Number. Boston: Thursday Morning, June 10, 1841. This is a special issue of the *Boston Notion*, of which George Roberts was publisher and proprietor, and is claimed to be "the largest printed sheet yet seen in this or any other country."

Contains several wood engravings after drawings by Johnston, including 7 "Scraps" and a portrait of Daniel Webster from a sketch taken at the Cunard dinner by Johnston, and "The Fruiterer at the Old South Church, N. Washington Street." The masthead also resembles his work. There is 1 illustration by J. H. Manning.

This special number contains 75 poems by Park Benjamin (see B.A.L., Vol. I, No. 1000) which are presented as "the first collected edition of his writings that has been published." It also contains a complete work by Henry William Herbert, "The Fortunes of the Maid of Arc." This had appeared in *The American Monthly Magazine* in 1835-1836 and was reprinted in *Chevaliers of France*, New York, 1853 (see William M. Van Winkle and David A. Randall, *Henry William Herbert*, Portland, 1936, p. 141).

1789. QUADRUPLE BOSTON NOTION. Boston: George Roberts, July 15, 1841. On the first page appear the portraits of President Tyler, Daniel Webster, John C. Calhoun, Henry Clay, General Scott, and Commodore Stewart, "representing the six most prominent candidates for the Presidency in 1844." They were drawn by Johnston and engraved on wood, "expressly for this sheet," by Mallory.

This number, which is stated to be the "second quadruple number of the Boston Notion," contains *The Eve of St. Bartholomew* by Henry William Herbert and extracts from *Reginald Wolfe*, "an unpublished novel by Charles F. Hoffman."

1790. BROTHER JONATHAN. A WEEKLY COMPEND OF BELLES LETTRES AND THE FINE ARTS, STANDARD LITERATURE, AND GENERAL INTELLIGENCE. Vol. I from January 1 to April

23, 1842, and Vol. II from April 30 to August 27, 1842. New-York: Wilson & Company [1842]. While *Brother Jonathan* was founded in 1839, these are the first 2 volumes of the Quarto Library Edition. It ran through December 23, 1843, there being 6 vols. altogether. H. Hastings Weld appears to have been its editor (see p. 438 of Vol. I).

Vol. I, including the "Extra" or "Supplement" which follows immediately after the first number, contains the first 23 chapters of *The Adventures of Tom Stapleton*, by John M. Moore [John McDermott Moore].* The final 3 chapters of the novel appear in Vol. II. These 26 chapters are illustrated with 23 wood engravings. Of these, 14 bear D. C. Johnston's initials and, beginning with Chapter XIX in the number for March 5, 1842, each chapter is headed with the words "Illustrated by D. C. Johnston." It seems likely that he made the drawings for them all with the exception of the final one on p. 53 of Vol. II which, in spite of the chapter heading, bears Manning's name as draftsman. For many of them R. Roberts was the engraver but on some the name "Rafael" appears. Strong engraved the cut by Manning referred to above.

Johnston also designed and Roberts engraved the illustration on p. 281 of Vol. I for John Neal's "Little Joe Junk," a story which appeared in the numbers for March 12 and March 19, 1842. The design which appears on the cover of each weekly number was also engraved by Roberts after a drawing by Johnston, a design also to be found on the title-page of Vol. I which, in this copy, is bound in at the end. Vol. II lacks a title-page. Roberts' engraving on p. 201 of Vol. II may also be after Johnston, for it looks somewhat like his work.

Vol. I contains an interesting letter (p. 15) from James Fenimore Cooper relating to his libel suits, including his "Lost Chapter" for *Home as Found*. At p. 113 of Vol. I will be found "Ambition," a poem by Walt Whitman. This was a revision, with some added lines at beginning and end, of "Fame's Vanity" which had appeared in the *Long Island Democrat* for October 23, 1839 (see *Index to Early American Periodical Literature 1728-1870*, New York, 1941, and Gay Wilson Allen, *The Solitary Singer*, New York, 1955, p. 45).

2 Vols. in orig. boards, with calf backs.

Accompanying these 2 vols. are (a) another copy of Vol. I in cloth and (b) a volume of *Brother Jonathan Supplements or Extras*, containing for the most part first American editions of stories by foreign authors. The dates run from

---

* This was published in book form in 1850 (see Wright I [1913], who locates 2 copies). The few illustrations in the book are entirely different from

those in the *Weekly* and are not by Johnston. There also appear to be some textual variations.

19. Darley. Wash drawing. (Item 1593)

20. Darley. *The Big Bear of Arkansas and Other Sketches*, 1845. (Item 575)

21. Darley. Pencil drawing.
(Item 1624[2])

22. Darley. *Evangeline*, 1867.
(Item 1624[1])

23. Darley. Pen drawing.
(Item 1593)

24. Darley. *Major Jones's Courtship*, 1844. (Item 573)

After paying a sorrowful visit to the tomb of our beloved Joshua, we tore ourselves away from the place of his burial to the place of his birth ; that *where* our joys had risen without limits, *there* our tears might flow without restraint. *Page 90*

25. Dearborn, *A Monument of Parental Affection to a Dear and Only Son*, 1812. (Item 1635)

CAPE COD AND GAY HEAD.

26. Downes. *The American Comic Almanac* [1834]. (Item 1643)

Behold me supporting a drawing of Miss Dormer's, with the innocent and benevolent Viola at my feet, trying her skill in a copy......Thus have I gained my POINT of brightest glory......*P.* 34.

THE HISTORY OF A PIN. As related by itself. INTERSPERSED WITH A Variety of Anecdotes : Pointing out to the Youth of both Sexes, the superiority of a generous Mind over one that is contracted.

Printed and Sold by Whittingham and John Gilman, Middle-street...Newburyport. Feb. 1808.

27. "I.G." *The History of a Pin*, 1808. (Item 1680)

ANDREW JACKSON, MAJOR GENERAL, United States' Army.

28. Hall. *Biographical Sketch of the Life of Andrew Jackson*, 1828. (Item 1691)

29. "C.G." "It was altogether a busy scene." *Tracts of the American Sunday School Union* [1830-1840]. (Item 1688a)

LESSON XLI. *Natural History of the Peacock.*

LESSON VIII. *Natural History of the Lion.*

30. Horton. *Academical Reader*, 1830. (Item 1742)

31. Homer. "Then she spreads her wings . . . to save the young eaglets from falling." *Leila Among the Mountains*, 1861. (Item 1727)

32. Homer. *What the Animals Do and Say*, 1858. (Item 1725)

33. Hoppin. Pen drawing, possibly first attempt at the "School Mistress" for *The Autocrat of the Breakfast-Table*, 1858. (Item 1736)

34. Hyde. *The Family Doctor*, 1868. (Item 1779)

DELAWARE STATION.

35. Lovie. *The Ohio Railroad Guide, Illustrated*, 1854. (Item 1804)

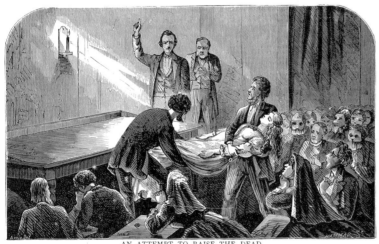

AN ATTEMPT TO RAISE THE DEAD.

"THE deep stillness which succeeded these words was awfully impressive. The door slowly opened, and two men entered bearing a corpse. It was the body of a young and beautiful female, clad in the white habiliments of death, and looking, oh! how ghastly and ghostly in the dim obscurity of the uncertain light."

36. Lovie. *The Mormon Wife*, 1873. (Item 1808)

"TRY TO FORGIVE ME, MAMMA."

37. Jewett. *The Moonstone*, 1868. (Item 1783)

August 17, 1842 to June 3, 1843. Bound in at the end are copies of *Brother Jonathan* for July 23, December 3, and December 10, 1842. There are few illustrations. In the extra for June 3, 1843, Johnston's drawing used in Vol. I to illustrate Neal's "Little Joe Junk" is used again to illustrate a different story. Orig. boards with calf back.

THE CARPET-BAG. Boston: 1851-1852. An illustration after a drawing by Johnston will be found at p. 1 of No. 12. The illustration on p. 1 of No. 28 also looks like his work. [See Item 2000]

1791. THE HOUSE THAT JEFF BUILT. Boston [*ca.* 1863]. 12 etchings by Johnston on a single sheet, each with descriptive poetry. Illustrated are a slave pen, a slave auction, and other scenes of slavery.

Elisha Kent Kane
1820-1857

Kane is best known as an explorer who in the 1850s searched the Arctic regions for Sir John Franklin, missing since 1845. Kane, who had become a surgeon in the United States Navy after graduation from the medical department of the University of Pennsylvania, was senior medical officer in the first expedition to search for Franklin and described his experiences in *The U.S. Grinnell Expedition in Search of Sir John Franklin*, published in 1853. On his return, he organized a second expedition of which he was in command. Franklin's party was not found but, in spite of illnesses and hardships, many important discoveries were made. Kane tells the story of this expedition in his *Arctic Explorations* listed below. It was immensely popular and made a fortune for its publisher, although Kane said of it, "The book, poor as it is, has been my coffin." He died in the year following its publication. See D.A.B., Vol. X, p. 256; Stanley J. Kunitz and Howard Haycraft, *American Authors 1600-1900*, New York, 1938, p. 429.

ARCTIC EXPLORATIONS . . . By Elisha Kent Kane, M.D. U.S.N. Philadelphia: 1856.
The illustrations were by James Hamilton, principally after sketches made by Kane. William Elder in his *Biography of Elisha Kent Kane*, Philadelphia, 1858, at p. 220, prints a letter from Hamilton in which the latter speaks most highly of Kane's sketches and the "air of simple, earnest truthfulness which pervades them." Elder makes them more dramatic by pointing out (p. 223) that "many of them were made in the open air, under a killing tempera-

ture, by a sick man, with the broad shoulders of Morton, Stephenson or McGary for his easel, and lead pencils for his implements." [See Item 1694]

William Keith
(*See Main Catalogue, p. 163*)

BROADSIDE. OVERLAND MAIL ROUTE TO OREGON. JULY 20, 1866. With wood engraving signed by both Keith and Harrison Eastman. [See Item 1647c]

S. S. Kilburn
(*See Main Catalogue, p. 164*)

THE HISTORICAL PICTURE GALLERY. Boston: 1856. Among the advertisements is an illustration by Kilburn. [See Item 1556]

THE WEEKLY NOVELETTE. Boston: 1857-1862. Illustrations signed "Kilburn, Del." or simply "Kilburn" or "K" will be found in Vol. II, pp. 288 and 345; Vol. III, pp. 200, 216, 217, 224, and pp. 38 and 50 of the July 1858 extra; Vol. IV, pp. 80 and 104; Vol. V, p. 137; Vol. VI, pp. 153, 208, and 416; Vol. VII, pp. 57, 120, 169, 185, and 240; Vol. VIII, pp. 24, 25, 64, 153, 168, 344, 345, 360, and 409; Vol. IX, pp. 8, 32, 89, 112, 185, 233, 248, 249, and 272; and Vol. X, pp. 48, 88, 89, 136, 137, 280, 281, 336, 368, and 416. They were probably engraved by Kilburn or his firm but occasionally the name of some other engraver appears, as Brightley (Vol. II, p. 288), Tarbell (Vol. IV, p. 80), John Andrew (Vol. V, p. 137), Peirce (Vol. VIII, pp. 24 and 409, and Vol. IX, p. 89), Damoreau (Vol. VIII, p. 64), and Bricher (Vol. IX, p. 249). [See Item 1545]

GLEASON'S WEEKLY LINE-OF-BATTLE SHIP. Boston: 1859. With 7 illustrations by Kilburn in the numbers for January 1, February 12, April 2, October 22, December 10 (2) and December 17, engraved on wood by Hayes (1), Pilliner (1), and Andrew (2), the others unsigned by the engraver. [See Item 1961]

THE NOVELETTE. Boston 186?. Novelettes Nos. 85, 90, and 102 contain illustrations by Kilburn. [See Nos. 4, 7, and 17 of Item 1546]

Peter Kramer
(*See Main Catalogue, p. 165*)

THE JOHN-DONKEY. New York: 1848. On p. 377 of Vol. I is a cartoon by Kramer, engraved on wood by C. T. Hinckley. [See Item 1597]

Kuchel & Dressel

This firm of San Francisco lithographers consisted of Charles Conrad Kuchel and Emil Dressel. Kuchel was born in Switzerland in 1820 and spent some time in Philadelphia before moving to San Francisco. Dressel came to San Francisco about 1853 and joined forces with Kuchel about 1855. The firm was active between 1855 and 1860 and apparently the partners were fairly proficient draftsmen as well as lithographers. Dressel had been in Oregon in the 1850s and made some views there, and perhaps he was the chief draftsman. See Groce and Wallace, pp. 189 and 377.

HUTCHINGS' ILLUSTRATED CALIFORNIA MAGAZINE. San Francisco: 1857-1861. On p. 295 of Vol. I is a view of Jacksonville signed "C.C. Kuchel-Dressel Del." and on p. 61 of Vol. II is a view of Shasta signed "Kuchel-Dressel Del." Both are engraved by W. C. Butler. [See Item 1874]

John LaFarge

(*See Main Catalogue, p. 165*)

THE BODLEYS TELLING STORIES. New York: 1878. Facing p. 228 is the illustration, "The Wise Men from the East" by LaFarge which first appeared at p. 529 of Vol. II of *The Riverside Magazine for Young People* [Item 958]. [See Item 1732]

George Cochran Lambdin

1830-1896

He was the eldest son of James Reid Lambdin, a Philadelphia portrait and miniature painter. He studied with his father and began exhibiting at the Pennsylvania Academy when he was 18 years old. He is best known as a portrait, genre, and flower painter. Except for two years in New York City, most of his life was spent in Philadelphia. See Groce and Wallace, p. 381.

SKETCHES OF LIFE AND CHARACTER. Philadelphia: 1850. The illustration facing page 290 is signed "G.C.L." and may be early work of G. C. Lambdin. It was engraved on wood by T. & L. [See Item 1583]

Garret Lansing

(*See Main Catalogue, p. 166*)

1792. MEMOIRS OF THE LIFE OF THE LATE LORD H. NELSON . . . New-York: E. Duyckinck, 1811.
The frontispiece, a portrait of Admiral Nel-

son, is signed "L." This is almost certainly the work of Garret Lansing. The book is similar in format to the *Life of Napoleon Bonaparte* (Item 964), published by Duyckinck also in 1811, where Napoleon's portrait is signed with the full name "Lansing." Both books appear to form part of a series of "Small Histories" published by Duyckinck, a list of which appears, in this Item, on the verso of the title-page. Orig. boards with leather back.

1792a. A NEW YEAR'S GIFT. New York: Published by S. Wood & Sons, No. 261, Pearl-street; And Samuel S. Wood & Co., No. 212, Market-street, Baltimore, 1818.
The frontispiece is signed "L" and is similar to the frontispiece in Item 969. However, this Item and 969 are different printings of the book and, while a number of the wood engravings which appear here will also be found in Item 969, there are many differences. This Item is probably the earlier of the 2. Orig. flowered wrappers.

1793. THE COLUMBIAN PRIMER, OR LADDER TO LEARNING. Newark: Benjamin Olds, 1825.
The cut on the title-page and cuts on pp. 15 and 19 are signed "L" and what may be meant for the letter "L" appears on the cut on p. 33. These may be the work of Lansing. Indeed, it is possible that all the small cuts in the book are his work. The frontispiece carries Anderson's "A." Orig. wrappers.

1794. THE HISTORY OF THE WESTERN STATES, ILLUSTRATED BY TALES, SKETCHES AND ANECDOTES. By Lambert Lilly, Schoolmaster [Francis L. Hawks?]. Boston: William D. Ticknor, 1839.
Contains 13 wood engravings (including that on the title-page), not badly done. 2 of these (facing pp. 37 and 48) are signed with the letter "L" which suggests that Lansing might have been employed on this book. Orig. boards, leather back.

Allen V. Lesley

A young artist "of much promise" in 1845 when he was making sketches for the book listed below.

1795. HISTORY OF SCHOHARIE COUNTY, AND BORDER WARS OF NEW YORK; CONTAINING ALSO A SKETCH OF THE CAUSES WHICH LED TO THE AMERICAN REVOLUTION; AND INTERESTING MEMORANDA OF THE MOHAWK VALLEY . . . By Jeptha R. Simms. Albany: Munsell & Tanner, Printers, 1845.

Contains a number of wood engravings, at least 8 of which (pp. 114, 134, 145, 241, 379, 437, 509, and 625) bear Lesley's name or initials as the draftsman. The engravers whose names or initials appear were Hall (probably J. H. Hall who was working in Albany at this time), E. Forbes* (who also made the drawings for at least 2 of the engravings, pp. 123 and 644), J. Fraser (probably J. Fraser of Elmira, N.Y., listed by Groce and Wallace on p. 240), and Pease.

Lesley also made the drawings for a full-page lithograph by Endicott (p. 629) and 3 full-page steel engravings (front. and pp. 355 and 474) which were engraved by Vistus Balch who was active in the first half of the 19th century and headed, from time to time, a number of firms in Albany and New York (see Groce and Wallace, p. 23).

Lesley's landscapes, especially those made for the lithograph and steel engravings, show considerable skill as a draftsman, but he was not so successful when it came to figure drawing. Simms, in his preface to the book, speaks of him as "a young gentleman of much promise, who sketched with accuracy the principal views with which the volume is embellished." He also thanks the engravers, particularly Messrs. V. Balch and E. Forbes, "who have done most of the engraving, for the skillful manner in which they have executed their trust."

Orig. boards.

Emanuel Leutze

(See Main Catalogue, p. 169)

1796. POEMS BY WILLIAM CULLEN BRYANT. With Illustrations by E. Leutze, Engraved by American Artists. Philadelphia: Carey and Hart, 1847.

Contains 19 steel engravings after designs by E. Leutze. Most of them are engraved by W. Humphrys. Other engravers whose work appears are J. Cheney, W. H. Dougal, J. J. Pease, G. H. Cushman, W. E. Tucker, and J. W. Steele. There is a 20th engraving, a portrait of the author, engraved by J. Cheney from a drawing by S. W. Cheney. In the advertisements at the end it is stated that Leutze's designs were made "expressly for this volume." For further information regarding this edition, see B.A.L., Vol. I, No. 1633. Orig. cloth.

VANITY FAIR. Vols. 1-6. New York: 1859-1862. Only 1 illustration by Leutze appeared in *Vanity Fair*, but this was specially featured. It was engraved on wood by Andrew & Filmer. [See Item 1933]

William J. Linton

(See Main Catalogue, p. 169)

1797. MOONFOLK. A TRUE ACCOUNT OF THE HOME OF THE FAIRY TALES. By Jane G. Austin. Illustrated by W. J. Linton. New York: G. P. Putnam's Sons, 1874. With full-page half title and numerous small wood engravings in the text, all probably drawn and engraved by Linton. Orig. cloth.

1798. THANATOPSIS AND THE FLOOD OF YEARS. By William Cullen Bryant. Undated but probably about 1878.

This is a set of artist's proofs of the illustrations drawn and engraved by Linton for these 2 books when they were published by Geo. P. Putnam's Sons. Someone has written in pencil the captions for many of the drawings and here and there in the text appear handwritten corrections. The spine is marked "Ms. J. B. Putnam."

There are 16 illustrations for *Thanatopsis* and Linton acknowledges his indebtedness to "David Scott and William Blake and (almost unknown as an artist) Isaac Taylor." There are 13 illustrations for *The Flood of Years* and these will also be found in Item 982. Timothy Cole's engraving of Bryant after a drawing by Wyatt Eaton, which had appeared in *Scribner's Magazine*, forms the frontispiece.

The Putnam edition of *The Flood of Years* came out in 1878. B.A.L. (1742) gives 2 Putnam editions of *Thanatopsis*, 1 attributed to 1877 and 1 to 1878. However, the illustrations in this Item (1798) could hardly have appeared before 1878 as, in an illustration of a graveyard, Linton has put the date 1878 on one of the tombstones.

Pasted in are 2 letters from Bryant to Geo. P. Putnam's Sons dated June 7, 1876 and December 27, 1876, respectively. The first requests the publisher, in response to a letter from a prisoner in the Nebraska State Prison, to send 2 of Bryant's titles to the prison library. The other requests the delivery to bearer of a copy of Tupper's *Proverbial Philosophy*.

Half morocco.

1799. THE HISTORY OF WOOD-ENGRAVING IN AMERICA. By W. J. Linton. Boston: Estes and Lauriat, 1882.

This is the first history of American wood engraving and is still a book of very real value. It has numerous illustrations, some of which had been engraved by Linton himself (following pp. 40, 44, 66, and 70). This copy is No. 70 of 1000 numbered and 26 lettered copies each autographed by the author. Cloth.

* This is probably Elisha Forbes, a wood engraver listed by Groce and Wallace on p. 234.

This history first appeared in the *American Art Review* in 1880. Accompanying the book are a large number of letters in Linton's hand, written by him in 1879 and 1880 to Sylvester R. Koehler who edited the *American Art Review*. They relate to the preparation of Linton's articles, the efforts to secure illustrations and to locate wood engravers, etc. Many are of particular interest because Koehler frequently attempted to persuade Linton to soften his attacks on the "New School" of wood engraving and a number of the letters relate to this controversy.

Benson J. Lossing

(*See Main Catalogue, p. 169*)

1800. THE HORSEMAN. A WORK ON HORSE-MANSHIP . . . TO WHICH IS ANNEXED A SABRE EXERCISE FOR MOUNTED AND DISMOUNTED SERVICE. By H. R. Hershberger, Instructor of Riding at the U.S. Military Academy. New York: Henry G. Langley, 1844.

Contains numerous interesting cuts showing various phases of horsemanship. All are engraved by Lossing. Possibly he also supplied the drawings, although they are not typical of his work. Perhaps Instructor Hershberger himself had some hand in the drawings. The signature of "Thos. B. Weld, West Point, Jany: 11th, 1845, N.Y." appears on the flyleaf. Orig. cloth.

THE ODD-FELLOWS' OFFERING FOR 1848. New York: 1848. Contains 2 wood engravings, printed in colors, one a view of Odd-Fellows Hall in New York and the other a presentation plate. They are unsigned but the preface states that 2 of the 12 engravings in the book are by "Bro. Benson J. Lossing" and, since the other 10 bear Matteson's name, these 2 must be Lossing's contribution. The list of embellishments indicates that Lossing was also the engraver. The first article in the book is also by him. [See Item 1830]

1801. A PICTORIAL HISTORY OF THE UNITED STATES. FOR SCHOOLS AND FAMILIES. By Benson J. Lossing. New York: F. J. Huntington-Mason Brothers [cop. 1854]. Contains over 200 wood engravings, many of which were undoubtedly after drawings by Lossing and all of which, it may be safely assumed, were engraved by Lossing-Barritt. The frontispiece was drawn by Doepler. Cloth. Presented by James H. Farrell.

1802. NOTICE AND ADVERTISEMENT, dated March 1, 1862, announcing the removal of the Engraving Establishment of Lossing & Barritt (which the notice states is the oldest wood engraving establishment in New York, commenced in 1838) from 71 Nassau Street to the building of the Nassau Bank at the corner of Beekman and Nassau Streets. It is signed by both Lossing and Barritt and holds out the firm as "prepared to execute orders of every kind for Designs, Drawings and Engravings on Wood, such as [here follows an engraving of the Nassau Bank building], Illustrations for Books, Magazines & Circulars . . . and every other kind of Illustration adapted to the art. The large experience of the senior partner (author of the *Pictorial Field Book of the Revolution* [Item 985] and numerous other books) in the Illustration of his own works, gives us special facilities in that department." It is an interesting advertisement in the wood engraving field.

1803. PICTORIAL HISTORY OF THE CIVIL WAR IN THE UNITED STATES OF AMERICA. By Benson J. Lossing. Philadelphia: George W. Curtis, 1866. 3 vols. Vols. II and III were published in Hartford by T. Belknap and are dated 1868.

Each volume, as stated on its title-page, was "illustrated by many hundred engravings on wood, by Lossing and Barritt, from sketches by the author and others." It seems safe to assume that Lossing was himself responsible for the great majority of the illustrations. He made a personal visit to the principal battlefields and other places of interest connected with the war, and the engravings, as the preface to Volume I attests, were prepared under his direct supervision. Orig. cloth.

Henri Lovie
Charles B. Bauerle

(*See Main Catalogue, p. 171*)

1804. THE OHIO RAILROAD GUIDE, ILLUSTRATED. Cincinnati to Erie, *via* Columbus and Cleveland. Columbus: Ohio State Journal Company, 1854. Fig. 35.

The list of illustrations calls for 28, but several illustrations were omitted from the list. The folding frontispiece, the "vignette title" and the illustrations facing pp. 24, 64, 80, 96, 112, and 120 were drawn by Lovie and engraved on wood by Shipley-Stillman. These illustrations were made before the formation of the firm of Lovie & Bauerle, and Bauerle's name appears nowhere. The illustrations facing pp. 20 and 28, which also were after drawings by Lovie, were engraved by Lenoble, apparently an engraver of Cincinnati. In fact, at the bottom of the last of these 2 appear the names "Lovie & Lenoble, Cin." which indicates that Lovie was for a time a member of an earlier firm before he joined forces with Bauerle.

3 of the illustrations are signed simply "Shipley," and 15 bear the name "Telfer," a Cincinnati engraver and designer, whose full name was John R. Telfer.

All of the illustrations have tinted backgrounds. While the drawing is none too good, they are interesting in the light they throw on the early days of railroading.

Orig. cloth.

1805. MAN-OF-WAR LIFE: A BOY'S EXPERIENCE IN THE UNITED STATES NAVY . . . [By Charles Nordhoff.] Cincinnati: Moore, Wilstach, Keys & Co. . . . 1856.

Contains 6 full-page illustrations, all signed "Lovie & Bauerle" except the frontispiece which is signed "L-B." A small cut on p. 237 is signed "L & B" and 2 other small cuts (pp. 199 and 206), while unsigned, are probably the work of Lovie & Bauerle also.

This was Nordhoff's first book, but this is not the 1st edition which was published in 1855. Orig. cloth.

1806. THE MERCHANT VESSEL: A SAILOR BOY'S VOYAGES TO SEE THE WORLD. By the Author of "Man-Of-War Life." [Charles Nordhoff.] Cincinnati: Moore, Wilstach, Keys & Co. . . . 1856. Contains a number of illustrations. 4 of them are signed with the name or initials of Lovie & Bauerle (pp. 33, 152, 200, and 256). This is not the 1st edition which was published in 1855. Orig. cloth.

1807. THE BOOK OF THE GREAT RAILWAY CELEBRATIONS OF 1857 . . . By Wm. Prescott Smith. New York: D. Appleton & Co., 1858.

Contains numerous wood engraved illustrations, including views of Baltimore, Cincinnati, St. Louis, and Columbus. The view of Morrow opposite p. 8 in Part II and that of Milford opposite p. 12 of Part II were drawn by Lovie and engraved on wood by Lenoble.

The cut opposite p. 14 of Part II is signed "Shipley" and was probably engraved either by Henry Shipley or his brother William, both Cincinnati wood engravers who were associated in business (see Groce and Wallace, p. 577). John R. Telfer was responsible for a few of the illustrations. Orig. cloth.

THE ILLUSTRATED CHRISTIAN WEEKLY. New York: 1871. The illustrations on pp. 197 and 213 are signed "Lovie Del." The engravers were R. A. Muller and T. Williams. [See Item 1627]

1808. THE MORMON WIFE; A LIFE STORY OF THE SACRIFICES, SORROWS AND SUFFERINGS OF WOMAN. A NARRATIVE OF MANY YEARS' PERSONAL EXPERIENCE, BY THE WIFE OF A MORMON ELDER, RECENTLY FROM UTAH [Maria Ward]. Hartford, Conn.: Hartford Publishing Company . . . 1873. Wright II (2632). Fig. 36.

Contains a steel engraved portrait of the authoress, and some wood engraved portraits of Mormon celebrities and views in Salt Lake City. The general view of that city at p. 89 is signed "A.H." which may mean that A. Hill was the draftsman. In addition there are a number of cuts illustrating scenes described in the text (see pp. 21, 131, 166, 173, 233, 255, and 325). With the exception of the 2 at pp. 131 and 166, these are signed "Lovie" or "H. Lovie" as the draftsman and "Hammar" as the wood engraver. The latter was probably George D. Hammar (see Groce and Wallace, p. 288). The illustration at p. 131 is well handled but unfortunately the writer has been unable to decipher the name of the draftsman. Lauderbach was the engraver of the cut at p. 166, but it is not signed by the draftsman. On the illustration at p. 255 Lovie has added the letters "N.Y." after his name, which may indicate that, after his work for *Leslie's* during the Civil War, Lovie made New York City his headquarters.

Orig. cloth.

Arthur Lumley
(See Main Catalogue, p. 171)

1809. WILD LIFE; OR, ADVENTURES ON THE FRONTIER. A TALE OF THE EARLY DAYS OF THE TEXAN REPUBLIC, by Capt. Mayne Reid. New York: Robert M. DeWitt [cop. 1859]. A presentation date on the front fly-leaf reads "Sept. 8/60."

With 8 full-page illustrations by Lumley, engraved on wood by N. Orr—Co. It is interesting to note that the name of Orr as the engraver of the "original designs" appears on the title-page, but no mention is made of Lumley. Orig. cloth.

1810. KIT KELVIN'S KERNELS. New York: Rollo, 1860. Wright II (1468). Contains 4 full-page illustrations, one signed "Lumley del." and the others probably his also. They are engraved on wood by J. C. Bruen. Orig. cloth.

1811. CAPTAIN BRAND, OF THE "CENTIPEDE." A PIRATE OF EMINENCE IN THE WEST INDIES: HIS LOVES AND EXPLOITS, TOGETHER WITH SOME ACCOUNT OF THE SINGULAR MANNER BY WHICH HE DEPARTED THIS LIFE. By

Harry Gringo (H. A. Wise, U.S.N.). New York: Harper & Brothers, 1864. Wright II (2775).

Contains 22 full-page illustrations, of which 5 are signed with Lumley's name or initials (pp. 69, 85, 116, 259, and 297). Some of the unsigned illustrations are probably by him also, as, for example, those facing pp. 12, 191, and 208. Several of the illustrations are signed "C.P." which are probably the initials of Charles Parsons. Orig. cloth.

1812. THE CULPRIT FAY. A POEM BY JOSEPH RODMAN DRAKE. With one hundred illustrations, by Arthur Lumley. New York: Carleton, 1867.

This is another copy of Item 996. It is of interest because it is inscribed by the artist to his fellow artist, H. W. Herrick. Tipped in is the presentation letter from Lumley to Herrick which reads "I send you by mail a copy of the 'Culprit Fay.' I know you cannot value it for its illustrations. Please accept it then, as a slight acknowledgment for your kindness to a poor disciple. With my compliments to the Ladies and to your noble self, Ever sincerely [sic] yours. Arthur Lumley."

Orig. cloth.

1813. A SCRAPBOOK formerly belonging to Lumley and containing a number of original drawings by him. There is also a copy of *The Culprit Fay* by Joseph Rodman Drake published by Carleton in New York in 1864 which Lumley has used in working up the illustrations for the edition of 1867 [Item 996]. Laid in it are a number of drawings which Lumley evidently intended for the book but which were discarded. It is an interesting study in the development of an illustrator's ideas.

Accompanying the above is a copy of the 1867 edition of *The Culprit Fay* inscribed "To Mrs. Abby S. Whipple with compliments of the Artist," with 3 letters from Lumley laid in.

HARPER'S BAZAAR. Vols. I-III. New York: 1867-1870. A Thanksgiving Day drawing by Lumley appears at p. 765 of Vol. II. [See Item 1729]

PEBBLES AND PEARLS FOR THE YOUNG FOLKS. Hartford: 1868. Contains 2 illustrations by Lumley. [See Item 1939]

1814. OUR NEW WEST. RECORDS OF TRAVEL BETWEEN THE MISSISSIPPI RIVER AND THE PACIFIC OCEAN . . . By Samuel Bowles. Hartford: Hartford Publishing Co. . . . 1869.

Contains 5 illustrations (pp. 30, 46, 177, 233, and 416) bearing Lumley's name or initial, 3 of which are engraved on wood by Knapp—Co. There are a number of other illustrations but none of them appear to be after Lumley. One, a view of Salt Lake City, is signed "G.P." and may have been drawn by Granville Perkins. Orig. cloth.

1815. TEN YEARS IN WALL STREET; OR, REVELATIONS OF INSIDE LIFE AND EXPERIENCE ON 'CHANGE . . . By Wm. Worthington Fowler. Hartford: Worthington, Dustin & Co. . . . 1870.

Including the portraits of Wall Street celebrities, there are 23 illustrations which are all stated to be from drawings by Arthur Lumley. His name appears on the "Illuminated Title Page" which is opposite the frontispiece and which was engraved on wood by Filmer. The only other engravers' names which appear are those of Wevill & Hammar (p. 151), Pierson (p. 183), Spiegle (p. 273), and Kingdon & Boyd (p. 305). Orig. cloth.

1816. THE HAND-BOOK OF WYOMING AND GUIDE TO THE BLACK HILLS AND BIG HORN REGIONS FOR CITIZEN, EMIGRANT AND TOURIST. By Robert E. Strahorn ("Alter Ego"), of the Western Press. Cheyenne: 1877.

The illustrations on pp. 65 and 193 are by Lumley, engraved on wood by N. Orr—Co. There are a number of other illustrations of Western interest, unsigned by the draftsman. At the end are some Cheyenne advertisements including that of a livery stable's "fine hearse that we run free." Orig. cloth.

R. Lusk
(See Main Catalogue, p. 172)

1817. SPARKLES FROM SARATOGA. By Sophie Sparkle [Jennie E. Hicks]. New York: American News Company, 1873. Wright II (1186).

Contains a frontispiece, presumably a portrait of "Sophie Sparkle," whose draftsman is unidentified, and 9 other illustrations, of which 4 are by Lusk, 3 by D. C. Hitchcock, 1 by J. Hyde, and 1 by Matt. Morgan. Lusk's drawings are somewhat exaggerated burlesques but are not without humor. Orig. cloth. Presented by Seven Gables Bookshop.

John L. Magee
(See Main Catalogue, p. 173)

GLEASON'S WEEKLY LINE-OF-BATTLE SHIP. Boston: 1859. With an illustration by Magee in the number for December 3. [See Item 1961]

Richard P. Mallory

A pupil of Abel Bowen, Mallory worked as a wood engraver in Boston for many years. He was a partner in the engraving firms of Chandler, Wright & Mallory (1836-1839), Wright & Mallory (1839-1852) and Kilburn & Mallory (1852-1865). A panoramic view of Boston, engraved by James Smillie, was drawn by him in 1848. See Groce and Wallace, p. 421.

GLEASON'S WEEKLY LINE-OF-BATTLE SHIP. Boston: 1859. A view from Cambridge Bridge, drawn by Mallory and engraved on wood by Worcester & Co. will be found in the number for December 24. [See Item 1961]

John H. Manning
(See Main Catalogue, p. 173)

1818. PEOPLES ALMANAC FOR 1842. Boston: S. N. Dickinson [1841]. On pp. 29, 31, 34, and 36 are wood engravings by Hartwell, the final 2 being signed by Manning as draftsman. There is an amusing cut for each of the months but these are probably copies of English cuts. Orig. wrappers.

QUADRUPLE BOSTON NOTION. Boston: 1841. Contains an illustration by Manning, engraved on wood by F. & W., showing a most unsightly female and titled "Mamma! why don't the men propose?" [See Item 1788]

BROTHER JONATHAN. Vols. I and II. New York: 1842. The final illustration on p. 53 of Vol. II of *The Adventures of Tom Stapleton* is engraved by Strong after a drawing by Manning. [See Item 1790]

1819. TALES OF THE OCEAN, AND ESSAYS FOR THE FORECASTLE, CONTAINING MATTERS AND INCIDENTS HUMOROUS, PATHETIC, ROMANTIC AND SENTIMENTAL. By Hawser Martingale [John Sherburne Sleeper]. Boston: S. N. Dickinson, 1842.
As listed on p. [viii], there are 44 illustrations, of which 29 are full-page. On 4 of them (pp. 12, 23, 37, and 383) Manning's name appears as draftsman and Hartwell as the wood engraver. Hartwell's name or initial appears on at least 27 others (half title and pp. 49, 57, 67, 83, 91, 126, 165, 185, 191, 201, 218, 220, 223, 231, 240, 243, 256, 279, 314, 331, 345, 358, 365, 406, 419, and 432). The style of most of the listed illustrations resembles that of Manning and it seems likely that most, if not all, of them were drawn by him and engraved by Hartwell. There are a number of un-listed and unsigned tailpieces with which Manning probably had nothing to do. Cont. boards, rebacked.
This is the 2nd edition, the 1st edition having appeared in 1841. Wright I (2446) locates only 1 copy of this 2nd edition, only 3 copies (2445) of the 1st edition, only 1 copy (2447) of the 3rd edition of 1845, and only 2 copies (2448) of the 4th edition of 1846.

1820. DAVY CROCKETT'S ALMANAC, 1844. Philadelphia: Turner & Fisher [1843]. Contains many wood engravings showing the incredible exploits of Davy Crockett. The third cut from the end, showing Crockett separating 2 wild cats, is signed "Manning" and probably many of the others are also after his drawings. Orig. wrappers.

1821. TURNER'S COMIC ALMANAC [for] 1849. Boston: James Fisher [1848]. With numerous comic illustrations. 4 of them carry Manning's initials and others are no doubt his work. Sewed.

1822. ROSALTHE: OR, THE PIONEERS OF KENTUCKY. A TALE OF WESTERN LIFE. By Dr. J[ohn] H[ovey] Robinson. Boston: F. Gleason's Publishing Hall, 1853. On p. 45 (repeated on the front wrapper) is an illustration signed with Manning's initials. Orig. wrappers.
Wright II (2081) locates only 1 other copy of this novel, that at the New York Public Library, but there is another copy in the Barrett Collection at the University of Virginia. In addition to *Rosalthe*, the book contains *The Isle of Crows*, by Mrs. E. C. Lovering.

HISTORY OF BOSTON, FROM 1630 TO 1856. Boston: 1856. Contains some work by Manning and his firm. [See Item 1763]

THE WEEKLY NOVELETTE. Boston: 1857-1862. An illustration by Manning, engraved on wood by Wurzbach, will be found in Vol. X, p. 232. [See Item 1545]

GLEASON'S WEEKLY LINE-OF-BATTLE SHIP. Boston: 1859. With 2 illustrations by Manning in the numbers for September 24 and December 3, both engraved on wood by Leslie. [See Item 1961]

Francis Samuel Marryat
1826-1855

Son of the English novelist, Frederick Marryat, Frank Marryat came to California in 1849 at the age of 23, settling in San Francisco. After a brief return to England in 1852, he came back to California for another year. He died in London at the early age of 29. See Groce and Wallace, p. 424.

1823. MOUNTAINS AND MOLEHILLS, OR RECOLLECTIONS OF A BURNT JOURNAL. By Frank Marryat. New York: Harper & Brothers, 1855.

Contains 8 full-page wood engravings, after drawings by Marryat, engraved by J. W. Orr (5) and Lossing-Barritt (1), the other 2 not being signed by the engraver. In addition there are 16 smaller engravings, several by Lossing-Barritt, also after drawings by Marryat. For the most part they depict scenes of life in California.

An edition of this book was published in London by Longman, Brown, Green and Longmans (see No. 52 of *The Zamorano 80*, Los Angeles, 1945) in the same year as the American edition. In the English edition there are 8 lithographs, "drawn on stone by Messrs. Honhart, from designs by Frank Marryat," which correspond with the 8 full-page wood engravings in the American edition, but a comparison shows that the wood engraver has omitted portions of the drawings in order to reduce their size. The 18 small wood engravings also appear in the English edition but it is stated that they were "drawn on wood by Mr. L. C. Martin, from designs by Frank Marryat." While these 18 cuts in the American edition appear at first glance exactly similar to those in the English edition, a study reveals the fact that the two sets have probably been cut by different hands. It seems likely that the English edition preceded the American.

Orig. cloth.

Theodore (?) Marsden

Marsden was a "Sporting artist best known for his *American Field Sports*, a series of four lithographs published in 1857, and for his horse prints." See Groce and Wallace, p. 424.

ALBUM OF WOOD ENGRAVINGS by John Andrew, etc. [*ca.* 1855-1875]. 1 engraving after Marsden. [See Item 1472(2)]

1824. HOW TO MAKE THE FARM PAY; OR, THE FARMER'S BOOK OF PRACTICAL INFORMATION ON AGRICULTURE, STOCK RAISING, FRUIT CULTURE, SPECIAL CROPS, DOMESTIC ECONOMY & FAMILY MEDICINE. By Charles W. Dickerman, Assisted by Hon. Charles L. Flint . . . Zeigler, McCurdy & Co., Philadelphia, Pa., Cincinnati, Ohio, Chicago, Ill., and St. Louis, Mo. [cop. 1869].

This is the Canvassing Book, used to obtain orders for *How to Make the Farm Pay*, which was issued both in English and German. It contains numerous sample pages from the book and a number of its 140 illustrations. 2 of the illustrations appearing in the Canvassing Book were drawn by Marsden, viz., the horse "Draco Prince" (Fig. 69) and the bull "Honest John" (Fig. 76), both engraved on wood by Matthews-Robinson. Other engravers whose work appears are Baker of Chicago, J. D. Ehlers (listed as John D. Ehlars by Groce and Wallace) of Baltimore, Carson of New York, Murry, and Whittemore. Before the title-page is a steel engraving by Sartain after a painting by P. Moran and a lithograph by Sinclair.

Orig. cloth. Presented by Seven Gables Bookshop.

? Martins

An artist who had established himself in Boston a short time before March 1834.

THE PEOPLE'S MAGAZINE. Vol. I. Boston: 1834. On p. 201 is a view of Lowell and the article regarding it states on p. 202 that "The sketch was taken by Mr. Martins, an artist of first rate abilities who has recently established himself in Boston." [See Item 1785]

Abraham John Mason
(*See Main Catalogue, p. 175*)

THE AMERICAN TRACT MAGAZINE. New York: 1829-1840. A wood engraving signed "Mason" appears in the issue for March 1830. Mason did not arrive in New York from London until December 1829 (see Groce and Wallace, p. 427). This cut, therefore, represents extremely early work of his in this country. [See Item 1440]

FOX'S BOOK OF MARTYRS. Philadelphia: 1832. 10 of the wood engravings bear Mason's name but some of the unsigned plates are no doubt also his work. [See Item 1444]

1825. A PORTFOLIO FOR YOUTH. By Robert Ramble [John Frost]. Philadelphia: J. Crissy, 1835. It was copyrighted in 1835 by John Frost.

With full-page frontispiece and some 55 smaller wood engravings in the text. That on p. 91 is signed "Mason" and, since this is a Philadelphia publication, it is tempting to assign most of these engravings to William Mason. However, they seem somewhat too elegant, and perhaps also too late, for William and hence they are credited here to A. J. Mason. They have the appearance of having been copied from English cuts. One of them bears Bowen's initials. Full cont. morocco.

THE PANORAMA OF PROFESSIONS AND TRADES. Philadelphia: 1836. With 3 or 4 exceptions, all of the illustrations in this book were engraved on wood by Mason. [See Item 1866]

William Mason
(See Main Catalogue, p. 176)

1826. AMERICANISCHER STADT UND LAND CALENDER AUF DAS 1815TE JAHR CHRISTI . . . Philadelphia: Conrad Zentler [1814]. On the second leaf is a wood engraving signed "Mason," depicting a lion hunt in the East Indies. It seems likely that this is the work of William Mason, generally supposed to have been Philadelphia's first wood engraver. Sewed.

1827. THE HISTORY OF LITTLE PHOEBE, AND THE RECLAIMED CHILD. [By Elizabeth Somerville.] Hartford: Hale & Hosmer, 1814.
Contains a number of rude cuts. That on p. 8 is signed "M" and it is possible that this is very early work of Mason, done while he was an apprentice of Abner Reed at Hartford. While he is supposed to have left Hartford for Philadelphia in 1810, some 4 years before the date of the book, the cut may well have been made earlier than this. Orig. wrappers. Presented by Sinclair H. Hitchings.

ALBUM containing over 1000 wood engravings probably used in books published by the American Sunday School Union in Philadelphia during the 1820s. One engraving signed "Mason" and another signed "M." [See Item 1674]

1828. DER HOCH-DEUTSCHE AMERICANISCHE CALENDER, AUF DAS JAHR 1825 . . . Germantaun, gedrucket und zu haben bey M. Billmeyer [1824]. On the front cover is Sower's old cut which Michael Billmeyer had no doubt acquired when he bought the Germantown almanac (see Items 104 and 62). On A² recto is a cut signed "Mason," which, in view of its early date, may well be the work of William Mason. Sewed.

Tompkins Harrison Matteson
(See Main Catalogue, p. 177)

1829. BROTHER JONATHAN. GREAT PICTORIAL BATTLE SHEET. AN ILLUSTRATED HISTORY OF THE VICTORIES AND CONQUESTS OF THE AMERICAN ARMY IN MEXICO. New-York: Wilson & Co., 1847.

This issue of Brother Jonathan consists of 8 pages, each approximately 32 inches long and 22 inches wide, and is devoted to "The Life of General Zachary Taylor, and a History of the War in Mexico." The first page is largely occupied by an enormous wood engraving of General Taylor on horseback and in full military dress. It is signed with Matteson's initials. There are numerous other wood engravings throughout, many of them of large dimensions. That of "American Troops in Monterey" on p. 4 is signed "T. H. Matteson" and was engraved by S. F. Baker & Bros. Matteson's initials appear on 2 illustrations on p. 5, one engraved by S. F. Baker & Bro. and the other by J. W. Orr.

1830. THE ODD-FELLOWS' OFFERING FOR 1848. Edited by James L. Ridgely and Paschal Donaldson. New York: Edward Walker, 1848. Contains 10 illustrations by Matteson, engraved on steel by Rice & Buttre. There are also 2 wood engravings after designs by B. J. Lossing. Orig. decorated cloth.

1831. (1) BROTHER JONATHAN—CHRISTMAS AND NEW YEARS, 1852. No. 25 of the quarterly issues of this periodical. Edited by Benjamin H. Day. New York: Wilson and Company, 1852.
The greater portion of the first page is occupied by a series of wood engravings by S. P. Avery, after designs by Matteson. It is entitled "Reverie of the Oldest Inhabitant" and depicts scenes of his boyhood and youth. The editor, in describing the engraving, speaks of Matteson as "our favorite artist."
The 2 center pages are entirely devoted to a series of wood engravings after Matteson's designs showing "Santa Claus' Christmas Journey." The editor expresses a good deal of enthusiasm for this "beautiful and spirited design" and goes on to say: "The block from which we take the impressions of this grand picture, has cost us within a fraction of One Thousand Dollars. We regard it as by far the most meritorious and costly Engraving on Wood that has ever been attempted." Several engravers were employed upon it. The names of Avery and Howland appear and the initials "J.A.C."
(2) Also a double page wood engraving or series of engravings after designs by Matteson showing "The Career of a Country Girl in New York." They depict the "progress of a lovely woman from innocence and happiness, through shame and infamy to despair and death." They follow her from her meeting with her seducer in "one of the splendid Ice Cream Saloons on Broadway" through nights of revelry, prostitution, theft, and suicide, with the horrified se-

ducer of her youth sitting as one of the coroner's jury. The enthusiastic editor does not hesitate to say: "The series of pictures of the Downward Road . . . is drawn with a truthfulness, a power, and an artistic talent, which must give to Matteson a high rank in the world of art. In many great qualities, these pictures compare favorably with the best works of Hogarth, Cruikshank, and Grandville." The engraver's name does not appear. Fig. 38.

On the back is an advertisement of *The Illustrated Family Almanac for 1851* as "just issued." It is probable that these engravings formed part of the Christmas number of *Brother Jonathan* for 1850.

Mott, Vol. I, pp. 359-62, tells something of *Brother Jonathan*.

THE CHILD'S PAPER. Vols. I-IV. New York, etc.: 1852-1855. An illustration on p. 3 of Vol. IV, signed T.H.M. and engraved on wood by P. Annin, is probably after a drawing by Matteson. [See Item 1605]

Ann Maverick
(See Main Catalogue, p. 178)

1832. THE CHIEF'S DAUGHTER: OR, THE SETTLERS IN VIRGINIA. New York: General Protestant Episcopal Sunday School Union and Church Book Society [n.d. but an inscription on the fly-leaf is dated January 8th, '68]. The frontispiece, dramatically depicting Pocahontas saving the life of John Smith, is signed "Ann Maverick." Orig. marbled boards, cloth back.

Christian Mayr
(See Main Catalogue, p. 179)

1833. NEW YORK IN SLICES: BY AN EXPERIENCED CARVER: BEING THE ORIGINAL SLICES PUBLISHED IN THE N. Y. TRIBUNE. Revised, Enlarged, and Corrected by the Author [George G. Foster]. New York: William H. Graham, 1849. 121 pp.

This is the 1st edition of Item 1030. It contains the same illustrations as Item 1030, except that Mayr's view of Broadway is not repeated on p. 116. Instead there appears a wood engraving of the American Art Union after a drawing by S. Wallin, unsigned by the engraver. Orig. boards, rebacked.

Wright I (980) locates only 1 copy of this book, that at Yale University, but there is also a copy in the Barrett Collection at the University of Virginia.

* Some of these difficulties are more fully discussed in the article in the first number (December 15,

Jervis McEntee
(See Main Catalogue, p. 179)

ALBUM of wood engravings by John Andrew, etc. [*ca.* 1855-1875]. 1 engraving after McEntee. [See Item 1472(2)]

John McLenan
(See Main Catalogue, p. 180)

1834. AUTOBIOGRAPHY OF AN ENGLISH SOLDIER IN THE UNITED STATES ARMY . . . New York: Stringer & Townsend, 1853. On the half title is a wood engraving by J. W. Orr after a drawing by McLenan. It is difficult to say whether the unsigned frontispiece, also engraved by Orr, is after McLenan. Orig. cloth.

1835. THE CRYSTAL PALACE COMIC ALMANAC [for] 1854. New York: T. W. Strong [1853]. The title-page cut is by McLenan and there are 35 comic illustrations throughout the text, 23 of which bear McLenan's initials. A few of them will be found in Item 1839 and it is probable that many of them had first seen the light of day in Strong's *Yankee Notions*. Sewed.

1836. THE ILLUSTRATED NEWS. Vol. I. January-July, 1853. New York: [P. T. Barnum, Special Partner, H. D. & A. E. Beach, General Partners, 1853].

This early illustrated weekly was at first a decided success, its circulation, within a month after the publication of the first number, reaching 70,000. However, as Barnum tells us, such enormous difficulties* arose that the two general partners became disheartened and at the end of 1853 the goodwill and the engravings were sold without loss to *Gleason's Pictorial* in Boston. The editor of *The Illustrated News* was Rufus W. Griswold assisted by Charles Godfrey Leland. [See P. T. Barnum, *Struggles and Triumphs*, Hartford, 1870, at p. 380, and Mott, Vol. II, pp. 43-44.] The 26 numbers of this first volume cover the first half of 1853. Only 22 additional numbers were issued before the sale of the paper.

The volume is full of wood engravings, many unsigned. McLenan has at least 14 drawings (pp. 78, 93, 108, 160, 184, 228, 312, 329, 333, 364, 408[2], 409, and 412). The only engravers whose names appear in connection with McLenan's drawings are J. W. Orr, J. F. Badeau, and Leslie. These drawings are very

1855) of *Frank Leslie's Illustrated Newspaper*, p. 5.

early work of McLenan and it is interesting to note that D. C. Hitchcock, who brought Mc-Lenan to New York, also has several drawings in the volume.

The work of numerous other illustrators will be found in the volume, such as Bellew, Billings, Dallas, Darley, Devereux, Doepler, Goater, Hinsdale, W. R. Miller, Parsons, Schussele, Waud, and others.

Much of the engraving for *The Illustrated News* was done by Frank Leslie, who came to New York at the end of 1852. He is supposed to have invented the process of cutting a wood block, after the drawing had been made on it, into a number of pieces and parceling these out among a number of engravers, thus enabling the block to be ready for printing much more quickly than if one engraver had cut the whole block. The double page view of the "Inauguration Ceremonies of the Crystal Palace" in the issue of *The Illustrated News* for July 30, 1853, marks a very early use of this process (see the article on Leslie in D.A.B., Vol. XI, p. 186).

1837. Love's Lesson. By the Author of "Timid Lucy." New York: General Protestant Episcopal S.S. Union, and Church Book Society, 1853. With frontispiece and half title engraved on wood by N. Orr after drawings by McLenan. Orig. boards with modern cloth back.

1838. The New York Journal; An Illustrated Literary Periodical. Vols. I and II. New York: [Printed and Published for the Proprietors, by P. D. Orvis, 75 Nassau Street, 1853-1854].

Illustrations by McLenan will be found on pp. 16, 32, and 48(3), engraved on wood by N. Orr and J. W. Orr. On pp. 360 and 361 in the issue for January 1854 are 2 of his illustrations from *Hot Corn* (Item 1043) which had been "just published" by DeWitt and Davenport.

Other American illustrators whose work appears are Chapin, Devereux, Gunn, Voight, and Wallin. There are many wood engravings of rather poor quality throughout, most of which appear to have been re-engraved from foreign sources. Some of the engravers used were the Orrs, S. M. Beck, Van Vranken, and Badeau.

This periodical began as a weekly, the first number being that for the week ending July 2, 1853. The last weekly issue was that for August 20, 1853. Thereafter it became a monthly. It was sold in December 1854 to Frank Leslie, who in January 1855 began a new series under the title *Frank Leslie's New York Journal of Romance, General Literature, Science and Art.* This was Leslie's second magazine, soon to be followed by his most famous periodical, *Frank Leslie's Illustrated Newspaper.* See Mott, Vol. II, p. 31.

Orig. cloth with leather back.

1839. The Know Nothing Almanac [for] 1855. New York: T. W. Strong [1854]. Contains numerous comic illustrations. 6 carry McLenan's initials and some of the others resemble his work. Illustrations by [Courtland?] Hoppin and Gunn are also to be found. Sewed.

1840. Mrs. Partington's Carpet-Bag of Fun. With 150 Engravings, from Designs by Darley, McLenan, Leech, Phiz, Henning, Cruikshank, Hine, Doyle, Tenniel, Goater, Crowquill, etc. By S. P. Avery. New York: Garrett & Co., 1854. Wright II (164).

This is the 1st edition of Item 1046 and contains the same illustrations. In addition there is a full-page design by McLenan on the front wrapper, which does not appear in the text, and on the verso of the front wrapper there is a design by McLenan illustrating *Scenes in the Life of an Actor.* Other illustrations signed with McLenan's initials will be found on the title-page and on pp. IV, 34, 245, 289, and 300. The same 2 illustrations by Darley are present which are contained in Item 1046. Orig. wrappers, in cloth case.

1841. Swell Life at Sea; or, Fun, Frigates, and Yachting: a Collection of Nautical Yarns. From the Log-Book of a Youngster of the Mess. New York: Stringer & Townsend, 1854. Wright II (2414). The half title is signed by McLenan and the frontispiece also looks like his work. Both are engraved on wood by N. Orr. Orig. cloth.

1842. Young America's Comic Almanac. 1855. New York: T. W. Strong [1854]. Contains numerous comic illustrations, many of which carry McLenan's name or initials. Sewed.

1843. Flora's Dictionary. By Mrs. E. W. Wirt, of Virginia. Baltimore: Lucas Brothers, No. 170 Baltimore Street [cop. 1855].

The half title and the presentation page (which shows that the book was presented to Miss Lucy F. Burke by her Friend George, December 25th, 1856) were lithographed and printed in colors by A. Hoen & Co. of Baltimore. They contain floral designs, and McLenan was the designer of both. The wood engraving by J. W. Orr on p. 20 may also be after a drawing by McLenan for it resembles his work. There are 6 other lithographed plates of flowers, printed in color but unsigned.

There are numerous small wood engravings, chiefly of flowers, in the text and wood engraved page-borders throughout. J. W. Orr was the engraver but the name of the draftsman does not appear. Possibly it was Orr himself. In this connection it is interesting to note that, while Orr's name appears on a vast majority of the pages, in only one instance is it followed by the letters Sc.—that of the engraving on p. 20 which, as suggested above, may be after a drawing by McLenan.

Orig. cloth, elaborately ornamented in gold, a delightful Victorian binding.

1844. PRINCE LIFE; A STORY FOR MY BOY. By an Old Author [G.P.R. James]. New-York: James S. Dickerson, 1855. With 3 full-page illustrations by McLenan, engraved on wood by Avery. Orig. cloth.

COLTON AND FITCH'S INTRODUCTORY SCHOOL GEOGRAPHY. New York: 1856. On p. 56 is an illustration whose signature appears to be that of McLenan. It is engraved on wood by Whitney & Jocelyn. [See Item 1986]

A NEW FLOWER FOR CHILDREN. New York: 1856. The cut on p. 154 bears McLenan's initials and the initials on the cut on p. 157 are possibly his also. Both cuts were probably engraved on wood by Avery. [See Item 1685]

HUTCHINGS' ILLUSTRATED CALIFORNIA MAGAZINE. San Francisco: 1857-1861. On p. 240 of Vol. V, under the caption "California Cartoons—No. II," is an illustration with McLenan's initials. It is also signed "A.A." which suggests Anderson as the engraver. It would be interesting to know how this specimen of McLenan's work drifted to California. [See Item 1874]

1845. AMERICAN WIT AND HUMOR. Illustrated by J. McLenan. New York: Harper & Bro's [cop. 1859].

Contains numerous comic drawings by McLenan. No wood engraver's name appears. The preface states that "This rich and readable book is gathered mainly from the Drawer of Harper's Magazine." For comments on the origin of "The Editor's Drawer" of *Harper's Magazine* and the character of its humor, see Mott, Vol. II, p. 388. Modern cloth.

VANITY FAIR. Vols. 1-6. New York: 1859-1862. A drawing by McLenan will be found on p. 7 of Vol. 2. [See Item 1933]

COLLEGE TRAMPS. New York: 1880. The illustration on p. 23 bears McLenan's initials.

It must represent the later use of an old cut. [See Item 1544]

William McLeod (or MacLeod)

McLeod, a landscape painter, exhibited in New York City in 1848 and again in 1852-1853. In 1857 we find him in Washington, D.C. His subjects included views on the Hudson, Delaware, and Susquehanna rivers, in the Highlands of Scotland and in New England. See Groce and Wallace, p. 417; Mary Bartlett Cowdrey, *American Academy of Fine Arts and American Art-Union, Exhibition Record 1816-1852*, New York, 1953, vol. 2, p. 239.

1846. HARPERS NEW-YORK AND ERIE RAILROAD GUIDE . . . New York: Harper & Brothers [cop. 1851].

Contains 136 wood engravings by Lossing and Barritt from original sketches made expressly for the work by McLeod. These neat little landscapes are well engraved and have genuine appeal. Orig. cloth.

J. McNevin
(See Main Catalogue, p. 185)

1847. LIFE OF COL. FREMONT. New York: Greeley & M'Elrath [cop. 1856]. With 2 illustrations (pp. 11 and 19) by McNevin. That on p. 19 is engraved on wood by J. W. Orr. Pamphlet issued without wrappers.

1848. ALE IN PROSE AND VERSE. By Barry Gray [Robert Barry Coffin] and John Savage. New York: Russell's American Steam Printing House, 1866.

This book has 3 sections: (1) "A Runlet of Ale," by Barry Gray; (2) "Ale: Antiquarian, Historical and Literary," by John Savage; and (3) "Albany Ale, an account of the rise and progress of the brewery of John Taylor & Sons."

"A Runlet of Ale" has 8 full-page illustrations which are stated to be by McNevin. Most of them are signed by him. They are lithographed by A. Brown. There is also a frontispiece by McNevin, lithographed by Brown. Orig. cloth.

Larkin Goldsmith Mead
1835-1910

Larkin G. Mead, a sculptor, was born in New Hampshire and raised in Vermont. From 1853 to 1855 he studied sculpture under Henry Kirke Brown. In 1862 he went to Italy where he married. Most of his life was spent in Italy with, however, numerous visits to the United States.

His brother was the Mead of McKim, Mead & White, the architects, and his sister married William Dean Howells. See Groce and Wallace, p. 435.

1849. SCHOOL DAYS AT RUGBY. By an Old Boy [Thomas Hughes]. Boston: Fields, Osgood, & Co., 1870. With 8 illustrations by Mead, engraved on wood by Kilburn-Mallory. The figures in these illustrations have a sculptural quality. Orig. cloth. Presented by Alexander D. Wainwright. Fig. 39.

Frank Thayer Merrill
1848-

Born in Boston in 1848, Merrill was educated at the Roxbury High School and studied art at the Lowell Institute and at the Museum of Fine Arts. He spent most of his life in his native city and was one of the founders of the Boston Etching Club. The bulk of his work as an illustrator, and his most important work, belongs to the period after 1880. However, some of his earlier work has been acquired for the collection. See *American Artists and their Works*, Vol. I, Boston [1889]; Weitenkampf, pp. 12 and 227; Fielding, p. 239.

ALBUM of wood engravings by John Andrew, etc. [*ca.* 1855-1875]. 20 engravings after Merrill. [See Item 1472(2)]

1850. THE HOLLANDS. By Virginia F. Townsend. Boston: Loring [cop. 1869]. Wright II (2507). With 4 illustrations by Merrill, engraved on wood by John Andrew-Son. Orig. cloth.

1851. MOODS. By Louisa M. Alcott, Author of "Little Women," "An Old-Fashioned Girl," "Hospital Sketches." Boston: Loring, *ca.* 1870. Fig. 40.

With 6 full-page illustrations (including the half title) by Merrill, engraved on wood by John Andrew-Son. *An Old-Fashioned Girl*, mentioned on the title-page, was published in 1870 and hence this book has been dated "*ca.* 1870." It is probably the 1st illustrated edition. Foley erred in stating that the 1st edition of 1864 was illustrated. Orig. cloth.

PUNCHINELLO. New York: 1870. With 6 illustrations by Merrill (Vol. I, pp. 120, 151, 174, 240, and 397, and Vol. II, p. 168). [See Item 1227]

1852. THE DEERINGS OF MEDBURY. By Virginia F. Townsend. Boston: Loring [cop. 1871]. Wright II (2536). With 4 illustrations by Merrill, engraved on wood by John Andrew-Son. Orig. cloth.

1853. THE MILLS OF TUXBURY. By Virginia F. Townsend. Boston: Loring [cop. 1871]. Wright II (2540). With 4 illustrations by Merrill, engraved on wood by John Andrew-Son. Orig. cloth.

1854. EIGHTY YEARS ASHORE AND AFLOAT, OR THE THRILLING ADVENTURES OF UNCLE JETHRO . . . By E. C. Cornell. Boston: Andrew F. Graves [cop. 1873]. These are "tales of Martha's Vineyard, Cape Cod, and all along shore."

With 3 illustrations. That facing p. 175 is by Merrill and engraved on wood by John Andrew-Son. The others are probably not Merrill's work. On the fly-leaf is a presentation inscription in the author's hand, dated January 31st, 1874. Orig. cloth.

THE MARVELLOUS COUNTRY. Boston: 1873. At least 3 illustrations by Merrill. [See Item 1942]

1855. BROUGHT TO THE FRONT; OR, THE YOUNG DEFENDERS. By Elijah Kellogg. Boston: Lee and Shepard . . . 1876. With 6 full-page illustrations, 3 of which are signed by Merrill. All are probably his. This is one of "The Forest Glen Series." Orig. cloth.

1856. THE GREAT BONANZA. ILLUSTRATED NARRATIVE OF ADVENTURE AND DISCOVERY IN GOLD MINING, SILVER MINING, AMONG THE RAFTSMEN, IN THE OIL REGIONS, WHALING, HUNTING, FISHING, AND FIGHTING. By Oliver Optic, R. M. Ballantyne, Capt. Chas. W. Hall, C. E. Bishop, Frank H. Taylor, and other Popular Writers. With Two Hundred Illustrations, by W. L. Sheppard, Frank Merrill, H. L. Stephens, Miss L. B. Humphrey, and other well-known Artists. Boston: Lee & Shepard . . . 1876.

According to the Table of Contents numerous illustrations by Merrill appear in the articles "The Great Bonanza," "Vacation in Petrolia," "Getting on Sea Legs," and "The Battle of Bunker Hill." Cuts signed with Merrill's name or initial will be found on the frontispiece and on pp. 36, 37, 42, 44, 45, 46, 103, 139, 146, 194, and 237. The only names of wood engravers to appear are those of John Andrew-Son and Kinnersley-Johnson. Orig. cloth.

PIONEERS IN THE SETTLEMENT OF AMERICA. Boston: 1876-1877. 2 illustrations by Merrill in Vol. I (opposite pp. 44 and 229). [See Item 1922]

1857. ADIRONDACK TALES. By W.H.H. Murray. Boston: The Golden Rule Publishing Co., 1877. With 8 full-page illustrations which are stated on the title-page to be "Designed by

Darley and Merrill. Engraved by James S. Conant." Merrill's name or initial appears on those facing pp. 12, 70, 220, and 442. The rest look like Merrill's work. None resemble the work of Darley. Orig. cloth.

1858. JUST HIS LUCK. Boston: Lee and Shepard . . . 1878. 6 full-page illustrations, several of which are signed "M." This is the first volume of "Our Lucky Series" written "by a famous writer for the young, whose name is withheld for 'Luck.'"

1859. THE PRINCE AND THE PAUPER. A TALE FOR YOUNG PEOPLE OF ALL AGES. By Mark Twain [Samuel L. Clemens]. Boston: James R. Osgood and Company, 1882. 1st American ed. An inscription on the fly-leaf is dated 1881.

Contains numerous illustrations by Merrill. Some of the illustrations, however, appear to be by a different hand. The only engraver's name to appear is that of Harley and his name or initial is not to be found on any of the cuts which are after Merrill's drawings. Orig. cloth, in half morocco case.

1860. OUR BASE BALL CLUB AND HOW IT WON THE CHAMPIONSHIP. By Noah Brooks. New York: E. P. Dutton and Company, 1884. With 10 full-page illustrations by Merrill. Orig. decorated cloth.

Miller (of Cincinnati or Philadelphia)

It is probable that the Miller whose name appears on 2 of the illustrations in the book listed below was a resident of Cincinnati, although at this time Barclay, the publisher, would sometimes use a Philadelphia craftsman in books copyrighted in Ohio (see Item 1886). It is possible that the Miller in question was William Miller (1835?-1907) who was a miniature painter and was working in Cincinnati about the time when the book was copyrighted (see Groce and Wallace, p. 445), although the illustrations hardly seem the work of a professional painter.

1861. THE STARTLING AND THRILLING NARRATIVE OF THE DARK AND TERRIBLE DEEDS OF HENRY MADISON, AND HIS ASSOCIATE AND ACCOMPLICE, MISS ELLEN STEVENS, WHO WAS EXECUTED BY THE VIGILANCE COMMITTEE OF SAN FRANCISCO, ON THE 20TH SEPTEMBER LAST. Edited by Rev. P. Shelden Drury. Cincinnati: Barclay & Co., 234 Main St. [cop. in Southern District of Ohio, 1857]. On the front wrapper the imprint is

Philadelphia: Barclay & Co., 734 Market Street.

The full-page frontispiece is signed "Miller Eng." and the full-page illustration facing p. 12 is signed "Miller." They are crude efforts and probably the wood engraver was the draftsman as well. There are 2 other full-page illustrations in the text, a smaller illustration on both front and back wrappers and a portrait of Miss Ellen Stevens on the title-page. All are unsigned and are more sophisticated than those by Miller. They do not appear to be his work. Orig. wrappers.

Wright II (793) locates only 2 other copies.

William Rickarby Miller
(See Main Catalogue, p. 186)

THE ILLUSTRATED NEWS. Vol. I. New York: 1853. Illustrations by Miller will be found on pp. 73, 108, 109, 116, 176, 196, 197, 204, 212, 232, 281, 288, 328, 336, 349, 372, and 373. They include views of Concord, N.H., Washington, D.C., the Naval Academy at Annapolis, Trinity College, Hartford, and Charleston, S.C. The only engravers whose names appear are Leslie, E. Hooper, S. J. Pinkney, and Swinton & Fay. [See Item 1836]

THE WEEKLY NOVELETTE. Boston: 1857-1862. Illustrations by Miller will be found in Vol. II, pp. 96 and 128; Vol. IV, p. 96; Vol. V, p. 329; Vol. VII, p. 9; Vol. IX, p. 345; and Vol. X, p. 360. The engravers whose names appear are Bricher, Strong, Major, Peirce, S. J. Pinkney, and C. Minton. [See Item 1545]

GLEASON'S WEEKLY LINE-OF-BATTLE SHIP. Boston: 1859. With 3 illustrations by Miller, one a view of The Narrows at New York (number for June 18), one of Yale (number for November 19) and one a view on the Baltimore & Washington Railroad (number for December 24). The 2 latter were engraved by S. E. Brown. [See Item 1961]

William Momberger
(See Main Catalogue, p. 186)

THE CARPET-BAG. Boston: 1851-1852. An illustration of the Patent-Office drawn by Momberger and engraved on wood by W. E. Bridges will be found on p. 5 of No. 28. [See Item 2000]

1862. FORM LETTER OR BROADSIDE, dated July 2, 1855, issued by George F. Cooledge of 323 Pearl Street, New York, addressed "to whomsoever this may come" and reading "Friend: Should you or any of your acquaintances at any time have any good Business Notes for which the money is wanted and a discount of one per cent per month perfectly agreeable, I shall be most happy to receive a call from either you or them . . . Respectfully Yours, Geo. F. Cooledge, N.S. Business-Note Shaver. Wm. P. Cooledge, Atty." The top half of the sheet contains a wood engraving by Anderson after a drawing by Momberger showing a gentleman standing outside the Cooledge establishment. It bears the caption "I've got some notes I'd like to get shaved. Wouldn't mind the *rate*!!"

1863. LILIES AND VIOLETS; OR, THOUGHTS IN PROSE AND VERSE, ON THE TRUE GRACES OF MAIDENHOOD. By Rosalie Bell. New York: J. C. Derby . . . 1855. The frontispiece, engraved on steel by J. C. Buttre, is after a drawing by Momberger and there are also 7 small wood engravings by N. Orr after drawings by Momberger.

This is an anthology, containing the work of many writers, and dedicated to "that fond and youthful sisterhood, the maidens of my native land." In commending it to her sex, the editor assures her readers that her labors will be far more than requited "if, happily, its perusal shall serve to encourage any daughter's footsteps to walk more diligently the path of Wisdom, Beauty, and Love."

Orig. cloth.

MILLER'S NEW YORK AS IT IS. New York: 1862. View of the old City Armory or Arsenal by Momberger (p. 44), engraved on wood by Richardson-Cox. [See Item 1971]

1864. THE UNION PACIFIC RAILROAD COMPANY, CHARTERED BY THE UNITED STATES. PROGRESS OF THEIR ROAD WEST FROM OMAHA, NEBRASKA, ACROSS THE CONTINENT. MAKING, WITH ITS CONNECTIONS, AN UNBROKEN LINE FROM THE ATLANTIC TO THE PACIFIC OCEAN. Five Hundred Miles Completed October 25, 1867. New York: Brown & Hewitt, Printers, 1867.

On the front wrapper is an elaborate wood engraving by Lossing-Barritt, after a drawing by Momberger, showing various scenes across the continent. It is an entirely different drawing from that in Item 1865. Orig. wrappers.

1865. PROGRESS OF THE UNION PACIFIC RAILROAD WEST FROM OMAHA, NEBRASKA, ACROSS THE CONTINENT, MAKING, WITH ITS CONNECTIONS, AN UNBROKEN LINE FROM THE ATLANTIC TO THE PACIFIC OCEAN. Eight Hundred and Twenty Miles Completed September 20, 1868. New York: published by the Company [Pamphlet Edition, September 20th, 1868].

On the front wrapper is an elaborate wood

engraving after a drawing by Momberger. The name of the engraver does not appear. The tailpiece on p. 5 is also after Momberger. Orig. wrappers.

Isaac W. Moore

A portrait and landscape painter working in Philadelphia in 1846-1858. See Groce and Wallace, p. 452.

ANNALS OF PHILADELPHIA AND PENNSYLVANIA, IN THE OLDEN TIME. Philadelphia: 1856. 1 illustration, which is probably by Isaac W. Moore, engraved on wood by Baxter & Harley. [See Item 1868]

Thomas Moran
(See Main Catalogue, p. 187)

THE GREAT SOUTH. Hartford: 1875. Contains over 50 illustrations by Moran. The wood engravers whose names appear are Bookhout, Varley, King, Speer, W. Roberts, Bogert, Miller, Lauderbach, David Nichols, J. P. Davis, and Treat. [See Item 1919]

McGUFFEY'S SECOND ECLECTIC READER. Cincinnati and New York [cop. 1879]. With 4 illustrations by Thomas Moran (pp. 43, 111, 119, and 139), engraved on wood by Jueng-Mill. [See Item 1907a(2)]

Matthew Somerville Morgan
1839-1890

Born in London, Morgan did not come to the United States until 1870. He was a painter and worked for a time in New York. Later he went to Cincinnati where he founded the Art Students' League. His series of large panoramic pictures of Civil War battles was exhibited in Cincinnati in 1883. He had his studio in New York where he died in 1890. See Fielding, p. 247.

SPARKLES FROM SARATOGA. New York: 1873. The illustration at p. 97 of "Miss Airs," whose style of walking resembled "the proud strutting of the peacock," is credited to Matt. Morgan in the List of Illustrations. [See Item 1817]

John Ludlow Morton
(See Main Catalogue, p. 189)

1866. THE PANORAMA OF PROFESSIONS AND TRADES; OR EVERY MAN'S BOOK. By Edward Hazen. Philadelphia: Uriah Hunt, 1836.

This is an earlier edition of *Popular Technology*, New York, 1843 [Item 1103]. It is probably the first appearance of the book. It is in one volume and contains all the same wood engravings which appeared in Item 1103, including Morton's frontispiece or half title. The cut at the head of the Preface on p. vii was not used in Item 1103. The text appears to be substantially the same except that in the later edition occasional paragraphs are added here and there. In the earlier edition, however, several paragraphs appear in the Preface which were dropped in the later edition and one of these tells us something about the artists involved. This reads: "In the embellishment of 'The Panorama,' great expenses have been incurred. . . . The designs were made by Messrs. Morton, Hoyle, Burton, and Gimber, of New York; and nearly the whole of the engraving was executed by Mr. A. J. Mason, of the same city, but lately from London. The first title,* the cut representing some of the operations of the manufacturer, and the illustrations of architecture and of optics, were engraved by R. S. Gilbert, of Philadelphia." The initials C.B. will be found on 4 of the cuts. These are probably the initials of C. Burton. None of the other illustrations is signed by the draftsman. Mason's name or initials appear on several of the cuts.

Morton's frontispiece will be found also on the back cover, and the cut of "The Author," which appears on the title-page and on p. 177, was used again on the front cover.

This copy is inscribed in pencil "To R. S. Gilbert, by the Author, Ed^d Hazen. July, 1836." These words have been traced over in ink, probably by Gilbert himself. Gilbert's own signature, "R. S. Gilbert Engraver on Wood Phila," appapers on the second fly-leaf. Orig. boards with leather back.

E. F. Mullen

(*See Main Catalogue, p. 189*)

VANITY FAIR. Vols. 1-6. New York: 1859-1862. Quantities of drawings by Mullen appear in these volumes. [See Item 1933]

1867. MRS. LEARY'S COW. A LEGEND OF CHICAGO. By C. C. Hine. New York: The Insurance Monitor, 1872. With many wood engravings, a number of which bear Mullen's name or initials. No doubt all are by him. This is a scarce pamphlet issued shortly after the Chicago fire to promote the cause of insurance. Orig. wrappers.

* This refers to Morton's frontispiece or half title.

H. Muller

LEILA AMONG THE MOUNTAINS. Boston [cop. 1861]. An illustration by Muller, engraved on wood by N. Orr, will be found on p. 59. [See Item 1727]

Thomas H. Mumford

(*See Main Catalogue, p. 190*)

1868. ANNALS OF PHILADELPHIA AND PENNSYLVANIA, IN THE OLDEN TIME; BEING A COLLECTION OF MEMOIRS, ANECDOTES AND INCIDENTS OF THE CITY AND ITS INHABITANTS, AND OF THE EARLIEST SETTLEMENTS OF THE INLAND PART OF PENNSYLVANIA, FROM THE DAYS OF THE FOUNDERS . . . Embellished with Engravings, by T. H. Mumford. By John F. Watson. In Two Volumes. Edition of 1856. Philadelphia: Whiting & Thomas, 1856.

In 20 numbers or parts, numbers 9 and 10 being bound together. At the beginning of each number are several illustrations, for the most part wood engravings and for the most part comprising views in or near Philadelphia. There are over 50 wood engravings. Mumford's name or initials will be found on some 14 of them (see Nos. 1, 4, 6, 7[3], 8[2], 9-10[2], 11[2], and 13[2]). The majority of the wood engravings bear the names of Van Ingen & Snyder, a firm of Philadelphia engravers, but in many instances these names probably relate to the ornamental borders surrounding the main engravings and not to the engravings themselves. In fact in the 4 instances where the letters "Sc." follow Mumford's name (see Nos. 4, 7, 8, and 9-10), the Van Ingen & Snyder signature appears between the main engraving and the ornamental border. It seems probable, from the wording of the title-page, that for most of the wood engravings Mumford was either draftsman, engraver, or both. In any event the work is well done and the wood engravings form an attractive series. The final engraving in No. 20 is signed "Moore Del." and is engraved by Baxter & Harley of Philadelphia. Moore may be the A. O. Moore listed in the Main Catalogue, but more likely Isaac W. Moore, the Philadelphia portrait and landscape painter (see Groce and Wallace, p. 452).

This book was first published by Carey & Hart in Philadelphia in 1830. Mumford's illustrations first appeared in an edition published for the author in 1844. Another edition published for the author was issued in 1850. This 1856 edition appears to be the third to contain the Mumford engravings. It is well printed and the impressions are good.

In orig. wrappers, except that the front wrapper of No. 20 is missing.

Nathan Winship Munroe

1789-

Munroe was born in Lexington, Mass., and is said to have been a pupil of Gilbert Stuart. He was a portrait painter and was working in Boston in 1813. He died while still in his youth. See Groce and Wallace, p. 461.

1869. ELEGY, IN REMEMBRANCE OF JAMES LAWRENCE, ESQUIRE: (Late Commander of the United States' Frigate Chesapeake). Fig. 42.

This is a broadside printed on silk, probably in 1813 and probably in Boston. At the top is a wood engraving showing a monument surrounded by cannon and battleflags and surmounted by a bust of Lawrence. On the cut appear the words "N. W. Munroe, Del." and "Eng'd on wood by G. Cobb." 2 verses are printed below the engraving and then follows the Elegy which closes with the words:

"Blest Shade! Farewell! Thy
    memory ever dear
Oft shall receive fair Freedom's
    holy tear;
In each fond heart shall live
    thy peerless name
And there shall rise thy
    Monuments of Fame."

H. A. Munson

1870. PICTURE OF SLAVERY IN THE UNITED STATES OF AMERICA. [By George Bourne.] Middletown, Con.: Edwin Hunt, 1834. With 11 wood engravings, which for the most part depict cruelties inflicted on slaves. That facing p. 144 is signed "H. A. Munson del. & sc." while that facing p. 106 is signed "Flag del." This latter illustration differs somewhat in style from the others and it seems probable that Munson drew and engraved most of the illustrations. Orig. cloth.

William Barksdale Myers

Son of a prominent lawyer, Myers became a painter of historical scenes and of portraits in Richmond, Va., and was apparently well known in artistic circles there. In 1857 he exhibited at the Washington Art Association. There is little record of what became of him after the Civil War but it would appear from the Items listed below that he drifted into commercial book illustrating, although it is, of course, possible that the W. B. Myers who illustrated these items was another Myers. See Groce and Wallace, p. 463.

1871. MABEL LEE. A NOVEL. By the Author of "Valerie Aylmer," "Morton House," etc. [Frances Christine (Fisher) Tiernan]. New York: D. Appleton and Company, 1872. Wright II (2508).

Contains 4 full-page illustrations by Myers, engraved on wood by J. Karst (1) and A. Bobbett (1), the name of the engraver of the others not appearing. Orig. cloth.

1872. MORTON HOUSE. A NOVEL. By the Author of "Valerie Aylmer." [Frances Christine (Fisher) Tiernan]. New York: D. Appleton and Company, 1872. Wright II (2509).

Contains 4 full-page illustrations by Myers. That at p. 17 is signed by J. Filmer as wood engraver and that at p. 79 is signed with what appears to be the name "Aylmar." The other 2 are not signed by the engraver. Orig. cloth.

Charles Christian Nahl
H. W. Arthur Nahl

(See Main Catalogue, p. 190)

1873. CALIFORNIA CHARACTERS, AND MINING SCENES AND SKETCHES. San Francisco: Bonestell & Williston, Wide West Office [ca. 1854 or 1855]. California Characters is by Whittlestick [H. C. Williston]. Mining Scenes and Sketches is by "an old Miner." The book was copyrighted on June 9, 1854 (see Robert Greenwood, California Imprints 1833-1862, Los Gatos, Cal., 1961, Appendix A, No. 53). In spite of the date of copyright, Greenwood dates the book [1855]. Howes (No. 507) dates it [ca. 1854]. Fig. 41.

The various sketches contained in the book, together with their illustrations, first appeared in The Wild West, a weekly published by Bonestell & Williston (see Mott, Vol. II, p. 118). The sketches ran from March 26, 1854 to June 11, 1854.

The book contains 12 wood engravings which are unsigned by the draftsman. They clearly resemble the work of Charles Nahl and both Greenwood, in the book above cited (No. 635) and Robert E. Cowan in his Bibliography of the History of California and the Pacific West, San Francisco, 1914, at p. 251, state, without qualification, that they are by Nahl. The subjects illustrated are "The Unsuccessful Miner," "The

Ranchero," "The Digger Indian," "The Grizzly Bear," "John Chinaman," "The French Boot-black," "The San Francisco Newsboy," "The Big Lump Man," "A Night on a Dam," "My Prospecting Tour," "Will Winkle's Nugget," and "Tunneling." The names or initials of Anthony & Baker of San Francisco appear on several of the cuts and that firm probably engraved them all.

Greenwood locates only 2 copies but there are also copies at Yale and Harvard. Orig. wrappers.

1874. HUTCHINGS' ILLUSTRATED CALIFORNIA MAGAZINE. Vols. I-V, all that were published, July 1856 to June 1861. San Francisco: Hutchings & Rosenfield, 1857-1861.

This is a very early California monthly magazine which has become quite scarce. It is of considerable value in connection with the early days of the Gold Rush. It was copiously illustrated with wood engravings and many of the drawings for these were made by the Nahl brothers.

Charles Nahl's name or initials will be found on cuts on pp. 10, 13, 242, 247,* 290, 293, 294, 491, and 533 of Vol. I; pp. 1, 5, 6, 7, 13, 51, 96, 105, 107, 145, 149, 151, 153, 193, and 199 of Vol. II; pp. 2, 4, 5, 6, 205, 289, 291, 292, 293, 295, 298, 351, 385, 392, 393, 433, 438, 443, and 445 of Vol. III; and pp. 105, 107, 109, 112,** and 329 of Vol. V. Undoubtedly, among the cuts unsigned by the draftsman, there are many others after drawings by C. Nahl. The engravers whose names appear in connection with these Nahl cuts are Durbin Van Vleck, Harrison Eastman, Eastman-Loomis, W. C. Butler, William F. Herrick, and Thomas Armstrong.

Arthur Nahl's name or initials will be found on cuts on p. 151 of Vol. I (probably A. Nahl made all the drawings for the cuts illustrating the article in which this signed cut appeared); pp. 59, 100, and 289 in Vol. II; and p. 147, of Vol. IV.

On the following cuts the name "Nahl" appears in a way making it impossible to determine which brother was the draftsman: pp. 349, 394, and 448 of Vol. I; pp. 55 and 94 of Vol. II; and p. 529 of Vol. IV.

Other illustrators whose work appears in the magazine are Harrison Eastman, William F. Herrick, Kuchel-Dressel, John McLenan, and A. E. (probably Alexander Edouart).

The principal engraver used, especially in the later volumes, was Thomas Armstrong. His portrait, engraved by Eastman-Loomis, appears on p. 433 of Vol. V. William Keith, the "California Turner," engraved 2 cuts to be found on pp. 57 and 104 of Vol. IV.

Uniformly bound in ¾ calf.

1875. SCENES OF WONDER AND CURIOSITY IN CALIFORNIA . . . By J. M. Hutchings. San Francisco: Hutchings & Rosenfield, Publishers, Montgomery Street [cop. 1860]. 236 pp. with 93 wood engravings. Through an error only 92 engravings are listed.

A number of the wood engravings are after Charles Nahl (see pp. 10, 42, 46, 54, 58, and 59) and others are after Harrison Eastman and George Tirrell. Robert Greenwood in his *California Imprints 1833-1867*, No. 1275, lists this as the 1st edition and lists that of 1861 (erroneously stated in Item 1117(1) of the Main Catalogue to be the 1st edition) as the 2nd edition (see Greenwood, No. 1475).

All of the illustrations appearing in the first 236 pp. of Item 1117(1) will be found in this earlier edition. Item 1117(1) has 3 additional chapters and 12 additional engravings, giving it 267 pp. and 105 engravings as against 236 pp. and 93 engravings in the 1st edition.

Greenwood calls this "The first work to promote the natural beauty and scenery of California."

Orig. cloth.

? Nanteuil

The only illustration by Nanteuil which the writer has seen is that in the book listed below. He may not have been an American artist and yet Trichon, the engraver of the illustration, was working in this country as early as 1855 (see Item 507) and the illustration seems to have been made for the book.

WESTERN BORDER LIFE. Philadelphia [cop. 1863]. An illustration signed "Del. Nanteuil," engraved on wood by Trichon, appears at p. 102. [See Item 1571]

Thomas Nast

(*See Main Catalogue, p. 192*)

ALBUM OF WOOD ENGRAVINGS by John Andrew, etc. [*ca.* 1860-1870]. 1 engraving after Nast. [See Item 1472(3)]

---

* The cuts on pp. 242 and 247 illustrate an article on "Packing, in the Mountains of California," and probably all the illustrations in this article were drawn by C. Nahl.

** These last 4 appeared in *The Adventures of James Capen Adams* by Theodore H. Hittell, published in 1860 [Item 1116].

1876. A COLLECTION OF 14 AUTOGRAPH LETTERS written by Nast, as follows:

(a) Letter of March 19, 1860, from London to Mr. Lexow (of the *New York Illustrated News*), sending sketches relating to the coming fight of Tom Sayers and John C. Heenan, one of the great sporting events of all time for which even Parliament adjourned. Nast, young as he was, had been sent over to cover the fight, and many of his sketches, including a number of the fight itself, appeared in the pages of the *New York Illustrated News*. 3 of the sketches enclosed in this letter of March 19, will be found in the issue of April 21, 1860.

(b) 3 letters to Sallie Edwards whom he later married, 2 written in April 1860, when he was in London for the Heenan-Sayers fight, and 1 written on July 30, 1860, from Messina, Sicily. That of April 24, 1860, contains 3 pen and ink drawings, 1 showing Sallie's brother making ardent love to the lady of his affections.

(c) Undated letter written to his wife Sallie from Fortress Monroe after the start of the Civil War when he was trying to get to the front. He tells of a meeting with A. R. Waud.

(d) 6 letters to Mr. Thomas (W. L. Thomas, an engraver on the *Illustrated London News* who had looked after Nast's pictures and remittances while in Italy [see Albert Bigelow Paine, *Th. Nast, his Period and his Pictures*, New York, 1904, p. 67]) of the following dates in the year 1860: July 7 from Palermo, July 9 and 14 from Naples, July 23 from Milazzo, July 25 from Messina, and October ? from Naples. After the Sayers-Heenan fight Nast decided to go to Sicily and Italy to follow the fortunes of Garibaldi, believing that he could dispose of his drawings to both the *New York Illustrated News* and the *Illustrated London News*. His letters to Thomas give interesting glimpses of Garibaldi and tell of some of the fighting, particularly that at Milazzo. With most of them he forwarded sketches and many of his sketches, some engraved by Thomas, appeared in the *London News* (see the issues for July 7, July 28, August 11 (Supp.), August 25, September 22, September 29, October 20 [drawings of the battle on the Volturno], November 3, and November 10, all in the year 1860).

(e) 3 letters, dated March 17, 1869, September 27, 1869, and February 18, 1872, respectively, to Col. and Mrs. Chipman, all full of amusing pen and ink sketches by Nast. One of these shows Nast's wife and his 3 children welcoming him at the door of "the second shanty west of fifth avenue in 125th," where the Nasts were then living, and another shows Nast with the mumps. In one he writes "I endorse and highly appreciate your sentiments as to the com-

parison between me and Doré, in fact, I dont think he can hold a candle to me. I feel like *some pumkins* [sic] and consider him *small potatoes*, speaking from a strictly vegetable point of view." These 3 letters have been bound in red leather.

Accompanying this letter collection is (1) a copy of *Solid for Mulhooly, a Political Satire* by Rufus E. Shapley, Philadelphia: Gebbie & Co., 1889 (see Item 1160), a presentation copy to Nast from the publishers, with notes regarding the illustrations, which may be in Mrs. Nast's handwriting, inserted and (2) a copy of the pamphlet, *The Man who made Santa Claus*, designed by Joseph Francis Weiler of The Marchbanks Press, New York, 1958.

THE NOVELETTE. Boston: 186?. Novelette No. 85 contains an illustration by Nast. [See No. 4 of Item 1546]

1877. A COLLECTION OF 200 WOOD ENGRAVINGS (including 2 or 3 duplicates) after drawings by Nast, removed from *Harper's Weekly*, 1862-1881, including the first appearances of the Democratic Donkey and the Republican Elephant and many well-known cartoons such as "The Tammany Tiger Loose," the first use of the tiger symbol.

1878. THE FIGHTING QUAKERS, A TRUE STORY OF THE WAR FOR OUR UNION. By A[ugustine] J[oseph] H[ickey] Duganne. New-York: J. P. Robens, 1866. Frontispiece by Nast, engraved on wood by J. P. Davis & Speer.

This book was printed for the "Bureau of Military Record," as a means of furnishing, by its sale, an honest living to returned soldiers, appointed agents. Orig. cloth.

1879. INCIDENTS AND ANECDOTES OF THE WAR . . . Edited by Orville J. Victor. New York: James D. Torrey [cop. 1866]. With 12 full-page illustrations by Nast, engraved on wood by J. P. Davis & Speer. Orig. stamped morocco.

1880. BEYOND THE MISSISSIPPI . . . By Albert D. Richardson. Hartford, Conn.: American Publishing Company . . . 1867.

This is the 1st edition of Item 1136. The illustrations are identical except that Item 1136, in the new reading matter at the end, has 11 additional illustrations. Orig. cloth.

1881. THE GHOST. By Wm. D. O'Connor. New York: G. P. Putnam & Son, 1867. Wright II (1813). Frontispiece and half title by Nast, engraved on wood by J. P. Davis-Speer. Orig. cloth.

HARPER'S BAZAAR. Vols. I-III. New York: 1867-1870. Contains some interesting work by

Nast. Illustrations by him are to be found at pp. 217, 253, 424, 425, 524, 568-69, 669, 688, 760-61, and 800 of Vol. II, and pp. 48, 345, 448, 512, 560(2), and 712-13 of Vol. III. [See Item 1729]

1882. THE SOLDIER'S STORY OF HIS CAPTIVITY AT ANDERSONVILLE, BELLE ISLE, AND OTHER REBEL PRISONS. By Warren Lee Goss. Boston: Lee and Shepard, 1867.

This is probably an earlier issue of the book than Item 1130. It has the 4 full-page illustrations by Nast, but not the presentation page. Item 1130 appears to have been a special edition, with Goss' portrait as frontispiece, a number of views of Andersonville (not by Nast) and at the end a list of the names of the Union soldiers buried at Andersonville. It was sold only by subscription. Orig. cloth.

1883. THE CRUISE OF THE DASHAWAY; OR, KATIE PUTNAM'S VOYAGE. By May Mannering. Boston: Lee and Shepard, 1868. 3 full-page illustrations by Nast, engraved on wood by Kilburn (2) and R.L. (1). This is one of "The Helping Hand Series" and the Series title is engraved by Kilburn after an anonymous draftsman. Orig. cloth.

1884. EKKOES FROM KENTUCKY. By Petroleum V. Nasby [David R. Locke]. Boston: Lee and Shepard, 1868. This is another copy of Item 1133 with the same illustrations by Nast. On the front flyleaf is an inscription reading "Thomas Nast from the publishers January 14th, 1868." Orig. cloth. Presented by the Seven Gables Bookshop.

E. M. Naylor

THE AMERICAN PIONEER. Cincinnati, O.: 1842-1843. The frontispiece for the August 1842 number (Vol. I, p. 266) is a view of Miami University drawn by E. M. Naylor and engraved on wood by Grosvenor. It is rather well handled. The article on Miami University in the August number was written by A. R. Naylor, probably some relative of the artist. [See Item 1946]

Victor Nehlig

(See Main Catalogue, p. 195)

1885. WILD SCENES IN SOUTH AMERICA; OR, LIFE IN THE LLANOS OF VENEZUELA. By Don Ramon Paez. New York: Charles Scribner, 1862.

Contains 2 wood engravings after Nehlig (pp. 113 and 338), the first of which is by Richard-son-Cox, and 7 full-page lithographs which bear Nehlig's name (front. and pp. 74, 90, 175, 189, 247, and 335). Jaubert's name as lithographer will be found on all but 2 of them, and he probably did them all. It appears from the preface that Nehlig's drawings were based on sketches made by the author and by Frederick Melby, a Danish artist. 2 wood engravings by Richardson-Cox after Melby appear on pp. 19 and 36. The book also contains 1 illustration by D. C. Hitchcock. There are 2 full-page wood engravings by Richardson and 1 by Van Ingen-Snyder where the name of the draftsman does not appear, but it is doubtful whether Nehlig had anything to do with these. Orig. cloth.

Charles F. Noble

Born about 1833, he was working as an engraver in Philadelphia in 1850 and after. He was a member of the firm of Scattergood and Noble in 1859 and of Noble & Nagle in 1860. See Groce and Wallace, p. 473.

1886. FEARFUL ADVENTURES IN PENNSYLVANIA'S WILDS; OR, THE STARTLING NARRATIVE OF ADELAIDE LANE. Philadelphia: Barclay & Co. [cop. 1857]. Wright II (893).

Contains frontispiece, 2 other full-page wood engravings in the text and a smaller engraving on the title-page. The latter is repeated on the front wrapper and the frontispiece on the back wrapper. The frontispiece is signed "Noble del" and "Grosvenor," and it seems probable that the same draftsman and the same engraver were responsible for the others.

Thomas M. McDade in his article on the "Publications of E. E. Barclay" in *The Pennsylvania Magazine of History and Biography*, Vol. LXXX, No. 4, p. 452, gives us some information regarding this publisher. Barclay started in New York, moved to Cincinnati in 1846 and in 1849 set up his publishing business in Philadelphia. He returned to Cincinnati in 1856 but stayed there only 2 years, after which he came to Philadelphia where he remained until his death. It is consistent with this vacillation between Philadelphia and Cincinnati that the present Item bears a Philadelphia imprint and was entered for copyright in the District Court of the Southern District of Ohio. It seems probable that Barclay used Charles Noble of Philadelphia to make the drawings for the illustrations in the book and Grosvenor of Cincinnati to engrave them. Orig. wrappers.

1887. THE WILD WOMAN; OR, THE WRECKED HEART. BEING THE TRUE AUTOBIOGRAPHY OF THE "WILD WOMAN," WHO

WAS RECENTLY EXHIBITED AT CINCINNATI, AND WAS RESCUED FROM HER PERSECUTORS BY THE CITIZENS OF THAT CITY, AND SENT TO THE INSANE ASYLUM AT DAYTON, OHIO. The History of this Strange Woman Furnishes Incidents of the most Thrilling Narrative ever Written, and is now Offered for the First Time. Philadelphia: Barclay & Co., 1864. The year of copyright is given as 1865. Fig. 43.

Contains 7 full-page wood engravings, 4 of which are signed "Noble del" and "T. Jones sc." (probably Theodore Jones of Cincinnati). They are in the lurid style which one expects of Barclay. The others are more restrained and better drawn and are by other hands. One (p. 50) is engraved by N. Orr. The frontispiece is repeated on the front wrapper. Orig. wrappers.

Not in Wright who may have excluded it as "true autobiography."

Johannes Adam Oertel
(See Main Catalogue, p. 195)

THE CHILD'S PAPER. Vols. I-IV. New York etc.: 1852-1855. Contains 3 illustrations by Oertel, viz.: p. 45 of Vol. I, engraved on wood by Peckham & Bookhout; p. 5 of Vol. II, engraved on wood by Ward; and p. 21 of Vol. II, engraved on wood by Hayes. [See Item 1605]

1888. LADY GODIVA or, PEEPING TOM OF COVENTRY. A ROMANCE OF THE OLDEN TIME. By the Author of "The First False Step," and "Rose Sommerville." New York: Williams & Co., 1852. This is the wording on the front wrapper. On what would normally be the title-page appear the words "The Lady Godiva; or, Peeping Tom. New York. For Sale by All Booksellers, 1851."

On the front wrapper is a wood engraving of a somewhat plump Lady Godiva, clothed only in her flowing hair and seated on her white horse. It bears the monogram J.O. which makes it appear likely that it was designed by Johannes Oertel. It may have been engraved by Avery as, on the title-page, there is a smaller cut of the same subject, signed "Avery." Orig. wrappers.

1889. ADVENTURES IN FAIRYLAND. By Richard Henry Stoddard. Boston: Ticknor, Reed, and Fields, 1853. With 5 full-page illustrations by Oertel. The name of the wood engraver does not appear, but according to the Cost Books of Ticknor and Fields, ed. by Tryon & Charvat, N.Y., 1949, p. 236, one of the plates was engraved by Baker, Smith & Andrew. Oertel received $25 for his drawings* and the engraver

* The facts given by Tryon & Charvat indicate that Oertel made 6 drawings for this book. It seems

was paid $90. This is the 1st edition of Stoddard's first prose work and is a difficult book to find. Orig. cloth.

John William Orr
1815-1887

Born in Ireland, Orr was brought to America at an early age and lived in Buffalo. After studying in New York City with William Redfield in 1836, he set up his wood engraving business in Buffalo in 1837, moving to Albany in 1842 and finally to New York City in 1844. He was one of the best known wood engravers of his generation. He was the older brother of Nathaniel Orr with whom he was in partnership in 1844-1846. See Groce and Wallace, p. 479.

1890. PECKS' TOURIST'S COMPANION TO NIAGARA FALLS, SARATOGA SPRINGS, THE LAKES, CANADA, ETC. . . . Buffalo: William B. & Charles E. Peck, 1845.

There are numerous wood engravings throughout the text and Orr's name appears on many of them (see pp. 28, 73, 80, 104, 124, and 125), but with nothing to indicate that he was more than the engraver. The frontispiece, however, a view of Niagara Falls from Prospect Point, is signed "J. W. Orr Del. & Sc." Orr's name appeared on countless engravings during his lifetime, but this frontispiece is the only one the writer has seen where Orr lays claim to have been the draftsman. It was made about the time of his move to New York City. It raises the possibility that Orr may have been the designer of many of those innumerable cuts which bear his name. Orig. cloth.

Harlan Page
1791-1834
(See Main Catalogue, p. 196)

Born in Coventry, Conn., "the son of pious parents," Page about 1823 became interested in the business of engraving which led to his being employed by the American Tract Society of Boston. In 1825, the year of the formation of the national American Tract Society in New York City, Page, after a short time spent in drawing and engraving in Norwich, Conn., came to New York to act as Agent of the General Depositary of the new American Tract Society. He appears, in addition to his other work, to have done drawing and engraving for the Society's publications. Early in the 1830s he resigned his superintendence of the tract distribution in order to assist in forming and

likely that a frontispiece is lacking in this copy.

sustaining the Brainerd Church in a destitute part of the city. Shortly thereafter he died. He was a man of extraordinary piety and was doubtless responsible for the salvation of many souls. See *Memoir of Harlan Page*, by William A. Hallock, New York, *ca.* 1835 (pp. 14, 120, 133, 185, 186, 191, and 230), and the article "Some American Wood Engravers 1820-1840" by Sinclair Hitchings in No. 4 of Vol. IX of *P.A.G.A.*, December 1961.

At the time of the publication of the Main Catalogue in 1958 the writer had not seen Hallock's memoir of Page and hence no facts regarding him are given in that Catalogue.

1891. MEMOIR OF HARLAN PAGE: OR THE POWER OF PRAYER AND PERSONAL EFFORT FOR THE SOULS OF INDIVIDUALS. By William A. Hallock, Corresponding Secretary of the American Tract Society. New-York: American Tract Society [cop. 1835]. Fig. 44.

On the half title is a copper engraving, after a drawing by Page, of his old home at Coventry. Facing p. 192 is a wood engraving by Anderson after a drawing by Page which will also be found in *The Life of Rev. David Brainerd* by President [Jonathan] Edwards (Item 308). It shows one of the scenes of the labors of David Brainerd. Page had visited the spot and drawn the sketch, and Anderson, shortly before Page's death, called to get Page's approbation of the engraving. As the incident is related in Hallock's *Memoir*, Anderson said, "You can cast your eye upon it now, and look at it again perhaps when you are stronger." "No," replied Page, "I shall never look at it again. My work here is *all done.*" Orig. boards.

Charles Parsons

(See Main Catalogue, p. 196)

THE ILLUSTRATED NEWS. Vol. I. New York: 1853. 2 illustrations by Parsons (pp. 13 and 21), engraved by Richardson-Cox (1) and Leslie (1). [See Item 1836]

1892. NARRATIVE OF A VOYAGE TO THE NORTHWEST COAST OF AMERICA IN THE YEARS 1811, 1812, 1813, AND 1814, OR THE FIRST AMERICAN SETTLEMENT ON THE PACIFIC. By Gabriel Franchere. Translated and Edited by J. V. Huntington. New York: Redfield, 1854.

Contains 3 full-page illustrations designed by Parsons, depicting "Astoria, as it was in 1813," "View of the Falkland Islands," and "Entrance of the Columbia River." All are engraved on wood by Avery.

This book was originally written in French and published in Montreal in 1820. This Eng-

lish translation published in 1854 is the 2nd edition and the first to contain illustrations. Washington Irving relied extensively on the French edition in writing his *Astoria.* In fact, one of the reasons which led Franchere to give his book an English dress was his desire to correct some of Irving's inaccuracies. Orig. cloth.

1893. ILLUSTRATED HISTORY OF THE PANAMA RAILROAD . . . By F. N. Otis. New York: Harper & Brothers, 1861.

Contains 30 wood engraved views along the Panama Railroad. They are well drawn. Parsons' name appears on 2 of them (pp. 37 and 179), and it seems likely that all are his. He became head of the art department of Harper & Brothers in the year this book was published. The only name of a wood engraver to appear is that of R. S. Bross (p. 112). Richardson engraved the 2 maps which follow the title-page. Orig. cloth.

CAPTAIN BRAND OF THE "CENTIPEDE." New York: 1864. 3 of the illustrations (pp. 29, 38 and 127) are signed "C.P." but some of the unsigned illustrations are probably by him also, as, for example, those facing pp. 44, 50, 97, 159, 180, 217, and 283. [See Item 1811]

HARPER'S BAZAAR. Vols. I-III. New York: 1867-1870. 3 illustrations of James DeMille's *Cord and Creese* are by Parsons. [See Item 1729]

1894. CORD AND CREESE. By the author of "The Dodge Club" [James DeMille]. New York: Harper & Brothers, 1869.

Contains numerous illustrations. Those on pp. 94, 100, and 133 are by Parsons. A number are signed "W.J." which are probably the initials of William S. L. Jewett (see Item 1729). Some are signed "B" or "C.B." and these are probably the work of Charles G. Bush. Orig. wrappers.

Granville Perkins

(See Main Catalogue, p. 197)

ANNALS OF THE ARMY OF THE CUMBERLAND. Philadelphia: 1863. 1 illustration (p. 309) is signed "G.P." [See Item 1979]

1895. THE NATURAL WEALTH OF CALIFORNIA . . . TOGETHER WITH A DETAILED DESCRIPTION OF EACH COUNTY . . . By Titus Fey Cronise. San Francisco: H. H. Bancroft & Company . . . 1868.

The frontispiece is a full-page wood engraving of the Golden Gate after a drawing by Perkins. There are numerous other wood engraved views of California and some of these may well be after Perkins also. The only name of an engraver to appear is that of Fay-Cox who engraved the view of Sutter's Fort at p. 48. Orig. cloth.

PEBBLES AND PEARLS FOR THE YOUNG FOLKS. Hartford: 1868. Contains 2 illustrations by Perkins. [See Item 1939]

OUR NEW WEST. Hartford: 1869. On p. 206 is a view of Salt Lake City signed "G.P." which may have been drawn by Perkins. It is engraved on wood by Knapp—Co. [See Item 1814]

SPECTACLES FOR YOUNG EYES. New York: 1869. Facing p. 60 is an illustration by Perkins, the name of the engraver not appearing. [See Item 1713]

1896. THE SHADOW OF MOLOCH MOUNTAIN. By Jane G. Austin. New-York: Sheldon & Company, 1870. Contains many small wood engravings by E. Sears. The first is signed "G.P." and it is probable that Perkins is the draftsman throughout. Orig. cloth.

THE ILLUSTRATED CHRISTIAN WEEKLY. New York: 1871. Illustrations on pp. 140 and 153 are signed "G.P." That on p. 140 is engraved on wood by Brightly. [See Item 1627]

THE GREAT SOUTH. Hartford: 1875. 8 illustrations by Perkins (pp. 74, 319, 320, 384, 392, 394, 409, and 412), engraved on wood by F. S. King (3), Varley (1), and Cullen (1), the names of the engravers of the others not appearing. [See Item 1919]

PIONEERS IN THE SETTLEMENT OF AMERICA. Boston: 1876-1877. 3 illustrations by Perkins (see plates opposite pp. 35 and 208 in Vol. I, and opposite p. 62 in Vol. II). [See Item 1922]

1897. THE TRUE CHURCH. By Theodore Tilton. Illustrated from Designs by Granville Perkins. Philadelphia: J. B. Lippincott & Co., 1876. The wood engraving at the beginning of the poem is after a drawing by Perkins. There are 8 full-page lithographs also after Perkins' designs. Orig. cloth.

THE BODLEYS TELLING STORIES. New York: 1878. Facing p. 160 is an illustration by Perkins, engraved on wood by Bogert. [See Item 1732]

James Poupard

(See Main Catalogue, p. 198)

1898. A PRELIMINARY ESSAY ON THE OPPRESSION OF THE EXILED SONS OF AFRICA. CONSISTING OF ANIMADVERSIONS ON THE IMPOLICY AND BARBARITY OF THE DELETERIOUS COMMERCE AND SUBSEQUENT SLAVERY OF THE HUMAN SPECIES; To which is added, A Desultory Letter Written to Napoleon Bonaparte, Anno Domini, 1801. By Thomas Branagan, Late Slave-trader from Africa, and Planter from Antigua; who, from conscientious motives, relinquished a lucrative situation in that island; and now from a deep sense of duty, publishes to the world the tragical scenes, of which he was a daily spectator, and in which he was unhappily concerned. Philadelphia: Printed for the Author, by John W. Scott, 1804. Fig. 45.

The frontispiece is a full-page cut, signed "James Poupard, Sculpt," showing a white man lashing a half-naked colored man and woman while in the background another white man is seen driving a gang of negroes with uplifted whip. In the sky appear a number of distressed angels who do not apparently operate as any deterrent to the slave traders. The caption reads: "The husband and wife, after being sold to different purchasers, violently separated . . . never to see each other more."

Cont. calf. From the Estate of William W. Staake.

1899. METAMORPHOSIS; OR, A TRANSFORMATION OF PICTURES, WITH POETICAL EXPLANATIONS, FOR THE AMUSEMENT OF YOUNG PERSONS. New York: Sold by Samuel Wood and Sons, No. 357, Pearl Street. Printed by J. Rakestraw, Philadelphia. 1816.

Contains the same cuts as those appearing in the 3 earlier editions of the *Metamorphosis* listed in Item 1168. Poupard moved to New York City sometime after 1807, but the blocks do not appear to have been recut for this edition. It is interesting to find these cuts of Poupard still in use after more than 40 years.

Harry B. Weiss in his article on Samuel Wood & Sons in the *Bulletin of The New York Public Library* for September 1942, lists an edition of the *Metamorphosis* published by Wood in 1814 and mentions another of 1815. The present copy would appear to be Wood's 3rd edition.

W. H. Prior

(See Main Catalogue, p. 199)

1900. WAR AND PEACE. A TALE OF THE RETREAT FROM CAUBUL. By A.L.O.E. [Charlotte Maria Tucker]. New York: Robert Carter & Brothers, 1863. Contains several illustrations. Those at pp. 41 and 245 are by Prior, engraved on wood by Jackson (1) and T. Bolton (1). Orig. cloth. Presented by M. Halsey Thomas.

E. Purcell

(See Main Catalogue, p. 199)

1901. THE PLEASANT JOURNEY; AND SCENES IN TOWN AND COUNTRY. By Thomas Teller. New Haven: S. Babcock [*ca.* 1850]. 8 wood engravings by Anderson after designs by E. P. The title-page cut was engraved by Lossing. Orig. wrappers.

THE CHILD'S PAPER. Vols. I-IV. New York, etc.: 1852-1855. An illustration by Purcell, engraved on wood by Whitney, will be found on p. 39 of Vol. IV. [See Item 1605]

Donald F. Read
James A. Read

The Read brothers were wood engravers of New York City but they were illustrators as well, working for a number of magazines, including *Yankee Doodle*. J. A. Read's "The Mass Meeting of Applewomen," which came out in that publication, is called by Murrell (Vol. I, p. 168), "one of the jolliest things in the volume," while the same writer says (p. 228) that J. A. Read's cartoons for *Vanity Fair* and *Phunny Phellow* are "really humorous." The best-known work of the Read brothers, however, is that listed below. See Groce and Wallace, p. 526.

1902. JOURNEY TO THE GOLD DIGGINS, by Jeremiah Saddlebags. Cincinnati: U. P. James [cop. by Stringer and Townsend, 1849]. Fig. 46.
Contains over 100 comic illustrations by J. A. and D. F. Read showing the lamentable experiences of Mr. Saddlebags in search of gold. Some of them are amusing but much of the humor seems a bit forced. 18 of the cuts are signed by Richardson as the wood engraver and 1 (p. 40) by Orr. The title-page cut is repeated on the front wrapper and on the back wrapper in an elaborate wood engraving (the name of the engraver indecipherable) advertising *Redstick: or, Scenes in the South*, published by U. P. James. Murrell (Vol. I, p. 179) reproduces one of the cuts. Orig. wrappers, in cloth slip case.
Another edition of this book was published by Stringer and Townsend in New York. It is not dated but it may precede the Cincinnati edition. A comparison of the 2 editions shows in the Cincinnati edition some breaks in the thin lines surrounding the cuts, breaks which do not appear in the New York edition. Except for this there is not much to choose between the 2 editions in the quality of the impressions.

J. (or C.) H. Reed

The name signed to the illustrations in the Item listed below is either J. H. Reed or C. H. Reed. If it is the latter, they were probably designed by Charles H. Reed, a Philadelphia engraver, whose name appears in the Philadelphia directory for 1867.

1903. AGNES WILBUR; OR, A DAUGHTER'S INFLUENCE. By Catherine M. Trowbridge. Philadelphia: J. C. Garrigues & Co., 1867. 2 illustrations designed by Reed, the name of the engraver not appearing. Orig. cloth.

J. F. Reiche

(See Main Catalogue, p. 200)

1904. EIN WOHL EINGERICHTETES DEUTSCHES A B C—BUCHSTABIR—UND LESEBUCH ZUM GEBRAUCH DEUTSCHER SCHULEN . . . Germantaun: Gedruckt bey Michael Billmeyer, 179[6]. A small hole in the title-page has obliterated the final figure in the date but the date is probably 1796, as this copy appears to correspond with Evans 31652. Evans lists 4 earlier editions (Nos. 24008, 24009, 25051, and 28118), but fails to locate a copy of any of them.
The frontispiece is a woodcut signed "F. Reiche fec." It is possible that the use of the abbreviation "fec" indicates that Reiche was draftsman as well as engraver. If so, his rating among early American draftsmen will hardly be a high one. Beginning on p. 67, there are 7 cuts illustrating "Auserlesene Fabeln," but they are unsigned and Reiche may have had nothing to do with them. The printer's mark of Billmeyer on the title-page deserves notice. Orig. boards.

Charles Stanley Reinhart

(See Main Catalogue, p. 200)

HARPER'S BAZAAR. Vols. I-III. New York: 1867-1870. On p. 332 of Vol. III Reinhart took over the illustrating of James DeMille's *The Cryptogram*, the opening chapters of which had been illustrated by W. J. (William S. L. Jewett). From p. 332 on, most of the illustrations for *The Cryptogram* are signed by Reinhart's initial or initials, and in all likelihood the unsigned ones are his also. He was also responsible for an excellent illustration on p. 572 of Vol. III. [See Item 1729]

1905. THE ISLAND NEIGHBORS. A NOVEL OF AMERICAN LIFE. By Antoinette Brown Blackwell. New York: Harper & Brothers, 1871. Wright II (306). 10 illustrations, of which 4 (pp. 16, 57, 85, and 99) bear Reinhart's initials. Cont. half calf.

1906. A Good Investment. A Story of the Upper Ohio. By William [Joseph] Flagg. New York: Harper & Brothers, 1872. Wright II (907). With full-page frontispiece and many smaller illustrations in the text by Reinhart. Modern cloth.

1907. A Fast Life on the Modern Highway; Being a Glance into the Railroad World from a New Point of View. By Joseph Taylor. New York: Harper & Brothers, 1874. Wright II (2436).

Contains 9 illustrations signed "C.S.R." (pp. 18, 22, 28, 34, 35, 111, 125, 169, and 202) and others may also be his. There are also a number by E. A. Abbey, who was only 22 years of age at the time of the book's publication. Modern cloth.

1907a. (1) McGuffey's First Eclectic Reader. By Wm. H. McGuffey, LL.D. Revised Edition. Van Antwerp, Bragg & Co., Cincinnati and New York [cop. 1879]. On the front cover are printed the words "Proof sheets of McGuffey's First Reader, Revised Edition." The text and illustrations appear only on the recto of each leaf, the other side being blank.

Contains 3 illustrations by Reinhart (pp. 34, 37 and 63), all engraved on wood by Jueng-Mill. There are numerous other illustrations, many of them by H. F. Farny. Orig. boards, with leather back.

(2) McGuffey's Second Eclectic Reader. Revised Edition. Van Antwerp, Bragg & Co., Cincinnati and New York [cop. 1879]. This also bears the words "Proof sheets" on the front cover, but, unlike (1) above, it is printed on both sides of the leaves and contains a Table of Contents giving the names of the illustrators. Reinhart has 2 illustrations (pp. 109 and 129), both engraved on wood by Jueng-Mill. Among the other illustrators are W. L. Sheppard, Thomas Moran, Mary Hallock Foote, and J. G. Brown. Orig. boards with leather back.

1908. The Pretty Sister of José. By Frances Hodgson Burnett. New York: Charles Scribner's Sons, 1889. With 12 illustrations by Reinhart. Orig. cloth.

W. Roberts
(See Main Catalogue, p. 202)

Manual of Geography. New York: 1861. On p. 91 is an illustration signed "W. Robberts [sic] Del. Sc." [See Item 1642]

Samuel Worcester Rowse
(See Main Catalogue, p. 203)

1908a. Celebrated Trial of Rev. Joy Hamlet Fairchild, for the alleged Seduction of Miss Rhoda Davidson . . . Contains the account of Fairchild's trial before an Ecclesiastical Council held on July 24, 1844, at Exeter, N.H., as reported by William B. English for the *Daily Mail*. On the final page is a portrait of Fairchild, "copied from a Daguerreotype taken by Plumbe, drawn by Rowse, and accurately engraved by Mr. F. E. Worcester." The man, as so portrayed, might have had some leanings toward "amativeness" but the testimony, in spite of the verdict against him, is not convincing. Disbound. Presented by Seven Gables Bookshop.

The Carpet-Bag. Boston: 1851-1852. A number of illustrations are signed "R," the initial resembling that used by Rowse (see Fig. 111 in the Main Catalogue). On p. 1 of No. 37 Rowse is stated to have been the draftsman of the illustration on that page, although it bears no initial. It seems probable that he made all those signed "R" and perhaps others in the periodical as well. Those with the initial will be found on p. 5 of No. 2, p. 1 of No. 10, pp. 1 and 5 of No. 19, p. 5 of No. 23, p. 4 of No. 26, p. 5 of No. 29, pp. 1 and 5 of No. 30, pp. 1 and 4 of No. 31, p. 4 of No. 34, and p. 4 of No. 37. The illustration at p. 1 of No. 27 is probably by Rowse also, although its initial "R" is quite different from the "R" used in the other illustrations. The wood engravers whose names or initials appear are N. Brown, G. H. Hayes, and W. J. Baker. [See Item 2000]

Album of wood engravings by John Andrew etc. [*ca.* 1855-1865]. 1 engraving after Rowse. [See Item 1472(1)]

John F. Runge
(See Main Catalogue, p. 203)

1909. Casper. By Amy Lothrop [Anna Bartlett Warner]. New York: G. P. Putnam & Co., 1856. This is Vol. IV of Ellen Montgomery's Book Shelf. Contains numerous small wood engravings by J. W. Orr. That on p. 25 bears Runge's name and doubtless others are after drawings by him. Orig. cloth.

The Illustrated Christian Weekly. New York: 1871. 4 illustrations on p. 132 are probably all by Runge. 1 is signed by him. The name of the wood engraver does not appear. [See Item 1627]

R. Sayer

(See Main Catalogue, p. 204)

1910. THE YOUNG CRUSADER. Vol. I (containing the 12 monthly numbers for 1869) bound with the first 2 numbers of Vol. II. Boston: 1869-1870.

Contains many illustrations, the drawing and wood engraving being quite mediocre. Very few names of either draftsman or engraver appear. On p. 105 is a drawing by R. Sayer of the building in which the Great Musical Festival, a National Thanksgiving for the return of peace, had been held in June 1869. It had been erected expressly for the Festival. Orig. cloth.

1911. RECOMPENSE. By Mrs. Mary H. Seymour. New York: T. Whittaker, 1874. The frontispiece is after a drawing by Sayer, and the 2 other full-page illustrations, which are unsigned, may be his work also. Orig. cloth.

F. B. Schell

Weitenkampf (p. 217) mentions an F. B. Schell whose name often appeared in the literature relating to the Civil War and who had been an artist correspondent in the field, although he may possibly be confusing him with Frank H. Schell. F. B. Schell was not one of the illustrators covered in the Main Catalogue as the writer never came across any work of his sufficiently early to warrant his inclusion. The volume noted below, however, now proves that he was illustrating by 1870.

1912. ALMOST A PRIEST. A TALE THAT DEALS IN FACTS. By Mrs. Julia McNair Wright. Philadelphia: McKinney & Martin, 1870. Wright II (2803). Contains 4 illustrations by Schell, engraved on wood by Probasco-Rea-Sharp. This is an anti-Catholic novel. Orig. cloth.

1913. CAST ADRIFT. By T. S. Arthur. Philadelphia: J. M. Stoddart & Co. . . . 1873. Wright II (88). With 8 full-page illustrations by F. B. Schell, engraved on wood by J. Dalziel of Philadelphia. Orig. cloth.

W. Schöner

(See Main Catalogue, p. 204)

1914. DER NEUE, AMERICANISCHE LANDWIRTHSCHAFTS-CALENDER, AUF DAS JAHR . . . 1821 . . . Reading (Penn.): gedruckt und zu haben bey Johann Ritter und Comp. [1820]. Fig. 47.

On the front cover is Schöner's cut of a man plowing which will also be found in Item 1197. On A³ recto there is a cut of "Alexander and Diogenes" which may also be the work of Schöner. Sewed.

Christian Schussele

(See Main Catalogue, p. 204)

THE ILLUSTRATED NEWS. Vol. I. New York: 1853. Double-page drawing (pp. 168-69) by Schussele, engraved by Leslie. [See Item 1836]

ORANGE BLOSSOMS. Philadelphia: 1871. 1 illustration by Schussele, engraved on wood by Lauderbach. [See Item 1496]

Hugo Sebald

A wood engraver and designer of Philadelphia.

1915. THE THRILLING NARRATIVE AND EXTRAORDINARY ADVENTURES OF MISS MADELAINE H. EVERETT, WHO WAS ABDUCTED FROM THE BLOOMINGTON LADIES' SEMINARY, IN FLORIDA; AND AFTER PASSING THROUGH THE MOST WONDERFUL AND PAINFUL SCENES, WAS FINALLY RESCUED BY HER FRIENDS AT AN AUCTION MART, IN HAVANA, WHERE SHE WAS ABOUT TO BE SOLD AS A SLAVE. Philadelphia: Barclay Co., 1859.

Contains 4 full-page wood engravings, one repeated on the front wrapper and another on the back wrapper. Each is signed "H. Sebald." Groce and Wallace (p. 567) list a Hobarth Sebald, an engraver who was in Philadelphia in 1860, and a Hugo Sebald, a wood engraver and designer whose name appears in the city directories of Philadelphia in 1855-1871. Of the 2, the latter would seem the most likely to have made the illustrations. Being both wood engraver and designer, it is quite possible that he was responsible not only for the engravings but for the drawings as well, which, on the whole, are quite effective. Orig. wrappers.

Wright II (2498) locates only the Library of Congress copy, but there are copies also at the American Antiquarian Society and Yale.

Jessie Curtis Shepherd

Jessie Curtis, afterwards Mrs. Shepherd, a native of New York City, studied art at Cooper Institute, where Mary Hallock Foote also studied, and later worked under Wilmarth at the Academy of Design. For the most part her drawings appeared in magazines, such as *Our Young Folks*. In an article about her in *American Art and Art Collections*, Boston, 1889, Vol. II, p. 689, it is said that she learned much about the art of drawing for wood engraving from William J. Linton and that her first good work was done, under his instruction, for the Item listed below. As to her artistic ability, or lack of it, the writer of the article above-mentioned reaches the conclusion that her "work may not be of the highest order, but it gives pleasure to many, and is evidently the work of a gifted and conscientious artist." See also Linton, pp. 31 and 33; Weitenkampf, p. 219.

1916. THE GATES AJAR. By Elizabeth Stuart Phelps [Mrs. Elizabeth Stuart (Phelps) Ward]. Boston: Fields, Osgood & Co., 1870. The 1st edition was published in 1869. This appears to be the 2nd edition and the first to be illustrated.

Contains 12 illustrations by Jessie Curtis, engraved on wood by W. J. Linton. Miss Curtis' drawings are weak and her figures wooden, but sometimes, thanks perhaps to Linton's instructions, she achieves a felicitous result. The book is a presentation copy to Mrs. Osgood from John G. Whittier. Whittier dates his inscription December 31, 1869, so the book was probably issued for the Christmas trade of 1869. Linton's engravings in *The Gates Ajar* must, therefore, have been done very soon after those in *Kathrina* by J. G. Holland, published in 1869 [Item 818], which he called his first important work in this country. Orig. cloth.

William Ludwell Sheppard

(*See Main Catalogue, p. 205*)

1917. BEECHENBROOK; A RHYME OF THE WAR. By Margaret J. Preston. Fifth Thousand. Baltimore: Kelly & Piet, 1867. Contains 6 illustrations by Sheppard, engraved on wood by J.D.E. (2), J. W. Torsch (2), N. Orr-Co. (1), and Kingdon-Boyd (1).

William M. Baskerville in his *Southern Writers: Biographical and Critical Studies*, Nashville, 1903, calls Miss Preston "the most notable poetess the South has produced." She was a sister-in-law of Stonewall Jackson. *Beechenbrook* appears to have been her most popular book. It was first published in an unillustrated edition in Richmond in 1865. The next edition was that of Kelly & Piet in Baltimore in 1866. This also was not illustrated. Kelly & Piet's 1867 edition marks the first appearance of the illustrations. Orig. cloth.

HARPER'S BAZAAR. Vols. I-III. New York: 1867-1870. Drawings by Sheppard are to be found on pp. 45, 120, 216, 217, 409, 605, 633,

665, and 729 of Vol. III. Many of these are from sketches by W. B. Myers and that on p. 216 is from a sketch by Thomas Worth. [See Item 1729]

1918. COUPON BONDS, AND OTHER STORIES. By J. T. Trowbridge. Boston: James R. Osgood and Company, 1873. With 10 full-page illustrations after drawings by Sheppard. *Coupon Bonds* was first published, unillustrated, in 1866 (Wright II, 2546). This appears to mark the first publication of the "other stories" (Wright II, 2547). Orig. cloth.

NINA'S ATONEMENT. New York: 1873. 2 full-page illustrations by Sheppard. 1 is engraved on wood by John Filmer. The name of the engraver of the other does not appear. [See Item 1666]

1919. THE GREAT SOUTH . . . By Edward King. Hartford, Conn.: American Publishing Company, 1875.

The title-page states that the book is "Profusely illustrated from original sketches by J. Wells Champney." As the writer has never seen anything done by Champney prior to 1871, his work has not been included in the Collection. However, many of his sketches for this book were redrawn for the engraver by Sheppard and the names or initials of both appear on a number of the cuts. Moreover, there are over 30 illustrations where only Sheppard's name or initials appear. There are also illustrations by Thomas Moran, Granville Perkins, and A. R. Waud. An extraordinary number of wood engravers were employed on the book. The following are some of the names: David Nichols, F. Juengling, J. M. Walker, Varley, F. A. Muller (these 5 engraved most of the illustrations on which Sheppard's initials appear without those of Champney), F. S. King, Bookhout, W. Roberts, Lauderbach, Cullen, Speer, J. P. Davis, Winham & Arnold, Bogert, Heinemann, Miller-Aikens, J. Minton, Harley, Annin, Gray, Pierson, Treat, Miller, and C. L. Cox.

This book is a record of a journey through the South and Southwest during 1873 and part of 1874. It was undertaken at the instance of *Scribner's Monthly* and much of the material first appeared in the magazine. Orig. cloth.

1920. THE LILY AND THE CROSS. A TALE OF ACADIA. By Prof. James DeMille. Boston: Lee and Shepard. . . . 1875. With 6 full-page illustrations, 2 of which are signed "W.L.S." All are probably by Sheppard. They are engraved on wood by John Andrew-Son. Orig. cloth.

1921. THE YOUNG SURVEYOR; OR, JACK ON THE PRAIRIES. By J. T. Trowbridge. Boston: James R. Osgood and Company, 1875.

Contains 7 full-page illustrations, 3 of which carry Sheppard's initials. All are probably his. In addition there are a number of smaller illustrations (pp. 36, 45, 49, 71, 102, 107, 129, 144, 168, 178, 187, 216, 256, and 288), many of which are signed "W.L.S." and most of which appear to be Sheppard's work. The engravers, whose names appear, are Bookhout, Smithwick, R. A. Muller, D.N. (David Nichols), F. French, F. Juengling, Treat, J.A.C., Miller-Aikens, J. M. Walker, and Mulet. Orig. cloth.

THE GREAT BONANZA. Boston: 1876. According to the Table of Contents, Sheppard was one of the illustrators of the article "The Camp in the Gulch." The cut on p. 111, engraved by John Andrew-Son, is probably his. [See Item 1856]

1922. PIONEERS IN THE SETTLEMENT OF AMERICA: FROM FLORIDA IN 1510 TO CALIFORNIA IN 1849. By William A. Crafts. 2 Vols. Boston: Samuel Walker and Company, 1876-1877.

Contains many wood engravings after drawings by Sheppard (see plates opposite pp. 28, 68, 83, 84, 101, 110, 116, 118, 127, 139, 165, 174, 201, 217, 218, 237, 263, 275, 277, 413, and 416 in Vol. 1, and opposite pp. 64, 220, 225, 229, 249, 263, 291, 311, and 382 in Vol. II). Other wood engravings are after drawings by F.O.C. Darley, Granville Perkins, F. T. Merrill, and A. R. Waud. All the engravings were executed under the supervision of George T. Andrew.

Cont. morocco, gold tooled, with name of A. N. Tripp on front cover.

MCGUFFEY'S SECOND ECLECTIC READER. Cincinnati and New York [cop. 1879]. With 5 illustrations by Sheppard (pp. 35, 61, 79, 81, and 117). [See Item 1907a(2)]

1923. IN THE BRUSH; OR, OLD-TIME SOCIAL, POLITICAL, AND RELIGIOUS LIFE IN THE SOUTHWEST. By Rev. Hamilton W. Pierson, D.D. New York: D. Appleton and Company, 1881. Contains 6 full-page illustrations by Sheppard, engraved on wood by Harley (2), Schults (1), and N. Orr-Co. (1), the others not being signed by the engraver. Orig. cloth.

Shipley and Stillman

This firm of early Cincinnati engravers consisted of Henry H. Shipley, William Shipley, and George K. Stillman. Henry H. Shipley was born in New York about 1830 and was working in Cincinnati from about 1850 to after 1860. At first he appears to have been associated only with his brother William but in 1853 the partnership with Stillman was formed. Stillman was born in Massachusetts about 1821 and worked as an engraver in Cincinnati from 1840 to 1860 and after. See Groce and Wallace, pp. 577 and 605.

1924. ELLEN; OR THE CHAINED MOTHER, AND PICTURES OF KENTUCKY SLAVERY. Drawn from Real Life. By Mary B. Harlan. Cincinnati: Published for the Author by Applegate & Co., 1853. Wright II (1100).

Contains 5 wood engravings by Shipley & Stillman. They may also have furnished the designs which are by no means masterpieces. The illustration on p. 151 is signed by Shipley alone. The others have the "S & S" or the full firm signature of Shipley & Stillman. Orig. cloth.

THE OHIO RAILROAD GUIDE. Columbus: 1854. Contains 6 wood engravings by Shipley and Stillman after drawings by H. Lovie and 1 wood engraving by them where the name of the draftsman does not appear (p. 25). 3 other illustrations are signed simply "Shipley" (pp. 16, 23, and 81), which may possibly be an indication that one of the Shipleys was the draftsman. [See Item 1804]

1925. "SAM:" OR THE HISTORY OF MYSTERY. By C[harles] W[ilkins] Webber. Cincinnati: H. M. Rulinson . . . 1855. Wright II (2671).

Contains 10 full-page wood engravings, of which 2 (pp. 96 and 400) are signed "Stillman." Shipley's name nowhere appears, which may indicate that the old firm had been dissolved and that George Stillman was again working alone as he had in the days before the firm was organized [see Item 769]. No draftsman's name is signed to the 2 illustrations and Stillman may have been the draftsman himself.

The frontispiece is engraved by Roberts of New York and the illustrations at pp. 16 and 88 are engraved by Theodore Jones of Cincinnati. No other names appear. Orig. cloth.

THE BOOK OF THE GREAT RAILWAY CELEBRATIONS OF 1857. New York: 1858. The cut opposite p. 14 of Part II is signed "Shipley" and was probably the work of either Henry Shipley or his brother, William. [See Item 1807]

1926. LENDERMAN'S ADVENTURES AMONG THE SPIRITUALISTS AND FREE-LOVERS; EXPLAINING HOW THE "RAPPINGS," "TABLE-TIPPINGS," PLAYING ON INSTRUMENTS, ETC., ARE DONE . . . By Lenderman. Cincinnati: People's Publishing House, 1858.

The frontispiece (which is repeated at p. 224) and 2 other full-page wood engravings are signed "Stillman." As in Item 1925, Shipley's name nowhere appears. Possibly Stillman himself was the draftsman. Not much can be said for either the drawing or engraving.

There is a fourth wood engraving signed "G. Kerr" but whether as draftsman or engraver or both does not appear.

The Union Catalogue locates only 2 copies. That at Duke University is dated 1857 and is probably the 1st edition, as that is the year of copyright. The copy at the Library of Congress bears the 1858 date. Orig. cloth.

1927. UNSEEN HAND. By Ruth Vernon [Stopford James Ram]. Cincinnati: J. R. Hawley, 1863. Wright II (199).

Contains 4 full-page illustrations. That facing p. 28 is signed "Stillman sc." That facing p. 94 is signed "Stillman." The others are unsigned. Here, again, Stillman appears to be working alone and may have been draftsman as well as engraver. Orig. cloth.

W. T. Russell Smith
1812-1896

A painter of portraits and landscapes, Smith was brought to this country in 1819, his parents finally settling in Pittsburgh in 1824. He was a pupil of James R. Lambdin, the noted portrait painter, for whom both Lincoln and Grant sat. Smith was also a panoramic artist and in 1851 went abroad to paint a panorama of the Holy Land. See Groce and Wallace, p. 590.

1928. A GEOGRAPHY OF PENNSYLVANIA . . . TO WHICH IS APPENDED A TRAVELLERS' GUIDE . . . By Charles B. Trego. Philadelphia: Edward C. Biddle, 1843. Howes, T 343.

Contains many pleasant wood engravings of Pennsylvania scenes. All are unsigned, but, in his preface, the author says "For the original drawings from which most of our engravings illustrative of natural scenery have been taken, we are indebted to the kind liberality of W. T. Russell Smith, an artist of acknowledged merit in his profession." Orig. roan.

Ephraim George Squier
1821-1888

Squier was a civil engineer but the depression of 1837 diverted him from this career. After editing the *Parlor Magazine*, the *Poets' Magazine*, and the *Hartford Daily Journal*, he went to Chillicothe, Ohio, in 1845 to edit the *Scioto Gazette*. It was at this time that, along with E. H. Davis, he investigated the ancient monuments of the Mississippi Valley which resulted in the Item listed below. He spent some

time in Central America as Chargé d'Affaires and in Peru as United States Commissioner. In 1860 he joined the publishing house of Frank Leslie, becoming chief editor. A complete breakdown forced him to retire. His wife, Miriam F. Folline of New Orleans, divorced him in 1873 and married Leslie. Squier was the author of numerous archaeological works. See Stanley J. Kunitz and Howard Haycraft, *American Authors 1600-1900*, New York, 1938, p. 709; Evert A. Duyckinck and George L. Duyckinck, *Cyclopaedia of American Literature*, New York, 1856, Vol. II, p. 695.

1929. ANCIENT MONUMENTS OF THE MISSISSIPPI VALLEY. By E. G. Squier, A.M., and E. H. Davis, M.D. New York: Bartlett & Welford, Cincinnati: J. A. & U. P. James, 1848.

Contains numerous lithographs and wood engravings prepared under Squier's supervision. The advertisement states that the wood engravings "were executed by Messrs. [N.] Orr & Richardson, and Mr. J. W. Orr, from drawings on the blocks, chiefly by Wm. Wade and Mr. Hamilton Brown." However, neither Wade's nor Brown's name or initials appear anywhere, while Squier's initials are to be found on at least 30 of the engravings. It is possible that Wade and Brown made the drawings on the blocks after sketches by Squier.

Most of the engravings bearing Squier's initials are slight but some 5 of them (pp. 139, 141, 161, 177, and 299) are sufficiently elaborate to warrant being called landscapes. Those on pp. 141, 144, 296, 297, and 299 are signed "E.G.S. del." N. Orr and Richardson engraved most, if not all, of the illustrations which bear Squier's initials. Squier's full name appears on only one cut, a somewhat elaborate illustration on p. 169 which was engraved by J. W. Orr. Many of the lithographed maps and surveys which appear in the book were drawn by Squier.

There are 2 colored lithographs after paintings by Charles Sullivan of Marietta.

This volume was the first publication of the Smithsonian Institution, having, as one of its title-pages shows, been accepted for publication in June 1847. The Smithsonian Institution permitted the authors to strike off from the same type and plates a small edition for their own benefit. The present copy is one of that "small edition." ¾ morocco.

Henry Louis Stephens
(See Main Catalogue, p. 208)

1930. CLARA MORELAND; OR, ADVENTURES IN THE FAR SOUTH-WEST. By Emerson Bennett. Philadelphia: T. B. Peterson, No. 98 Chesnut [*sic*] Street [cop. 1853]. Wright II (271). Contains 6 full-page illustrations which the title-page states are from original designs by Stephens. They are engraved on wood by Beeler. Cont. boards with leather back.

ALBUM OF WOOD ENGRAVINGS by John Andrew, etc. [*ca.* 1855-1875]. 1 engraving after Stephens. [See Item 1472(2)]

1931. THE WONDERFUL AND THE BEAUTIFUL; OR, APPLES OF GOLD IN VESSELS OF SILVER. Philadelphia: H. C. Peck & Theo. Bliss, 1857. This is the 1st edition of Item 1217, with the same 8 illustrations. Orig. cloth.

1932. THE LIFE OF BILLY VIDKINS. BEING ILLUSTRATIONS OF THE POETS, TAKEN FROM PASSAGES IN THE LIFE OF LITTLE BILLY VIDKINS. Philadelphia: T. B. Peterson & Brothers [n.d. but after 1858]. With 32 illustrations "engraved from original designs drawn by Henry L. Stephens." Orig. wrappers.

OLD NURSE'S BOOK OF RHYMES, JINGLES, AND DITTIES. Philadelphia: 1859. The illustration on the back wrapper is by Stephens. [See Item 1493]

1933. VANITY FAIR. Vols. 1-6. December 31, 1859—December 27, 1862, being, with the exception of Vol. 7, all the numbers published. The following 8 numbers, however, are missing—No. 29 of Vol. 2, No. 81 of Vol. 4, and Nos. 140, 147, 150, 151, 156, and 157 of Vol. 6. Frank J. Thompson was the publisher until April 28, 1860, when Louis H. Stephens became the publisher. Since Vol. 1 is discussed in Item 1219, this entry will be confined to the volumes following.

H. L. Stephens was the principal illustrator and there is scarcely a number which does not contain some of his work. The principal feature in each issue was a full-page cartoon and most of these were done by Stephens. While not very powerful, they are on the whole adequate. In fact Mott, at p. 523 of Vol. II, says of them, "The caricatures of H. L. Stephens in *Vanity Fair* entitle him to be ranked at or very near the top of the list of cartoonists who were prominent before Nast and Keppler."

The work of Mullen, as usual somewhat coarse and overly exaggerated, appears with great frequency in all the volumes.

Although Mott, at p. 523 of Vol. II, says McLenan drew occasional pictures for *Vanity Fair*, the only one signed with his name is at p. 7 in Vol. 2. It is the full-page cartoon for the number of June 30, 1860.

Toward the end of Vol. 2, J. H. Goater's work begins to appear and he has a number in Vol. 3. In the latter volume he began to illustrate Fitz-Hugh Ludlow's "The Primpenny Family," but for some reason he soon ceased to do so. In Vol. 4 he had only 6 illustrations and thereafter his name disappears.

W. Fiske first appears with 2 illustrations in Vol. 2 but the number of his illustrations gradually increases.

E. Leutze has a double-page Christmas drawing at pp. 308-09 of Vol. 2 but this appears to be his only contribution to any of the volumes.

Geo. W. Carleton's small bird appears on a drawing on p. 243 of Vol. 3.

Elihu Vedder has some drawings in Vol. 4 (pp. 196, 222, 242, and 257—the last done by the Graphotype process).

Benjamin Day has an illustration at p. 48 of Vol. 5, and possibly those at pp. 126, 130, and 221 of Vol. 4 are also his.

J. H. Howard does not appear until Vol. 5 but he has a number of drawings in that volume and in the next volume.

Robert Wylie, the painter, is given the full-page cartoon in No. 115 (p. 119) of Vol. 5.

A number of the cuts are signed with initials which the writer has been unable to identify.

In the beginning Wevill, Stephens' brother-in-law, did a good deal of the wood engraving, but toward the end of Vol. 2 Andrew and Filmer were brought into the picture. However, in the final number of Vol. 2 Bobbett and Hooper engraved the full-page cartoon and thereafter they appear to have done most of the engraving.

Vols. 1 and 5 are bound. The others are in the orig. wrappers.

1934. THE NEW NIGHT-CAPS TOLD TO CHARLEY. By the author of "Night-Caps," "Life Among The Children," "Aunt Fanny's Stories" &c. [Frances Elizabeth (Mease) Barrow]. New York: D. Appleton & Company . . . 1860.

Contains a number of illustrations, for the most part unsigned by the draftsman. Opposite p. 41 is an illustration by Stephens, the name of the wood engraver not appearing. There is also an illustration by Thwaites. Orig. cloth.

1935. DEATH AND BURIAL OF POOR COCK ROBIN. From Original Designs by H. L. Stephens. One Hundred Proof Copies, Printed for Subscribers by Julius Bien, Lithographer. New York: Hurd & Houghton [cop. 1864]. Title-page and 15 illustrations by Stephens, lithographed by Bien. Orig. cloth.

1936. GOLDEN-HAIRED GERTRUDE: A STORY FOR CHILDREN. By Theodore Tilton. New York: Tibbals & Whiting, 1865. Contains 6 full-page illustrations by Stephens. The author is chiefly notable for the suit which he brought in 1874 against Henry Ward Beecher for alleged adultery with Mrs. Tilton, which caused a nationwide scandal. Orig. cloth.

THE NEW HOUSE THAT JACK BUILT. New York [cop. 1865]. Stephens was one of the illustrators of this pamphlet. [See Item 1982]

1937. PUSS IN BOOTS. With Original Illustrations by H. L. Stephens. Printed in Oil Colors by J. Bien. New York: Hurd and Houghton . . . 1866. There are 6 illustrations by Stephens. Orig. cloth.

1938. QUEER LITTLE PEOPLE. By Harriet Beecher Stowe. Boston: Ticknor and Fields, 1867. This is the 1st edition of Item 1225 with the same illustrations. In addition to the illustrators mentioned in Item 1225, J. N. Hyde is represented by 1 illustration. Orig. cloth.

1939. PEBBLES AND PEARLS FOR THE YOUNG FOLKS. By Abby Sage. Hartford, Conn.: American Publishing Company, 1868.

Contains 4 illustrations by Stephens. Other illustrators whose work will be found are Tudor Horton, George G. White, H. W. Herrick, Edwin Forbes, Arthur Lumley, A. C. Warren, Granville Perkins, and Beaulieu (probably E. F. Beaulieu although listed as G. F. Beaulieu). All illustrations are full-page and all were engraved on wood by Fay & Cox. Orig. cloth.

1940. GOLDEN HOURS: A MAGAZINE FOR BOYS AND GIRLS. I. W. Wiley, D.D., Editor. S. W. Williams, A.M., Ass't. Editor. Vol. I. Cincinnati, Chicago, and St. Louis: Hitchcock and Walden . . . 1869.

Contains 4 full-page illustrations by Stephens (front. and opposite pp. 49, 145, and 529) and 2 smaller illustrations by him on pp. 196-97. The wood engravers were Gulick (2) and New York Bureau of Illustration (4). A few illustrations by E. J. Whitney will also be found. The work of Stillman & Adams, engravers of Cincinnati, also appears (pp. 5, 55, 75, 78, 120, 193, and 549). If the Stillman of this firm is George K. Stillman, this would indicate that, after the dissolution of Shipley & Stillman (see Item 1925) he formed a new firm and continued his work as a Cincinnati engraver.

Golden Hours was a Cincinnati monthly which ran from 1869 to 1881. Half morocco.

1941. ADVENTURES OF ONE TERENCE MC-GRANT. A BREVET IRISH COUSIN OF PRESI-DENT ULISSES S. GRANT, WHO GRADUATED FROM A WESTERN POOR-HOUSE—TERENCE DID, NOT ULISSES—AND WHO HAS BEEN HAV-ING CONSIDERABLE TROUBLE ABOUT GETTING PROPERLY SETTLED INTO A PAYING OFFICE, NOTWITHSTANDING HIS RELATIONSHIP . . . CONTAINS LETTERS FROM THE SEASIDE, EN-TERTAINING READING FOR THE FIRESIDE, AND INVALUABLE INFORMATION FOR THE SUICIDE. By George W. Peck. New York: James H. Lambert, 1871. Wright II (1865).

Contains 5 full-page illustrations by Stephens, all of which were probably engraved on wood by Wevill, although his name appears on only 2 (pp. 12 and 251). Eugene Field's copy with his signature and bookplate. This is the first of the humorous works of George Wilbur Peck, the originator of *Peck's Bad Boy*. Orig. cloth.

1942. THE MARVELLOUS COUNTRY; OR, THREE YEARS IN ARIZONA AND NEW MEXICO, THE APACHES' HOME . . . By Samuel Woodworth Cozzens. Boston: Shepard and Gill, 1873.

Contains 27 full-page wood engravings, and numerous smaller engravings, showing views of Arizona and New Mexico and scenes of Apache life. Many of them are of considerable interest, but unfortunately only a few disclose the name of the draftsman or the engraver. The frontispiece was designed by Stephens and engraved by John Andrew-Son. Frank Merrill's initials appear on the full-page illustration at p. 228, which was engraved by John Andrew-Son, while Merrill's name will also be found on the smaller illustrations on pp. 315 and 418. Probably he designed many of the others. Warren was responsible for the small drawing at p. 472. The only engraver's name to appear is that of John Andrew-Son (see front. and illustrated title-page and pp. 228, 238, 271, 295, 302, 400, 410, 475, and 513).

Orig. cloth.

THE GREAT BONANZA. Boston: 1876. According to the Table of Contents, Stephens was the designer of the 35 illustrations in the article "Among the Raftsmen." John Andrew-Son appear to have been the engravers. [See Item 1856]

David Hunter Strother
(Porte Crayon)
(See Main Catalogue, p. 210)

1943. THE LIFE OF GENERAL WINFIELD SCOTT. By Edward D. Mansfield, Esq. New York: A. S. Barnes & Co., 1846.

Contains 3 full-page illustrations signed by Strother and another, unsigned, which is probably also by him. The wood engravers were R. Roberts, H. W. Herrick, and J. W. & N. Orr.

All of these illustrations appeared in the 1852 edition of the book and in the 1861 edition (Item 1237).

This is the 1st edition of Mansfield's book. Full morocco, gold tooled, a.e.g., and evidently meant for presentation to General Scott's daughter, Camilla Adeline Scott, whose name in gilt appears on the cover. On the front end paper are the words "Presented by the Publishers."

1944. (1) THREE TRACTS published in New York by The American Tract Society from its 150 Nassau-Street address, probably about 1850, viz.:

THE FARMER AND SOLDIER, by Mrs. L. H. Sigourney.
LOUISA AND THE LITTLE BIRDS.
ADVICE TO SABBATH-SCHOOL CHILDREN.

The tracts are numbered 13, 14, and 15 and are probably reprints. Each has a frontispiece engraved on wood by R. Roberts after a drawing by Strother. There are other wood engravings as well (some of which are by W. Howland) and each tract is in its original wrappers. They are attractive little volumes.

(2) Another copy of ADVICE TO SABBATH-SCHOOL CHILDREN, substantially the same as that listed in (1) above, except that the wording of the back wrapper is somewhat different, the number of the tract is not given, and there are numbers on the inner margins of the pages greater than those on the outer margins which paginate the tract itself, indicating that the tract was intended to be used as part of a larger publication. It seems likely that this copy is somewhat later in date than that listed in (1).

1944a. BROADSIDE, 30 by 22-½ inches, containing scenes in the Life of General Scott, with text in 4 columns, bordered by portrait and 16 historical wood engravings, many of which are after drawings by Strother. No doubt the broadside was used in connection with Scott's campaign for the Presidency in 1852. All of the cuts will be found in Item 1233, which, however, contains 7 cuts not present in this item. Whoever selected the blocks for the broadside was either martially minded, since they are mainly the battle scenes, or else felt that such scenes would attract the most votes.

1945. A PEN AND INK DRAWING signed "D.H.S., 1862," showing Lincoln, the sweat pouring down his cheeks, trundling McClellan in a wheelbarrow past a sign reading "To Richmond." McClellan is in full regimentals and

holds an umbrella over his head and a spade over one shoulder. It is an excellent caricature.

Accompanying the drawing is an autograph letter from Pierre Morand to W. H. Lambert, dated September 3, 1901, in which Morand writes, "Of the two carricatures [sic] you inquire about, I know only that I had last seen them with a number of others in the hands of Mr. Drahosh (?), Ed. of the Parkersburg Times . . . Mr. D. was personally acquainted with Col. Strother who may be the author of the 'Lincoln and McClellan,'* since all the carricatures on that subject originated with Gen. Pope's staff. . . . The fact that many pictures relating to the Civil War are unsigned is probably owing to the small value attached to them at the time of their origin, when they did not possess the historical interest attached to them in after years. Even Porte Crayon had difficulty in finding a market for his productions."

Charles Sullivan
1794-1867

While Sullivan painted portraits, he was first and foremost a landscape painter. He was a Pennsylvanian by birth and, after studying under Thomas Sully, he painted for a while in Philadelphia and its vicinity, spending some time also in Georgia and Tennessee. After a few years in Wheeling, W.Va., he came to Marietta, Ohio, in 1833 and lived there until his death. See Edna Maria Clark, *Ohio Art and Artists*, Richmond [1932], pp. 104-06; Groce and Wallace, p. 613.

1946. THE AMERICAN PIONEER, A MONTHLY PERIODICAL, DEVOTED TO THE OBJECTS OF THE LOGAN HISTORICAL SOCIETY . . . Cincinnati, O.: Edited and Published by John S. Williams, 1842-1843. 2 vols. Vol. I is the 2nd edition, the 1st edition of Vol. I having been published in Chillicothe, Ohio. The 2 volumes contain all the numbers that were published.

The frontispiece to the March 1843 number (Vol. II, p. 98) is drawn by Sullivan and engraved on wood by John H. Lovejoy. The frontispiece to the June 1843 number (Vol. II, p. 242) is drawn by Sullivan and engraved on wood by Grosvenor. As the scenes shown in these illustrations are in the vicinity of Marietta, it seems probable that the Sullivan whose name appears upon them is Charles Sullivan, the landscapist of Marietta. The cut on p. 243 of Vol. II may also be his work.

The title-page of each of the bound volumes

* There can be little doubt of Strother's being the draftsman. Morand may have forgotten that his

initials were on the drawing.

38. Matteson. "The Career of a Country Girl in New York—Ice Cream Saloon." *Brother Jonathan*, 1850. (Item 1831[2])

HARE-AND-HOUNDS.

39. Mead. *School Days at Rugby*, 1870. (Item 1849)

41. Nahl. "The Grizzly's respect for the right of property, judging from his performances, must be extremely rare." *California Characters* [ca. 1854-1855]. (Item 1873)

40. Merrill. "He looked down at her as she went beside him. . . ." *Moods* [ca. 1870]. (Item 1851)

THE WILD WOMAN

OR THE

WRECKED HEART:

BEING THE

True Autobiography of Miss Alice Galon, who was recently exhibited in the South and West as the "Wild Woman."

"HOW sleep the Brave, who sink to rest,
By all their country's wishes blest;
When Spring, with dewy fingers cold,
Returns to deck their hallow'd mould;
She there shall dress a sweeter sod,
Than Fancy's feet have ever trod.

By Fairy hands their knell is rung,
By forms unseen their dirge is sung;
There Honour comes, a pilgrim grey,
To bless the turf which wraps their clay;
And Freedom shall awhile repair,
To dwell a weeping Hermit there."

ELEGY,

IN REMEMBRANCE OF

JAMES LAWRENCE, ESQUIRE:

(LATE COMMANDER OF THE UNITED STATES' FRIGATE CHESAPEAKE.)

42. Munroe. Broadside, *Elegy in Remembrance of James Lawrence, Esquire* [1813?]. (Item 1869)

" What devilish impulse suggested to Clarence Withrow the thought of speculating upon his crazed and unhappy victim, is a mystery of wickedness too deep to comprehend. Arraying her in a manner suitable to his scheme, assisted by wily accomplices, he exhibited her as a wild woman, who had been captured in the mountains.—PAGE 80.

PHILADELPHIA:
PUBLISHED BY BARCLAY & CO., 602 ARCH STREET.

43. Noble. *The Wild Woman*, 1864. (Item 1887)

View of the Creek and Village of Crosswicks, New-Jersey, July, 1833.

44. Page. *Memoir of Harlan Page* [1835]. (Item 1891)

And lo ! he darts his piercing eye profound,
And looks majestically stern around !

— *The husband and wife, after being sold to different pur-chasers, violently separated....never to see each other more.*

45. Poupard. *A Preliminary Essay on the Oppression of the Exiled Sons of Africa,* 1804. (Item 1898)

47. Schöner. *Der Neue Americanische Landwirthschafts-Calender for 1821.* (Item 1914)

Feeling satisfied with it, he starts home with a light heart.

He becomes fatigued.

He gives way under his burden.

He meets with an overland party, who are run short of provisions.

46. D.F. and J.A. Read. *Journey to the Gold Diggins* [1849]. (Item 1902)

48. Tuel. *The Doleful Tragedy of the Raising of Jo. Burnham*, 1832. (Item 1958)

49. Wolcott. Pencil drawing of "Mrs. Partington." (Item 2000[2])

MRS. RUTH PARTINGTON, RELICT OF CORPORAL PAUL PARTINGTON, U.S.A.

50. Wolcott. *The Carpet Bag*, 1851. (Item 2000[1])

51. Imitator of Wolcott. "Aunt Polly," *The Adventures of Tom Sawyer*, 1876. (Item 1291)

is by John Cranch. Illustrations will also be found by W. Hall, E. M. Naylor, and John S. Williams, the editor. ¾ morocco.

ANCIENT MONUMENTS OF THE MISSISSIPPI VALLEY. New York and Cincinnati: 1848. Contains 2 colored lithographs by Sarony and Major after paintings by Sullivan. [See Item 1929]

M. A. Sullivan

1947. BILL ARP, SO CALLED. A SIDE SHOW OF THE SOUTHERN SIDE OF THE WAR . . . [By Charles Henry Smith.] Illustrated by M. A. Sullivan, New York: Metropolitan Record Office, 1866.

Contains half title, and in the text 15 full-page illustrations of which all but 4 are signed "M.S." The frontispiece is a portrait of Smith. The half title is engraved by Hoey, but no engraver's name appears on the full-page illustrations. Orig. cloth.

James Gilchrist Swan
1818-1900

Born in Medford, Mass., Swan came of settler stock. An ancestor of his had come to America in 1680 and the battle of Bunker's Hill was fought on land belonging to the Swans. After working as a ship chandler for many years, Swan caught the gold-rush fever and went to California in 1850. It was in 1852 that he first visited the Pacific Northwest and here, except for 2 years at Washington, D.C., when he was acting as secretary to Isaac I. Stevens, the first Congressional Delegate from Washington Territory, he spent the rest of his life. He held numerous positions in the Territory and he made a study of the Indians and wrote a number of articles about them. For a full account of Swan, see Guy Allison, *Forgotten Great Man of Washington History, James G. Swan* [cop. 1951 by *The Longview Daily News*]. It reproduces a series of articles that had appeared in the *Daily News*. Mr. Allison calls Swan "one of Washington's most illustrious citizens."

1948. THE NORTHWEST COAST; OR, THREE YEARS RESIDENCE IN WASHINGTON TERRITORY. By James G. Swan. New York: Harper & Brothers, 1857.

Contains numerous wood engravings. 12 of them, as shown in the List of Illustrations, are after sketches by the author. None of these 12 carries the engraver's name except that on p. 105 which is signed "J.L.L." (probably James L. Langridge). The frontispiece is after a sketch by John Sykes, a draftsman of Vancouver, while the illustration on p. 93 is after a drawing by Thwaites. Avery engraved the cut on p. 52. The map of the Western Part of Washington Territory is present.

Mr. Allison, in his article referred to above, says that this book "contains the most authentic history thus far written on conditions in the state of Washington during its early territorial days." A full-page notice of it appeared in *Harper's Weekly* for August 22, 1857, Vol. I, p. 532, where 4 of the author's illustrations are reprinted. Orig. cloth with the bookplate of Edwin Stanton Fickes.

John R. Telfer

Telfer was a wood engraver and designer who was working in Cincinnati in 1850-1858. See Groce and Wallace, p. 621.

THE OHIO RAILROAD GUIDE. Columbus: 1854. Contains 15 illustrations which bear Telfer's name (pp. 5, 21, 29, 33, 44, 45, 53, 56, 60, 76, 83, 84, 85, 97, and 100). Since Telfer was both an engraver and a designer, it seems probable that he was responsible for both the drawing and the engraving of these illustrations. [See Item 1804]

THE BOOK OF THE GREAT RAILWAY CELEBRATIONS OF 1857. New York: 1858. The illustrations opposite pp. 6, 15, and 16 of Part II are signed by Telfer. It is probable that he both drew and engraved them. [See Item 1807]

Robert Telfer

A wood engraver of Philadelphia. He was a member of the firm of Telfer & Lawrie in 1849 and of Scattergood & Telfer in 1852-1854. Occasionally he acted as draftsman. Thus one cut in *Philadelphia as it is, in 1852* was both engraved and designed by Telfer (see Item 467) and he may be responsible for the views engraved and designed by Scattergood-Telfer in *The Pictorial Sketch Book of Pennsylvania* (Item 695). See Groce and Wallace, p. 621.

1949. THE MEMOIRS OF A PREACHER; OR, THE MYSTERIES OF THE PULPIT. By George Lippard. Philadelphia: T. B. Peterson & Brothers, 306 Chestnut Street [cop. 1864].

Contains 8 full-page wood engravings, one repeated on the front wrapper. That facing p. 84 is signed "Telfer, Del. Sc." Its caption reads "There are pistols, Edmund Jervis. There is a phial of prussic acid, Edmund Jervis. You can take your choice." As the other 7 illustrations are somewhat similar in style, it seems likely that Robert Telfer must take the responsibility for all of them. Orig. wrappers.

This book is not in Wright, although in Vol. I, No. 1685, Wright lists *The Man with the Mask: a Sequel to the Memoirs of a Preacher*, Philadelphia: Jos. Severns and Company [1849]. The 1st edition of *The Memoirs of a Preacher* must, therefore, have antedated *The Man with the Mask* and the Peterson edition is a late reprint. Apparently any edition of the book is scarce.

George Thomas
(See Main Catalogue, p. 212)

1950. PIRATICAL AND TRAGICAL ALMANAC FOR 1845. Philadelphia: John B. Perry . . . [1844]. Contains 21 wood engravings portraying bloodcurdling scenes of murder and piracy. That on p. 21 is signed "G. Thomas" and the others appear to be the work of the same draftsman. Orig. wrappers.

THE ILLUSTRATED NEWS. Vol. I. New York: 1853. On p. 1 of the first number, under Hitchcock's masthead, there is a drawing of the "Birth of the New Year" engraved by Leslie and signed "Thomas Del." It seems quite possible that this is the work of George Thomas. [See Item 1836]

William H. Thwaites
(See Main Catalogue, p. 213)

1951. NED MUSGRAVE; OR THE MOST UNFORTUNATE MAN IN THE WORLD. A COMIC NOVEL. By Theodore Hook. New York: Stringer & Townsend, 1854. On the front wrapper is an illustration by Thwaites showing "Edward horsewhipping Fitzallan." It is engraved on wood by N. Orr. Orig. wrappers.

1952. ROSE AND LILLIE STANHOPE; OR, THE POWER OF CONSCIENCE. By M. J. McIntosh. New York: D. Appleton and Company . . . 1855. With a frontispiece by Thwaites, engraved on wood by Bobbett-Hooper. Orig. cloth.

1953. GOLD AND SILVER. By A.W.H. New York: Dix, Edwards & Co., 1857. 7 full-page and 3 smaller illustrations by Thwaites, engraved on wood by Bobbett-Hooper and A. Bobbett. Presentation copy from the author. Orig. cloth.

THE NORTHWEST COAST. New York: 1857. The illustration on p. 93 is by Thwaites. The name of the wood engraver does not appear. [See Item 1948]

1954. CHRISTMAS VIGILS; OR, KITTY CLARKE'S DREAM. By Miss Mary. New York: Gen. Prot. Episcopal Sunday School Union and Church Book Society, 1859. Frontispiece of the Nativity drawn by Thwaites and engraved on wood by N. Orr. Orig. cloth.

1955. FAVORITE FAIRY TALES. FOR LITTLE FOLKS. With Seventy Illustrations by Thwaites and others, Engraved by the Best Artists. New York: James Miller, 1860.

Contains the stories of *Cinderella*, *Tom Thumb*, *Little Red Riding Hood*, *Beauty and the Beast*, *Puss in Boots*, and *Jack the Giant Killer*, each with separate pagination. The title-page as given above appears before *Cinderella*. The title-page to each of the others has the imprint of Loomis & Co., Engravers and Printers, while the copyright notices are in the name of Brown, Loomis & Co., and are dated 1855, except that of *Puss in Boots*, which is dated 1857.

Thwaites appears to have drawn all the illustrations. At least no other draftsman's name is to be found. The only engravers whose names appear are N. Orr, Bobbett & Hooper and Sears. Orig. cloth.

THE NEW NIGHT-CAPS TOLD TO CHARLEY. New York: 1860. 1 illustration by Thwaites (p. 81), the name of the wood engraver undecipherable. [See Item 1934]

Charles Winfield Tice
1810-1870

A portrait, landscape, and still-life painter, Tice spent most of his life at Newburgh, N.Y. He exhibited at the National Academy between 1837 and 1849. See Groce and Wallace, p. 630.

1956. HISTORY OF THE TOWN OF NEWBURGH. By E. M. Ruttenber. Newburgh: E. M. Ruttenber & Co., 1859.

Contains numerous wood engraved illustrations which the title-page states are "by Charles W. Tice, Artist, Newburgh." David Nichols engraved most of them. The artist must have derived a good deal of innocent satisfaction from these neat little views of his native town. Modern cloth.

George Tirrell
(See Main Catalogue, p. 214)

SCENES OF WONDER AND CURIOSITY IN CALIFORNIA. San Francisco [cop. 1860]. Work by Tirrell will be found on pp. 143, 149, and 221. [See Item 1875]

William Torrey

1814-

Torrey was born in the town of Wilbraham, Mass., and at the age of 12 left his family to seek his fortune. He then commenced his adventures as told in the Item listed below.

1957. TORREY'S NARRATIVE: OR, THE LIFE AND ADVENTURES OF WILLIAM TORREY. WHO FOR THE SPACE OF 25 MONTHS, WITHIN THE YEARS 1835, '36 AND '37, WAS HELD A CAPTIVE BY THE CANNIBALS OF THE MARQUESAS . . . Written by himself. Illustrated with Engravings of his own Sketching. Boston: Press of A. J. Wright, 1848.

The frontispiece is a portrait of Torrey and there are 5 full-page wood engravings in the text which are probably after Torrey's sketches. While somewhat amateurish, the designs are on the whole good and in some instances dramatic. No engraver's name appears. There are also a number of tailpieces with which Torrey had probably nothing to do. On one of them (p. 32) are the initials A.B., so that Abel Bowen may have been its engraver. Orig. cloth.

Benjamin Tuel

A jeweler's apprentice of Woodstock, Vt.

1958. THE DOLEFUL TRAGEDY OF THE RAISING OF JO. BURNHAM, OR THE "CAT LET OUT OF THE BAG." In Five Acts. Illustrated with Engravings. By Timothy Tickle [B. F. Kendall]. Woodstock, Vt.: William W. Prescott, 1832. Fig. 48.

Contains 5 amusing wood engravings which R. A. Perkins, a former Woodstock resident, in his account of the "Jo. Burnham" affair written for Gilman's *Bibliography of Vermont*, unequivocally states were made by Benjamin Tuel, a local jeweler's apprentice (see *The Bibliography of Vermont*, prepared by M. D. Gilman, Burlington, 1897, p. 144).

According to the story which Perkins tells, Jo. Burnham was convicted of the rape of one Sarah Avery of Pomfret and was sent to State Prison where he was supposed to have died in 1826. Later it was rumored that he had been seen in New York and, since both Burnham and the superintendent of the prison were Masons, it was surmised that Burnham had been allowed to escape and that the body of someone else had been substituted for his. It was a time of violent Anti-Masonic excitement and the Burnham case added fuel to the fire. Finally the corpse that had been buried in 1826 was exhumed and proved indubitably to be that of Burnham. The "Jo. Burnham farce" became so famous that Dr. David Palmer of Woodstock, by way of a sarcastic squib, wrote to the *Woodstock Courier* promising a book on the subject. When this was taken seriously and orders for the book began to pour in, B. F. Kendall, the editor of the *Courier*, decided to carry through the jest and produced the "Doleful Tragedy" under the pseudonym of Timothy Tickle. The characters were all taken from life and, when the "Doleful Tragedy" was put on the boards, it drew crowded houses for two weeks.

Orig. wrappers.

Elihu Vedder

(See Main Catalogue, p. 214)

VANITY FAIR. Vols. 1-6. New York: 1859-1862. Some drawings of his appear in Vol. 4. [See Item 1933]

1959. WATSON'S MANUAL OF CALISTHENICS: A SYSTEMATIC DRILL-BOOK WITHOUT APPARATUS, FOR SCHOOLS, FAMILIES, AND GYMNASIUMS. With Music to Accompany the Exercises. By J. Madison Watson. New York and Philadelphia: Schermerhorn, Bancroft & Co. . . . 1864.

Contains numerous cuts of calisthenic exercises, "illustrating positions actually taken and movements executed by the author." The preface states that they were drawn on wood by Geo. G. White and E. Vedder and engraved by N. Orr & Co. As they are unsigned, it is impossible to state which are by White and which by Vedder.

Vedder, returning penniless from Europe to New York on the very day Fort Sumter was fired on, was forced during the war years to resort to various pot-boilers in order to live. In his *Digressions of V.*, Boston and New York, 1910, p. 199, he tells us something of the calisthenic Mr. Watson: "And then a rosy-gilled, prosperous calisthenics man gave me much work in the way of illustrating a book he was getting up, the drawings consisting of figures showing the action by dotted lines until they looked like multitudinously armed Indian gods . . . This person would go through his exercises whistling 'Yankee Doodle,' and looking the while like a great ape; and I used to pretend not to catch the idea until he was in a raging perspiration, thus making him take his own medicine."

Orig. cloth.

1960. MISS MARTHA BROWNLOW; OR THE HEROINE OF TENNESSEE . . . By Major W. D.

Reynolds. Philadelphia: Barclay & Co. [cop. 1865]. The book appears to have first been published about 1863 (see Wright 2022).

On the final page is an illustration entitled "Fiend of Secessia," drawn by Vedder, and reproduced by the graphotype process. The cut on the back wrapper, which is repeated at p. 42 of the text, is signed "F.S." or "S.F." Orig. pictorial wrappers.

Lewis Towson Voigt (or Voight)

A portrait and miniature painter and fashion artist, Voigt was in Maryland between 1839 and 1845, later moving to New York City where he continued to paint portraits and do fashion drawings for some 20 years. According to Groce and Wallace he was also a poet. See Groce and Wallace, p. 650.

THE ILLUSTRATED NEWS. Vol. I. New York: 1853. A number of Voigt's fashion designs appear in its pages (see pp. 308, 324, 340, 388, and 416). The engravers whose names appear are C. Edmonds, Roberts, and Caughey. [See Item 1836]

THE NEW YORK JOURNAL. Vols. I and II. New York: 1853-1854. With a number of fashion designs by Voigt (Vol. I, pp. 109, 200, 201, 264, 265, 320, and 321, and Vol. II, pp. 166, 167, 214, and 215). The engravers are Van Vranken, Badeau, W. Roberts, Edmonds, and Hinckley. [See Item 1838]

THE ILLUSTRATED AMERICAN BIOGRAPHY. New York: 1854. Illustrations for advertisements designed by Voigt will be found on pp. 57, 173, 181, and 266. The engravers were Caughey (2), Roberts, and Van Vranken. [See Item 1964]

William Wade

(*See Main Catalogue, p. 214*)

THE CHILD'S PAPER. Vols. I-IV. New York etc.: 1852-1855. An illustration by Wade, engraved on wood by Bobbett & Edmonds, will be found on p. 19 of Vol. IV. [See Item 1605]

THE WEEKLY NOVELETTE. Boston: 1857-1862. Illustrations by Wade will be found in Vol. V, p. 185, and Vol. X, p. 208, the latter engraved on wood by Peirce. [See Item 1545]

1961. GLEASON'S WEEKLY LINE-OF-BATTLE SHIP. Boston: F. Gleason, 1859. Vol. I, January 1—December 24, 1859. A complete file of the new Series, there having been only 8 numbers of the previous Series issued. It is not paginated and hence references are not made to pages but to dates of issue. It is lavishly illustrated but most of the cuts are not signed. However, the work of a number of American illustrators, although not the leading ones, will be found in its pages. Among the illustrations are many interesting views of Boston and New York. It is quite possible that a number of them had been previously used by Gleason.

Contains 11 illustrations by Wade, chiefly views of New York City and views of shipping (see the numbers for January 8, May 14 (2), June 11, June 25, August 20, August 27, September 17, October 8, October 29, and December 24. The wood engravers were Pilliner, Peirce, Leslie, Hedge, W. & P. (Worcester & Peirce), and Worcester.

Other illustrators whose work will be found are A. Hill, Kilburn, Devereux, Warren, W. R. Miller, Croome, Mallory, Manning, W. Waud, Champney, and Magee. Orig. boards with leather back.

THE NOVELETTE. Boston: 186?. Novelettes Nos. 9 and 90 contain illustrations by Wade. [See Nos. 5 and 7 of Item 1546]

William Wagner
1800-1869

Wagner was born in York, the grandson of the Rev. Daniel Wagner, pastor of the Zion Reformed Church. In his early years William was "a skillful engraver, displaying remarkable talent in that field of art." He designed 50 or more seals for states, cities, and towns throughout the country. In 1834 he engraved a seal for the borough of York, containing "the only design in existence of the first locomotive in America that burned anthracite coal." He also made steel engravings for books, beginning as early as 1825. In 1845 he was elected cashier of the York County Bank, a position he held until his death. See *History of York County, Pennsylvania*, by George R. Prowell, Chicago, 1907, Vol. I, p. 477. Groce and Wallace (p. 653) call attention to his view of York Springs which appeared in *Portfolio* in 1827.

1962. (1) DER GEMEINNÜTZIGE LANDWIRTHSCHAFTS CALENDER, AUF DAS JAHR . . . 1827 . . . Lancaster (Pennsylvanien); gedruckt und zu haben bey William Albrecht [1826].

On A² recto there is a cut of the capture of a hyena in the East Indies. It is signed "Wagner sc. York" and is almost certainly the work of William Wagner. It does not show quite the talent which Mr. Prowell suggests. The cover cut of this almanac is an interesting one, showing a man ploughing with, in the distance, a town and grazing cattle, but, as it was used at least as early as 1812, it cannot be the work of Wagner. Accompanying this item is a copy of the almanac for 1812 with a much finer impression of the cover cut. Both almanacs sewed.

(2) DER GEMEINNÜTZIGE LANDWIRTHSCHAFTS CALENDER, AUF DAS JAHR . . . 1829 . . . Lancaster (Pennsylvanien): gedruckt und zu haben bey William Albrecht [1828].

On [A²] recto there is an elaborate full-page cut which, in view of Wagner's work in the 1827 almanac, it would seem plausible to ascribe to him. Sewed.

1963. HISTORY OF YORK COUNTY, FROM ITS ERECTION TO THE PRESENT TIME. By W. C. Carter and A. J. Glossbrenner. York, Pa.: A. J. Glossbrenner, 1834. The frontispiece is a wood engraving of the courthouse at York by Wagner.

It was to this courthouse that the Continental Congress retired after Howe occupied Philadelphia in 1777 and here they sat from September 28, 1777 to June 27, 1778. York was none too popular with the members of Congress. Cornelius Harnett of North Carolina wrote to a friend in December, 1777: "Believe me it [York] is the most inhospitable scandalous place I ever was in. If I once more can return to my family all the Devils in Hell shall not separate us" (see Edmund Cody Burnett, *The Continental Congress*, New York, 1941, p. 321).

Orig. calf.

Samuel Wallin

(*See Main Catalogue, p. 215*)

NEW YORK IN SLICES. New York: 1849. Contains one full-page illustration by Wallin [See Item 1833]

THE BATTLE SUMMER. New York: 1850. The half title is drawn by Wallin and engraved on wood by J. W. Orr. [See Item 1602]

THE CHILD'S PAPER. Vols. I-IV. New York, etc.: 1852-1855. Contains 2 illustrations by Wallin, viz.: p. 1 of Vol. III, engraved on wood by Hayes, and p. 33 of Vol. IV, which is not signed by the engraver. [See Item 1605]

THE ILLUSTRATED NEWS. Vol. I. New York: 1853. Wallin has large portraits of President Pierce and ex-President Fillmore on pp. 161 and 337. Many smaller portraits by him will be found throughout the volume, for the most part drawn from dauguerreotypes. [See Item 1836]

THE NEW YORK JOURNAL. Vols. I and II. New York: 1853-1854. On p. 11 of Vol. II is an illustration by S. Wallin, engraved on wood by S. H. Wallin. [See Item 1838]

1964. THE ILLUSTRATED AMERICAN BIOGRAPHY; CONTAINING CORRECT PORTRAITS AND BRIEF NOTICES OF THE PRINCIPAL ACTORS IN AMERICAN HISTORY . . . One Volume to be Issued Annually. By A. D. Jones. Volume II. New York: J. Milton Emerson & Co., 1854.

Contains a great many portraits of persons prominent in American history, drawn for the most part by Wallin and engraved on wood by J. W. Orr.

In spite of its title, this is essentially an advertising annual with many full-page and half-page advertisements of concerns not only in New York City but also in other cities, such as Philadelphia, Albany, Buffalo, Troy, Providence, and Boston. For each page devoted to a biography, there is a page of advertisement. Numerous wood engravers were employed in connection with these advertisements, including such men or firms as Lossing-Barritt, J. W. Orr, W. Roberts, Whitney, Jocelyn & Annin, N. Orr, Howland, Leslie & Hooper, Caughey, Felter, T. Horton & Co., Devereux, Van Vranken, Telfer, Waitt, Baker, Smith & Andrew, Ten Eyck, R. H. Carson of Albany, N. F. White of Troy, Henry Pease of Albany, Thompson & Crosby of Providence, Wightman of Buffalo, S. E. Brown of Boston, and Peirce of Boston.

The advertisements of the wood engravers are of particular interest. J. W. Orr has an amazingly intricate design to display his virtuosity at p. 81. Whitney, Jocelyn, & Annin at p. 114 show 2 of their engravings, one after Darley and the other after Kensett, both of which had appeared in Frederic Cozzens' *Prismatics* (Item 949). Leslie & Hooper, at p. 273, state that they are prepared to make contracts for any amount of illustrations and claim credit for the largest engraving ever executed in the United States. And Baker, Smith & Andrew, at p. 477, point with pride to a silver medal awarded them by the Massachusetts Mechanics' Charitable Association for the Best Wood Engraving, October 1853.

Not many of the best draftsmen seem to have been employed, but Barry, Elisha Forbes, Goater, Abram J. Hoffman of Albany, Voigt, J. Wells, and Wilson contribute drawings of sufficient interest to warrant mention. Orig. decorated cloth, spine defective.

ALBUM OF WOOD ENGRAVINGS by John Andrew, etc. [*ca.* 1855-1875]. 1 engraving after Wallin. [See Item 1472(1)]

THE WEEKLY NOVELETTE. Boston: 1857-1862. Illustrations by Wallin will be found in Vol. III, p. 24 and p. 50 of the June 1858 extra, the latter engraved by John Andrew. [See Item 1545]

A. Coolidge Warren
(See Main Catalogue, p. 216)

ALBUM OF WOOD ENGRAVINGS by John Andrew, etc. [*ca.* 1855-1875]. 1 engraving after Warren. [See Item 1472(2)]

THE WEEKLY NOVELETTE. Boston: 1857-1862. Illustrations by Warren will be found in Vol. I, p. 48; Vol. II, pp. 64, 376, 377, and 400; Vol. III, pp. 89 (Amherst), 96 (Harvard), 208, and p. 26 of July 1858 extra; Vol. VI, p. 281; Vol. IX, p. 184; and Vol. X, pp. 200 and 201. The engravers whose names appear are Bricher, Tarbell, Peirce, and John Andrew. [See Item 1545]

1965. THE BRIGHTS OF SUFFOLK, ENGLAND; REPRESENTED IN AMERICA BY THE DESCENDANTS OF HENRY BRIGHT, JUN., WHO CAME TO NEW ENGLAND IN 1630, AND SETTLED IN WATERTOWN, MASSACHUSETTS. By J. B. Bright. Boston: Printed by John Wilson and Son, 1858.
Contains 7 full-page English views which bear Warren's initials, the name of the wood engraver not appearing. 4 other such views (opposite pp. 62, 74, 99, and 111), on which the initials are lacking, may be his also, but it should be noted that 2 of these were engraved by Dalziel. It is doubtful whether this could have been the Philadelphia engraver and, if they are the work of the English Dalziel, the draftsman may also have been an English artist.
This book was written by an American Bright and privately distributed as a tribute to his English ancestors. Orig. cloth, with a presentation inscription by the author.

GLEASON'S WEEKLY LINE-OF-BATTLE SHIP. Boston: 1859. With 2 illustrations by Warren, one a view of Harvard (number for April 30) and one a view of the navy yard at Charlestown, Mass. (number for October 1), the latter engraved on wood by C. W. Wright. [See Item 1961]

ALBUM OF WOOD ENGRAVINGS by John Andrew, etc. [*ca.* 1860-1870]. 1 engraving after Warren. [See Item 1472(3)]

PEBBLES AND PEARLS FOR THE YOUNG FOLKS. Hartford: 1868. Contains 1 illustration by Warren. [See Item 1939]

SPECIMEN PAGES AND ILLUSTRATIONS FROM APPLETONS' JOURNAL. [New York: 1870.] With a folding wood engraving after Warren, "Elm Arcade, New Haven," engraved by John Filmer, which had accompanied the number of the *Journal* for January 15, 1870. 4 smaller views of New Haven, drawn by Warren, one engraved by Richardson and one by C. Cullen, will be found on pp. 57, 58, 59, and 60 of the number for January 15, 1870. Also a drawing by Warren of "The Belvidere, Central Park," will be found on p. 304 of the number for October 23, 1869. [See Item 1731]

THE ILLUSTRATED CHRISTIAN WEEKLY. New York: 1871. Illustrations by Warren will be found on pp. 45, 68, 69, 85, 156, 173, and 188. The only wood engravers whose names appear are Winham-Arnold, T. Williams, and Smithwick. [See Item 1627]

THE STORY OF THE GREAT FIRE. Boston: 1872. Among the advertisements are 2 illustrations by Warren. [See Item 1516]

THE MARVELLOUS COUNTRY. Boston: 1873. At least 1 illustration by Warren. [See Item 1942]

William DeHartburn Washington

Born in Virginia, he worked in Washington, D.C., in 1856-1860. He was a painter of portraits and historical scenes, and in 1868 was painting in New York City. He exhibited at the Pennsylvania Academy and the Washington Art Association. See Groce and Wallace, p. 664.

HARPER'S BAZAAR. Vols. I-III. New York: 1867-1870. A full-page drawing by Washington, showing a baptism in Grace Church, New York City, is to be found at p. 76 in Vol. II. [See Item 1729]

Alfred R. Waud
(See Main Catalogue, p. 217)

THE CARPET-BAG. Boston: 1851-1852. On p. 5 of No. 38 is an illustration signed "Waud" and engraved on wood by G. H. Hayes. [See Item 2000]

THE ILLUSTRATED NEWS. Vol. I. New York: 1853. Illustrations which are probably by A. R. Waud will be found on pp. 37 and 236. [See Item 1836]

THE HISTORICAL PICTURE GALLERY. Boston: 1856. Among the advertisements is an illustration by Waud. [See Item 1556]

THE WEEKLY NOVELETTE. Boston: 1857-1862. 2 of the illustrations in *The Phantom of the Sea* by Durivage and 2 of those in *The Ocean Martyr* by Sylvanus Cobb, Jr., are signed by Waud and probably all the illustrations in these 2 novelettes are his. Peirce's name appears on several of them, as the engraver. Miscellaneous illustrations by A. R. Waud will be found in Vol. VI, pp. 89, 96, 112, and 201; Vol. VII, pp. 16, 249, 345, and 384; Vol. VIII, p. 128; Vol. IX, pp. 16, 121, 137, 232, 240, and 296; and Vol. X, p. 345. The engravers for these illustrations whose names appear are Hayes, Fox, Smith-Damoreau, Damoreau, Peirce, John Andrew, and Tarbell. [See Item 1545]

ALBUM OF WOOD ENGRAVINGS by John Andrew, etc. [*ca.* 1860-1870]. 1 engraving after Waud. [See Item 1472(3)]

THE NOVELETTE. Boston: 186?. Novelettes Nos. 13, 14, and 96 contain illustrations by A. Waud. [See Nos. 26, 11, and 19 of Item 1546]

1966. THIRTY YEARS OF ARMY LIFE ON THE BORDER . . . By Colonel R. B. Marcy, U.S.A. New York: Harper & Brothers, 1866. With 13 full-page illustrations of which 3 bear Waud's name (front. and pp. 177 and 247), but some of the others may be his also. No engraver's name appears. Orig. cloth.

1967. SIEGE OF WASHINGTON, D.C. WRITTEN EXPRESSLY FOR LITTLE PEOPLE. By F[rancis] Colburn Adams, Capt. New York: Dick & Fitzgerald [cop. 1867].

The title-page calls for 26 illustrations but there are only 25, of which 8 are full-page (one of these is omitted from the list of illustrations). Nothing is missing. The title-page further states that the illustrations are by "A. W. Waud" which is obviously an error. As the initials "A.R.W." appear on the frontispiece, it seems reasonably safe to attribute all the illustrations to A. R. Waud. The names of J. P. Davis-Speer appear frequently as the wood engravers and probably they were responsible for all the engravings. Orig. cloth.
Presented by Seven Gables Bookshop.

THEATRICAL MANAGEMENT IN THE WEST AND SOUTH. New York: 1868. With 4 illustrations by A. R. Waud (pp. 80, 118, 183, and 200). The name of the engraver does not appear. [See Item 1625]

1968. HANNAH'S TRIUMPH. By Mary A. Denison [Mrs. Mary (Andrews) Denison]. Philadelphia: Alfred Martien, 1870. 3 full-page illustrations by Waud, engraved on wood by Probasco-Rea-Sharp. This is one of "The Denison Series" and the Series title is also by Waud, engraved by the same engravers. Orig. cloth.

SPECIMEN PAGES AND ILLUSTRATIONS FROM APPLETONS' JOURNAL. [New York: 1870.] With 3 folding wood engravings after Waud, viz.: "The Levee at New Orleans," engraved by John Karst, "Yachting-Rounding the Stake-Boat," engraved by Speer, and "A View on the Hudson River," engraved by N. Orr & Co. These had accompanied the numbers of the *Journal* for May 1, 1869, June 5, 1869, and November 20, 1869. [See Item 1731]

1969. GARNERED SHEAVES FROM THE WRITINGS OF ALBERT D. RICHARDSON, COLLECTED AND ARRANGED BY HIS WIFE; TO WHICH IS ADDED A BIOGRAPHICAL SKETCH OF THE AUTHOR. Hartford, Conn.: Columbian Book Company . . . 1871. Illustrations by A. R. Waud will be found at pp. 257, 280, and 318, the name of the engraver not appearing. 1 illustration (at p. 88) bears W. Waud's initials. Orig. cloth.

THE GREAT SOUTH. Hartford: 1875. 2 illustrations by Waud (pp. 294 and 309), engraved on wood by Bogert (1) and J. P. Davis (1). [See Item 1919]

GUARDING THE MAILS. Hartford: 1876. All the illustrations in Chapter 3 are signed with Waud's name or initials, except that on p. 81 which is by Williams and that on p. 102 which is unsigned but is clearly the work of Waud. All the illustrations in Chapter 7 are signed with Waud's name or initials except that on p. 159, which is probably by Williams, and that on p. 185, which is unsigned but is probably by Waud. The wood engravers were J. E. Hassildine and Van Ingen-Snyder. [See Item 1998]

PIONEERS IN THE SETTLEMENT OF AMERICA. Boston: 1876-1877. 6 illustrations by Waud in Vol. II (half title and opposite pp. 284, 305, 334, 344, and 399). [See Item 1922]

William Waud
(See Main Catalogue, p. 218)

ALBUM OF WOOD ENGRAVINGS by John Andrew, etc. [*ca.* 1855-1875]. 1 engraving after Waud. [See Item 1472(2)]

THE WEEKLY NOVELETTE. Boston: 1857-1862. Illustrations by W. Waud will be found in Vol. V, pp. 25 and 104; Vol. VII, pp. 121 and 320; and Vol. IX, p. 208. The engravers whose names appear are Tarbell, Hayes, Fox, and Peirce. [See item 1545]

GLEASON'S WEEKLY LINE-OF-BATTLE SHIP. Boston: 1859. With 4 illustrations by W. Waud (see numbers for October 1, 8, 15, and 29), engraved on wood by Fox (1), Leslie (1), and Worcester & Co. (1), the name of the engraver of the other not appearing. [See Item 1961]

THE NOVELETTE. Boston: 186?. Novelettes Nos. 82 and 117 contain illustrations by W. Waud. [See Nos. 21 and 18 of Item 1546]

THE LITTLE FLORENTINE. Boston: 1870. Waud has 1 illustration, engraved on wood by Rudd. [See Vol. II of Item 1780]

GARNERED SHEAVES. Hartford, Conn.: 1871. An illustration opposite p. 88 carries W. Waud's initials. [See Item 1969]

John Ferguson Weir
1841-1926

Weir was born in West Point, N.Y., and was both a sculptor and a painter. He was director of the Yale School of Fine Arts from 1869 to 1913. He was the author of *John Trumbull and his Works*, published in 1902. See Fielding, p. 397.

OUT OF TOWN. New York: 1866. At p. 114 is an illustration by J. F. Weir, engraved on wood by J. P. Davis-Speer. [See Item 1673]

Robert Walter Weir
(*See Main Catalogue, p. 219*)

1970. THE OLD MAN'S HOME. By the Rev. William Adams. New York: General Prot. Episcopal S.S. Union, 1848. 2 full-page illustrations by Weir, engraved on wood by Howland. Orig. cloth.

J. Wells
(*See Main Catalogue, p. 219*)

THE ILLUSTRATED AMERICAN BIOGRAPHY. New York: 1854. A drawing of the Seaman's Bank Building at 78 Wall Street by Wells, engraved on wood by Lossing-Barritt, appears at p. 118. [See Item 1964]

SKETCH OF ST. ANTHONY AND MINNE-APOLIS. St. Anthony: 1857. 3 of the illustrations are signed by Wells as draftsman and he may have been responsible for all of the illustrations. [See Item 1467]

MANUAL OF GEOGRAPHY. New York: 1861. On p. 89 is an illustration signed "J. Wells." He also drew the double-page map on pp. 24 and 25 and another map on p. 78. [See Item 1642]

1971. MILLER'S NEW YORK AS IT IS; OR STRANGER'S GUIDE-BOOK TO THE CITIES OF NEW YORK, BROOKLYN AND ADJACENT PLACES . . . New York: James Miller, 1862.

Contains at least 15 New York City views drawn by Wells and engraved on wood by Richardson-Cox (9) and J. W. Orr (1), the names of the engravers of the others not appearing. There are other New York views by Hitchcock, Doepler, Momberger, Goater, and Charles. Orig. cloth.

August Wenderoth
1825-

Wenderoth was a painter of historical scenes, animals, landscapes, and portraits and was also a lithographer. A native of Cassel, Germany, where he studied art, he arrived in America about 1848 and first lived in Brooklyn. In 1854 he was in San Francisco in partnership with Charles Nahl, also a native of Cassel, under the title of "daguerreotype artists." According to Harry T. Peters, he seems to have been a lithographer of unusual ability. With Nahl he drew on stone B. F. Butler's "Miners Cabin" and "A Miner Prospecting." He returned East and was in Philadelphia in 1858. He remained active until at least 1863. See Groce and Wallace, p. 672 and *California on Stone*, by Harry T. Peters, Garden City, N.Y., 1935, pp. 172 and 203.

HUTCHINGS' ILLUSTRATED CALIFORNIA MAGAZINE. San Francisco: 1857-1861. On pp. 574, 575, and 576 of Vol. II there are 11 comic illustrations, most of which are signed "W," and on p. 81 of Vol. V there is an illustration, also signed "W," and engraved by Armstrong, all very much in Nahl's style and evidently influenced by him. It is suggested* that these illustrations are the work of Wenderoth. [See Item 1874]

Samuel B. Wetherald

Wetherald was a Baltimore portrait painter who exhibited at the Maryland Historical Society in 1848. He apparently was in partner-

---

* The suggestion first came from Warren R. Howell of San Francisco.

ship with a man by the name of Resin, as Resin & Wetherald appear in Baltimore directories for 1853 and 1855. The business of the partnership is not stated. See Groce and Wallace, p. 676.

1972. SKETCH OF THE LIFE OF "POOR OLD MOSES!" Published at the request of "Poor Old Moses'" friends. For sale at Weishampel & Son's Literary Emporium, No. 11 Fayette Street, opposite Christ Church [Baltimore: *ca.* 1845].

This is a broadside to commemorate "Poor Old Moses," for many years a vender of ice cream and oysters, and apparently well known to Baltimoreans. At the top is a drawing of the faithful negro, who never entertained a notion of leaving Baltimore because he loved "the ladies and gent'men too much for that." The illustration is drawn by Wetherald and engraved on wood by Horton. The latter is probably John S. Horton, an engraver of Baltimore (see Groce and Wallace, p. 327). As he moved to New York about 1845, the date of *ca.* 1845 has been suggested for the broadside.

Merrill G. Wheelock
(See Main Catalogue, p. 219)

ALBUM OF WOOD ENGRAVINGS by John Andrew, etc. [*ca.* 1860-1870]. At least 50 engravings after Wheelock. [See Item 1472(3)]

George G. White
(See Main Catalogue, p. 220)

1973. TEN NIGHTS IN A BAR-ROOM, AND WHAT I SAW THERE. By T. S. Arthur. Philadelphia: J. W. Bradley, 1854. This appears to be the second printing of the book, the name of Lippincott, Grambo & Co. having been dropped from the title-page and that of J. W. Bradley appearing alone. See Wright II (131).

In this edition there is no half title and, for the wood engraved frontispiece after a drawing by White of the 1st edition [see Item 1274], there has been substituted a steel engraving by Sartain also after a drawing by White. While this new drawing shows the same barroom it is totally different from White's frontispiece for the 1st edition. Whitman Bennett in his *Practical Guide to American Book Collecting*, New York [1941], at p. 113, suggests that White's new drawing was intended to show "the same scene precisely as rendered in the dramatic version of the story which was made almost immediately and was a tremendous hit for those times."

In this edition, the father and daughter, who are shown in gold on the front cover and in blind on the back cover, are taken from the original drawing in the 1st edition. Orig. cloth.

ALBUM OF WOOD ENGRAVINGS by John Andrew, etc. [*ca.* 1855-1875]. 5 engravings after White. [See Item 1472(2)]

1974. WHAT NOT. By Mrs. Mary A. [Andrews] Denison. Philadelphia: Lippincott, Grambo & Co., 1855. Wright II (734). With frontispiece, half title, and 4 full-page illustrations in the text, all by White, engraved on wood by W. H. Van Ingen. The frontispiece was used again in Item 1975. Orig. cloth.

1975. NOBODY'S BOY. WRITTEN EXPRESSLY FOR AND RESPECTFULLY DEDICATED TO JAMES LYNCH, ESQ., OF SANFORD'S OPERA TROUPE, By Frank Drayton, author of "I have no Home." —"Sweet Flowers."—"The Old Man's Darling." —"I went to Gather Flowers."—"Weep not for me, my Mother Dear." Philadelphia: Winner & Shuster [cop. 1856].

This is a piece of sheet music written for the guitar. On the title-page is a drawing by White of the "helpless lad, without a friend, without a home."

1976. WHAT CAN WOMAN DO? By T. S. Arthur. Philadelphia: J. W. Bradley, 1856. With a mezzotint frontispiece engraved by Gross after a drawing by White.

Wright II (145) lists a copy with the imprint "Philadelphia: J. W. Bradley, 1855," but suggests that, as the copyright notice is dated 1856, the imprint date is possibly a printer's error. This error had evidently been corrected when the present copy came off the press. Wright gives 4 different imprints but locates only 5 copies of all issues. Orig. cloth.

1977. OLD WONDER-EYES; AND OTHER STORIES FOR CHILDREN. By Mr. and Mrs. L. K. Lippincott. (Grace Greenwood.) Philadelphia: Gaut & Volkmar, H. Cowperthwait & Co., 1858. With 6 full-page illustrations by White, engraved on wood by Van Ingen-Snyder (3) and Waitt (3). Orig. cloth.

1978. LIFE OF MAJOR GENERAL HENRY LEE, COMMANDER OF LEE'S LEGION IN THE REVOLUTIONARY WAR, AND SUBSEQUENTLY GOVERNOR OF VIRGINIA; TO WHICH IS ADDED THE LIFE OF GENERAL THOMAS SUMTER OF SOUTH CAROLINA. By Cecil B. Hartley. Philadelphia: G. G. Evans, 1859.

Contains 5 full-page illustrations and half title, all of them unsigned. The title-page states that the book is "illustrated with engravings, from original designs, by G. G. White." If so, these are not White's best work. Orig. cloth.

1979. ANNALS OF THE ARMY OF THE CUMBERLAND: COMPRISING BIOGRAPHIES, DESCRIPTIONS OF DEPARTMENTS, ACCOUNTS OF EXPEDITIONS, SKIRMISHES, AND BATTLES; ALSO ITS POLICE RECORD OF SPIES, SMUGGLERS, AND PROMINENT REBEL EMISSARIES. TOGETHER WITH ANECDOTES, INCIDENTS, POETRY, REMINISCENCES, ETC., AND OFFICIAL REPORTS OF THE BATTLE OF STONE RIVER. By an Officer [John Fitch]. Philadelphia: J. B. Lippincott & Co., 1863.

Contains numerous steel engraved portraits and vignettes and 9 wood engravings, probably all of which were engraved by Lauderbach. 2 of them (pp. 510 and 618) are signed by White as the draftsman, but others may well be his work also. One bears the initials "G.P." and was probably drawn by Granville Perkins. Orig. cloth.

1980. THE AMERICAN BOY'S BOOK OF SPORTS AND GAMES: A REPOSITORY OF IN-AND-OUT-DOOR AMUSEMENTS FOR BOYS AND YOUTH. Illustrated with over Six Hundred Engravings, designed by White, Herrick, Wier [sic], and Harvey; and engraved by N-Orr. New York: Dick & Fitzgerald [cop. 1864]. On the front flyleaf is the presentation date of "Christmas, 1864" and it would seem likely that this is a copy of the 1st edition.

Contains numerous wood engravings, many signed by N. Orr. The only ones bearing White's name as the draftsman are the frontispiece and half title and 6 frontispieces to the 6 parts of the book. The names of Herrick, Weir, and Harvey nowhere appear. Orig. cloth.

1981. CYCLOPAEDIA OF COMMERCIAL AND BUSINESS ANECDOTES; COMPRISING INTERESTING REMINISCENCES AND FACTS, REMARKABLE TRAITS AND HUMORS, AND NOTABLE SAYINGS, DEALINGS, EXPERIENCES, AND WITTICISMS OF MERCHANTS, TRADERS, BANKERS, MERCANTILE CELEBRITIES, MILLIONNAIRES, BARGAIN MAKERS, ETC. ETC. IN ALL AGES AND COUNTRIES. Designed to Exhibit, by Nearly Three Thousand Illustrative Anecdotes and Incidents, the Piquancies and Pleasantries of Trade, Commerce, and General Business Pursuits. . . . By Frazar Kirkland. 2 vols. New York: D. Appleton and Company . . . 1864.

Contains numerous portraits on steel and 25 wood engravings. Of the latter those facing pp. 174, 325, 514, 619, and 749 bear White's characteristic "W." Some of the others may be his work also, e.g., those facing pp. 129, 377,

451, 676, 694, and 738. A. H. Jocelyn was the engraver. Orig. boards with leather backs.

LARRY LOCKWELL. Boston: [cop. 1864]. 2 illustrations by White in the catalogue at the end, both for "My Favorite Library," 1 engraved on wood by Van Ingen-Snyder and 1 by Van Ingen. [See Item 1547]

WATSON'S MANUAL OF CALISTHENICS. New York and Philadelphia: 1864. White was one of the draftsmen of the illustrations in this book, but it is impossible to tell which are his work. [See Item 1959]

1982. THE NEW HOUSE THAT JACK BUILT. AN ORIGINAL AMERICAN VERSION. By L. Whitehead, Sr. New York: Beadle and Company [cop. 1865]. 12 illustrations (including 1 repeated), designed by H. L. Stephens and G. G. White, none of them signed. The only wood engraver's name to appear is that of N. Orr-Co.

This is a patriotic fable about the Civil War. Thus the rat is slavery, the cat is vigilance, the dog is secession, and so forth. Orig. wrappers.

1983. CHINCAPIN CHARLIE. By Nellie Eyster. Philadelphia: Duffield Ashmead, 1867. With 3 full-page illustrations by White. The name of the wood engraver is undecipherable. Orig. cloth.

PEBBLES AND PEARLS FOR THE YOUNG FOLKS. Hartford: 1868. Contains 2 illustrations by White. [See Item 1939]

1984. THE GENERAL; OR, TWELVE NIGHTS IN THE HUNTERS' CAMP. A NARRATIVE OF REAL LIFE. [By Willard Barrows.] Boston: Lee and Shepard, 1869. 4 full-page illustrations by White, engraved on wood by John Andrew-Son. Orig. cloth.

1985. POSTER advertising for agents to sell "The New Book, Sunlight and Shadow, by John B. Gough . . . Superbly Illustrated by Eminent Artists. Sold by Canvassing Agents Only." Hartford, Conn.: A. D. Worthington & Co. [ca. 1881].

The poster speaks of Sunlight and Shadow (see Item 686 and p. 221 of Main Catalogue) as "The Great Selling Book of the Year" and as "the most exciting and intensely interesting book ever published." At the 4 corners and in the center appear 5 illustrations from the book. 2 are by White, engraved on wood by John Karst, which will be found at pp. 126 and 270 of the book. There is 1 by Darley, 1 by Frederick Dielman, and 1 by S. G. McCutcheon.

Elias J. Whitney

(See Main Catalogue, p. 221)

1986. COLTON AND FITCH'S INTRODUCTORY SCHOOL GEOGRAPHY. By George W. Fitch. New York: J. H. Colton and Company . . . 1856.

Contains many small illustrations, most of which were drawn by Whitney and engraved on wood by his firm, Whitney & Jocelyn. Since both the title-page and the preface stress the fact that the maps in the book are new and drawn expressly for the work, it may perhaps follow that the illustrations had appeared previously. They must have added considerably to whatever pleasure the study of geography may have. The work of other illustrators such as Eytinge, Hitchcock and possibly McLenan will also be found. Orig. boards, with one of Whitney's illustrations on the front cover.

1987. THE RESCUED BOY, AND OTHER BOOKS FOR CHILDREN AND YOUTH. New York: The American Tract Society [*ca.* 1860].

The book contains 4 stories, each with its own title-page and pagination. Whitney made the drawings for the title-page of the book, which was engraved on wood by Felter, and also those for the title-pages of "Ellen Stone" and "Hopie Stratton; or, The Charms of Early Piety." It seems likely that he was responsible for all illustrations in those 2 stories. In fact his initials appear on the frontispiece to "Hopie Stratton." Herrick drew the frontispiece for "The Rescued Boy," which was engraved on wood by Bookhout, and may have been responsible for the other illustrations in this story. There is nothing to indicate the illustrator of the remaining story, "Albert Raymond." Orig. cloth.

LARRY LOCKWELL. Boston: [cop. 1864]. 2 illustrations by Whitney, one of them for the "Fernside Library" and the other, engraved on wood by Felter, for the "Boardman Library." Both are to be found in the catalogue at the end of the book. [See Item 1547]

THE OLD DISTILLERY. Boston: 1865. The illustration at p. 311 is by Whitney, engraved on wood by Felter. [See Item 1776]

1988. WHERE IS ROSA? A STORY FOR GIRLS AND BOYS. By June Isle. Cincinnati: Poe & Hitchcock [cop. 1865]. With a frontispiece by Whitney, engraved on wood by Felter. Orig. cloth.

ONE-ARMED HUGH. Boston: 1866. The illustration facing p. 101 is drawn by Whitney and engraved on wood by Felter. [See Item 1778]

GOLDEN HOURS. Cincinnati: 1869. Illustrations by Whitney appear on pp. 14, 62, 64, and 66. Probably those on pp. 13 and 16 are also his. [See Item 1940]

1989. THE BLACK VALLEY: THE RAILROAD AND THE COUNTRY; WITH AN ACCOUNT OF THE INTRODUCTION OF WATER. AN ALLEGORY. By S. W. Hanks, Boston: Congregational Publishing Society [cop. 1871]. This is a temperance allegory describing the railroad which, first stopping at Sippington, passes through various stations such as Drunkard's Curve, Brothelton, Deliriumton, and Horrorland, and finally reaches Destruction. At the end appear the diagrams of Dr. Sewall showing the internal condition of the human stomach at different places on the railroad's route. It was no wonder that it "saved many from a drunkard's grave."

The book contains numerous full-page wood engravings relentlessly depicting a drunkard's career. That facing p. 94 is after a drawing by Whitney. It seems likely that many of the others are also his work. The engravers whose names appear are Butterworth & Heath, Peirce, D. T. Smith, John Andrew, Felter, and Andrew & Filmer. Orig. cloth.

THE ILLUSTRATED CHRISTIAN WEEKLY. New York: 1871. The illustration on p. 152 is by Whitney, engraved on wood by Felter. [See Item 1627]

1990. JOHN-JACK. By Lynde Palmer. Troy, N.Y.: H. B. Nims & Co., 1873. 3 full-page illustrations by Whitney, engraved on wood by Felter. This is one of "The Magnet Stories" and the Series title is signed "Kilburn." Orig. cloth.

George D. Wightman

A wood engraver of Buffalo, active 1848-1896. Possibly the George Wightman of 74 Fulton Street, New York City, who exhibited a wood engraving at the American Institute in 1847. See Groce and Wallace, p. 684.

1991. THE POETICAL GEOGRAPHY, DESIGNED TO ACCOMPANY OUTLINE MAPS OR SCHOOL ATLASES. TO WHICH ARE ADDED THE RULES OF ARITHMETIC IN RHYME. By George Van Waters. Published at Louisville [Cincinnati is substituted for Louisville on the front cover], Philadelphia, Hartford, New York, and Boston, 1851.

On p. 70 is a wood engraved view of the Niagara River Suspension Bridge signed "Wightman, Buffalo, N.Y." As this was near

Wightman's home, he may well have made the drawing as well as the engraving. The map on p. 74 of the Sacramento and San Joaquin Valleys was also done by Wightman.

On p. [iv] are 2 interesting wood engravings of San Francisco in 1848 and in 1849, each signed "Brainerd," who was an early Ohio engraver and drawing teacher, active in Cleveland in 1849-1859 (see Groce and Wallace, p. 76). In Bayard Taylor's *Eldorado*, New York, 1850, there are 2 lithographic views, one of "San Francisco in November, 1848" from a sketch by J. C. Ward, and the other of "San Francisco in November, 1849" probably from a drawing by Bayard Taylor himself. While Brainerd did not slavishly copy them, his 2 wood engravings seem almost certainly to have been made from these lithographs. Their use in this 1851 *Poetical Geography* probably marks their first appearance, for they are not to be found in the 1849 Cincinnati edition of the *Poetical Geography*.

There are a number of other wood engravings in the book, the engravers whose names appear being J. W. Orr, H.C.C. (probably Henry C. Chowing, Jr., of Buffalo), Richardson of Buffalo, and B. J. Lossing.

One example of Mr. Van Waters' wonderful prosody might be given:

> Trenton, that takes from Jersey's
>   shore her fare,
> Is on the eastern side of Delaware,
> Then Bordentown, from Trenton south
>   is seen,
> With Burlington and Camden
>   down the stream.
> Freehold in Monmouth, known for
>   Monmouth battle.
> Princeton N.E. from Trenton,
>   deigns to settle.

Orig. boards.

1992. ZILLA FITZ JAMES, THE FEMALE BANDIT OF THE SOUTH-WEST, OR, THE HORRIBLE, MYSTERIOUS, AND AWFUL DISCLOSURES IN THE LIFE OF THE CREOLE MURDFRESS [*sic*], ZILLA FITZ JAMES, PARAMOUR AND ACCOMPLICE OF GREEN H. LONG, THE TREBLE MURDERER, FOR THE SPACE OF SIX YEARS. An Autobiographical Narrative, Edited by Rev. A. Richards. Little Rock, Ark.: A. R. Orton, 1852.

Contains 4 wood engravings, 2 signed by Wightman of Buffalo as both draftsman and engraver and 2 signed by Wightman as engraver only. Both drawing and engraving are of unusual crudity, considering the date of the book. The frontispiece, a portrait of Zilla, is repeated on the front wrapper, and the illustra-

tion of "Zilla's initiation at the Cave" is repeated on the recto of the back wrapper. Modern cloth with leather back, the orig. wrappers bound in.

The book is listed in Wright II (2024) but he locates no copy.

1993. A TERRIBLE HISTORY OF FRAUD AND CRIME. THE TWIN BROTHERS OF TEXAS, LIVES, TRIAL, CONFESSION, AND EXECUTION, AT SAVANNAH, GEORGIA, FOR THE CRUEL, BUT MISTAKEN MURDER OF THEIR BEAUTIFUL SISTER, EMILY EGANUS. WITH FULL CONFESSION OF MANY OTHER AWFUL MURDERS, INCENDIARIES, HIGHWAY ROBBERIES, AND GARROTTING, WHILE CONNECTED WITH THE LAWLESS BAND OF LAND PIRATES IN TEXAS AND KANSAS. Philadelphia: M. A. Milliette, No. 320 Chestnut Street [cop. 1858].

On the front wrapper is a wood engraving of the twin brothers signed "Wightman." There are 6 additional illustrations, 5 in the text and 1 on the back wrapper. These are unsigned except that on p. 27 which bears Butler's name as the engraver. It is possible that Wightman was the draftsman for these illustrations but, if so, his drawing ability must have considerably improved since the publication of *Zilla Fitz James* [Item 1992] in 1852. As a matter of fact, while some of the illustrations bear titles which appear to relate to the book, it is doubtful, in the writer's opinion, whether (with the exception of that on the front wrapper) they were actually drawn for the book.

The twin brothers eventually confess their crimes to a clergyman who signs his name, Rev. A. Ransom, at the end of the book. This is somewhat the same method of presentation used in *Ellen Irving, the Female Victimizer* [Item 1568] which was copyrighted by A. R. Orton, but published by his successor, M. A. Milliette. Orig. wrappers.

Wright II (1996) locates only the Library of Congress copy.

John S. Williams
1790-

Williams' family were North Carolina Quakers who moved to Ohio at about the turn of the century. He became a civil engineer and worked on the Chesapeake and Ohio Canal and on laying out some Ohio railroads. He was a resident of Chillicothe when he began to edit *The American Pioneer*. In 1843 he moved to Cincinnati where he became ill. His illness prevented him from getting out any further volumes of *The American Pioneer*. Some of his early reminiscences will be found in the October 1843 number of the periodical.

THE AMERICAN PIONEER. Cincinnati, O.: 1842-1843. The frontispiece to the October 1843 number (Vol. II, p. 434) is signed "Wms del" and was probably drawn by John S. Williams. It is engraved on wood by Grosvenor. [See Item 1946]

True W. Williams

(See Main Catalogue, p. 223)

HARPER'S BAZAAR. Vols. I-III. New York: 1867-1870. An illustration signed T.W.W. appears on p. 376 of Vol. III. [See Item 1729]

1994. STRUGGLES AND TRIUMPHS: OR, FORTY YEARS' RECOLLECTIONS OF P. T. BARNUM. Written by Himself. Hartford: J. B. Burr & Company, 1869.

In addition to the steel engraved portrait of Barnum which forms the frontispiece, there are 32 wood engravings by Fay & Cox. Many of these carry Williams' initials (pp. 32, 138, 146, 184, 243, 327, 432, 530, 562, 603, and 680). Most, if not all, of the others are probably his also. Orig. cloth. A presentation copy from P. T. Barnum to Miss Lucy Carnahan, December 4, 1869.

1995. AFOOT AND ALONE; A WALK FROM SEA TO SEA BY THE SOUTHERN ROUTE. ADVENTURES AND OBSERVATIONS IN SOUTHERN CALIFORNIA, NEW MEXICO, ARIZONA, TEXAS, ETC. By Stephen Powers. Hartford, Conn.: Columbian Book Company, 1872.

Contains 8 full-page illustrations by Williams (frontispiece and facing pp. 88, 140, 172, 208, 216, 268, and 281). No wood engraver's name appears. There are also a few smaller wood engravings and numerous tailpieces, unsigned by the draftsman.

The *Zamorano 80*, No. 61, calls this "A highly interesting book by the first man, probably, who ever walked alone from one coast to the other. . . . He walked from Raleigh, N.C., to San Francisco, a distance of 3556 miles." Orig. cloth.

MY OPINIONS AND BETSEY BOBBET'S. Hartford: 1873. Contains at least 5 small illustrations (pp. 84, 156, 187, 224, and 305) by Williams. [See Item 1750]

1996. PEOPLE FROM THE OTHER WORLD. By Henry S. Olcott, Profusely Illustrated by Alfred Kappes, and T. W. Williams. Hartford, Conn.: American Publishing Company, 1875.

This is a book on spiritualism, many of the illustrations showing spirits "materialized." Williams' name appears on pp. 63, 73, 81, 178, 295, 312, 322, 330, 371, 388, and 451 (some of the page numbers in the list of illustrations are wrong and some of the illustrations at the end are not listed). No doubt other illustrations are by Williams, for many resemble his work. Orig. cloth.

1997. GABRIEL CONROY. By Bret Harte. Hartford, Conn.: American Publishing Company, 1876. 33 illustrations by Williams reproduced by the Photo. Engraving Co., N.Y.

This is the rare issue in which the copyright notice is in smaller type than in the normal first edition and the word "copyright" instead of "copyrighted" is used. While the probabilities would seem to favor the view that the issue here listed, of which only a few copies appear to be known, is the first issue, B.A.L. (No. 7285) discreetly states that the sequence of the 2 issues has not been determined. Cont. half-leather, probably the publisher's binding.

Also a copy of the normal 1st edition with the same illustrations. Orig. cloth in a half morocco case.

1998. GUARDING THE MAILS; OR, THE SECRET SERVICE OF THE POST OFFICE DEPARTMENT. Illustrative Sketches. By P. H. Woodward, Chief Special Agent under Postmaster-General Jewell. Hartford, Conn. . . . Dustin, Gilman & Co., 1876.

Contains numerous illustrations by Williams. He was probably responsible for all the illustrations in Chapters 1, 4, 6, 8-15, 17, 18, and 19, since his name appears on many of them and the others are in his style. The illustrations in Chapters 5, 16, and 21 are all unsigned but they resemble Williams' work. Most of the illustrations in Chapters 2, 20, and 22 are signed by Day and probably all are his work, except the first in Chapter 2 which is by Williams. Chapters 3 and 7 are illustrated chiefly by A. R. Waud. Orig. cloth.

1999. MY WAYWARD PARDNER; OR, MY TRIALS WITH JOSIAH, AMERICA, THE WIDOW BUMP, AND ETCETERY. By Josiah Allen's Wife [Marietta Holley]. Hartford, Conn.: American Publishing Company, 1880. With 132 illustrations by Williams, of which 36 are full-page. Half-leather, publisher's binding.

Wilson

None of the descriptions of the many Wilsons listed by Groce and Wallace seem particularly to fit the draftsman of the illustrations mentioned below. Perhaps they were work of James Claudius Wilson.

THE ILLUSTRATED AMERICAN BIOGRAPHY. New York: 1854. A fascinating view of the Belgian Gallery of Paintings at 547 Broadway, New York, drawn by Wilson and engraved by Pinkney, will be found at p. 18. [See Item 1964]

MANUAL OF GEOGRAPHY. New York: 1861. Illustrations on pp. 34 and 64 are signed "Wilson," no engraver's name appearing. That on p. 60 is signed "Wilson Del" and is engraved by Edmonds. Wilson also drew the maps on p. 10 (engraved by Edmonds), p. 12 (no engraver's name), and p. 16 (engraved by Richardson-Cox). [See Item 1642]

Josiah Wolcott

A portrait painter, active in New England from 1835 to 1857. He exhibited at the Boston Athenaeum in 1837. He was one of the illustrators of the *Carpet-Bag*, a weekly published in Boston in the early 1850s. The editors said of him in their opening number of March 29, 1851, that "He has a peculiar genius for designing, and we expect many rich things from his pencil." See Groce and Wallace, p. 698.

2000. (1) THE CARPET-BAG. Boston: 1851-1852. The first vol. of this weekly, containing 52 numbers running from March 29, 1851, to March 27, 1852, both inclusive, no number for the week ending April 5 having been published. There was only one other volume, the last number being that for March 26, 1853.* Silas W. Wilder and B. P. Shillaber (the creator of Mrs. Partington) were the original editors, and Snow and Wilder, the original publishers, but in September 1851 Snow dropped out and Wilder, Shillaber, and S. T. Pickard became both editors and proprietors, acting under the firm name of Wilder, Pickard & Co. Fig. 50.

Wolcott drew the heading which appeared in all 52 numbers. On its left side this heading shows the well-known figure of Mrs. Partington at her knitting. It was engraved on wood by N. Brown. On p. 1 of No. 13 the same figure of Mrs. Partington is shown in a much larger drawing by Wolcott, a drawing which discloses the fact that Wolcott was clearly the creator graphically of Mrs. Partington and hence indirectly of Aunt Polly in *The Adventures of Tom Sawyer* (see Items 503 and 1291). Wolcott's drawing was probably engraved by N. Brown, although it is hard to decipher the name.

The first appearance of Mrs. Partington in book form was in *The Life and Sayings of Mrs. Partington, and Others of the Family*, published

in 1854 [Item 503]. The unsigned frontispiece of the book is a copy of Wolcott's drawing in No. 13 of the *Carpet-Bag*. For the book it was redrawn (possibly by Coffin who made many of the other illustrations for the book), because minor differences are apparent. In the book there is far more shading, the teapot and snuff box are smaller and so is the cup which no longer is partly concealed by Mrs. Partington's shoulder, while the design of the Constitution and Guerrière on the handkerchief in Mrs. Partington's lap, cherished relic of Corporal Partington, her deceased mate, is now no longer distinguishable. But the general design and, in particular, Mrs. Partington's "liniments" are substantially the same, and Coffin, in other illustrations in the book depicting Mrs. Partington, has made her conform to Wolcott's portrait of her; so to Wolcott must be given the credit.

The portrait of Aunt Polly at p. 274 of *The Adventures of Tom Sawyer* [Item 1291] is an exact reproduction of the frontispiece in *The Life and Sayings of Mrs. Partington*. Either the original block was used or a photo-mechanical reproduction made. Samuel Clemens in his youth must have been a reader of the *Carpet-Bag*, for his first known contribution (he was then only 17 years old) appeared in the number for May 1, 1852. Clemens, consciously or unconsciously, fashioned his Aunt Polly after Mrs. Partington (see Walter Blair, *Native American Humor*, pp. 150-53). It is not surprising, therefore, that Wolcott's drawing of Mrs. Partington should have been used for Aunt Polly.

It might be noted that the small drawing in the heading of the *Carpet-Bag* closely follows the larger drawing in No. 13, except that the figure of Mrs. Partington's nephew stealing a lump of sugar from the sugar bowl has been introduced. Wolcott's larger drawing had originally appeared in *The Boston Pathfinder*, also published by Snow and Wilder, and a full description of the illustration is given in No. 13 of the *Carpet-Bag*.

Other illustrations by Wolcott will be found in Vol. I of the *Carpet-Bag*, namely at p. 4 of No. 1, p. 5 of No. 1 (another of Mrs. Partington), p. 5 of No. 5, and pp. 1 and 5 of No. 14. N. Brown, whose initials appear on some of them, was probably the engraver.

A number of illustrations in the *Carpet-Bag* are probably the work of Samuel W. Rowse. It is amusing to note that on one occasion, Wolcott having met with an accident which prevented his working (see p. 4 of No. 2), Rowse attempted a drawing of Mrs. Partington which

---

* For a description of the *Carpet-Bag* see Franklin J. Meine's article in the *Collector's Journal*, issued by

James Madison in Los Angeles, Calif., Vol. 4, No. 2, October-December 1933, p. 411.

makes her far more youthful in appearance than did Wolcott's portrait. It appeared at p. 5 of No. 2.

Other illustrators whose work will be found in Vol. I of the *Carpet-Bag* are D. C. Johnston, Momberger, and Waud.

Modern cloth.

(2) A pencil drawing signed by Wolcott of Mrs. Partington. The illustration in the *Carpet-Bag* follows this drawing very closely. The chief change is in the photograph or drawing of Paul Partington which hangs on the wall. In the illustration this has been reversed and made to look like a silhouette. There are also a few other minor changes. This drawing may quite possibly be Wolcott's original portrait of Mrs. Partington, the changes noted having been introduced when the portrait was redrawn on the wood block for the engraver. In any event, Wolcott, the creator graphically of Mrs. Partington, has here drawn his original concept of her. It seems fair to say that this drawing represents the graphic genesis of 2 characters famous in American literature, Mrs. Partington and Aunt Polly. Fig. 49.

Henry Worrall
1825-1902

A native of Liverpool, Worrall was brought to this country at the age of 10. His early years were spent mainly in Buffalo and Cincinnati. In 1868 he went to Topeka, Kansas, and shortly thereafter was painting oil portraits. In the late 1860s caricatures of his began to appear in Kansas publications. His caricature "Drouthy Kansas" in the *Kansas Farmer* for November 1869 made him famous in Kansas. He contributed many drawings to *Harper's Weekly* and *Frank Leslie's Illustrated Newspaper*. In the book field he illustrated not only the item listed below but also Joseph G. McCoy's *Historic Sketches of the Cattle Trade* published in Kansas City in 1874. See Robert Taft, *Artists and Illustrators of the Old West*, New York, 1953, pp. 117, *et seq.*; Groce and Wallace, p. 703.

2001. BUFFALO LAND: AN AUTHENTIC ACCOUNT OF THE DISCOVERIES, ADVENTURES, AND MISHAPS OF A SCIENTIFIC AND SPORTING PARTY IN THE WILD WEST . . . By W. E. Webb, of Topeka, Kansas. Cincinnati and Chicago: E. Hannaford & Company . . . 1873.

With 52 illustrations of which 9 are from photographs. The rest were drawn by Worrall. They were engraved by the Bureau of Illustration, Buffalo, N.Y. At the time of the book's appearance, *The Kansas Magazine* called all of Worrall's illustrations good, "and some of them,

particularly the frontispiece, of striking excellence." Orig. cloth.

Thomas Worth
(*See Main Catalogue, p. 225*)

A NEW FLOWER FOR CHILDREN. New York: 1856. On p. 305 the cut of a nun praying is signed "T.W." Quite possibly these initials are those of Thomas Worth. If so, this is very early work of his. According to Groce and Wallace (p. 703) it was in 1855 that he sold his first comic sketch to Currier. [See Item 1685]

HARPER'S BAZAAR. Vols. I-III. New York: 1867-1870. Illustrations by Worth will be found at pp. 560 and 592 (4) of Vol. I, pp. 32 (2), 48, 320, 348, 384, 432, 457, 489, and 636 of Vol. II, and pp. 56, 125, and 192 of Vol. III. The illustration on p. 216 of Vol. III appears to have been drawn by Sheppard from a sketch by Worth. [See Item 1729]

2002. FIVE ACRES TOO MUCH. A TRUTHFUL ELUCIDATION OF THE ATTRACTIONS OF THE COUNTRY, AND A CAREFUL CONSIDERATION OF THE QUESTION OF PROFIT AND LOSS AS INVOLVED IN AMATEUR FARMING, WITH MUCH VALUABLE ADVICE AND INSTRUCTION TO THOSE ABOUT PURCHASING LARGE OR SMALL PLACES IN THE RURAL DISTRICTS. By Robert B. Roosevelt. New York: Harper & Brothers, 1869. Wright II (2123).

Contains 16 humorous illustrations all of which are probably by Worth. His initials can be seen plainly on the cuts on pp. 174 and 247 and indistinctly on several others. Orig. cloth.

2003. MASONRY EXPOSED. [By George G. Small.] New York: Winchell & Small, 1871.

Contains 15 wood engravings, including front wrapper and title-page. They display the somewhat exaggerated humor which one connects with Thomas Worth and 4 of them (front wrapper, title-page, and pp. 18 and 31) are signed "T.W." Probably he was responsible for all of the illustrations. W. M. Avery engraved the front wrapper. This is the only name of an engraver to appear.

Wright lists this in his *Additions and Corrections to American Fiction 1851-1875*, San Marino, Calif., 1965, as No. 2247a, and locates only 1 copy, that at the Huntington Library. Orig. wrappers.

2004. GOING TO THE CENTENNIAL, AND A GUY TO THE GREAT EXHIBITION. By Bricktop [George G. Small]. New York: Collin & Small, 1876. With 33 illustrations by Worth. The illustrations on the front wrapper are also by Worth. Orig. wrappers.

D. E. Wyand

(See Main Catalogue, p. 226)

SPECIMEN PAGES AND ILLUSTRATIONS FROM APPLETONS' JOURNAL. [New York: 1870.] With 2 folding wood engravings after Wyand, viz.: "Christmas Eve" and "New-Year Calls," both engraved by John Karst, which accompanied the numbers of the *Journal* for January 1, 1870, and January 8, 1870. [See Item 1731]

Robert Wylie
1839-1877

Born in England, Wylie came to America as a child. He studied at the Pennsylvania Academy from 1859 to 1862 and went to France in 1863 where he spent the rest of his life. He was a genre painter and sculptor. See Groce and Wallace, p. 707.

VANITY FAIR. Vols. 1-6. New York: 1859-1862. Wylie drew the full-page cartoon at p. 119 of Vol. 5. It was engraved on wood by Bobbett & Hooper. [See Item 1933]

INDEX

OF ILLUSTRATORS AND ENGRAVERS

References are to pages. Where the illustrator or engraver is one of those listed in Part II of the Supplement, the number of the page (or pages) containing the main entry relating to him is italicized.

INDEX OF AUTHORS

References are to pages and, where more than one page number follows an entry, the number of the page on which the main description of the book appears is italicized. An asterisk before a title indicates that the book is not in the collection.

INDEX OF TITLES

References are to pages and, where more than one page number follows an entry, the number of the page on which the main description of the book appears is italicized. Where the author (or in some cases the editor) is known, his name follows immediately after the title. Otherwise, the place and date of printing are given. In many instances it has seemed preferable to refer the reader to entries under the author's name in the author index, especially where the book is frequently cited or where more than one edition is in the collection. An asterisk before a title indicates that the book is not in the collection.